The Peaceful Atom in Foreign Policy

The Peaceful Atom
in Foreign Policy

by

ARNOLD KRAMISH

Published for the
Council on Foreign Relations
by
HARPER & ROW, Publishers
New York and Evanston

THE PEACEFUL ATOM IN FOREIGN POLICY

FIRST EDITION

Library of Congress catalog card number: 63-8128
Printed in the United States of America
by Capital City Press, Inc., Montpelier, Vermont

Published by Harper & Row, Publishers, Incorporated

COUNCIL ON FOREIGN RELATIONS

The Council on Foreign Relations is a non-profit institution devoted to study of the international aspects of American political, economic and strategic problems. It takes no stand, expressed or implied, on American policy.

The authors of books published under the auspices of the Council are responsible for their statements of fact and expressions of opinion. The Council is responsible only for determining that they should be presented to the public.

For a list of Council publications see pages 275 and 276.

To Vivian

Preface

I was tempted to title this book "The Unfulfilled Promise," having in mind the hopes aroused by President Eisenhower's Atoms for Peace plan of December 1953. In the decade that has passed, those hopes have faded. To assume the task of dissecting a policy which many consider to have "failed," and to attempt to find the usable remnant of it is not an easy decision. Certainly if it has not failed, the foreign policy of the peaceful atom has remained unexerted and uninspired for several years now, while technological advances have continued to accelerate and difficult situations, which our original Atoms for Peace plan had sought to avoid, are now reality.

To one who had observed this degeneration of a hope from a vantage point somewhat closer than the fringes, the Council on Foreign Relations' invitation to devote a period of study to the problems of the peaceful atom in U.S. foreign policy seemed opportune. It was natural for the Council to be interested in the implications for American policy of the peaceful uses of atomic energy, since it had earlier sponsored Henry A. Kissinger's important book *Nuclear Weapons and Foreign Policy.*

Early in the study it was seen that the emphasis might favor one of two approaches: the technological or the political. An attempt, however, has been made to serve both. Consequently, the specialist may find the text deficient within the narrower scope of his discipline. This is only one of several ascribable shortcomings. Another is perhaps an element of audacity in the number, scope and content of the proposals which have emerged in the course of this study. These probes are not necessarily meant to stand as ideal solutions, but to stimulate controversy and possibly to elicit more acceptable alternative solutions.

I am most grateful to the Chairman of our Study Group, Philip D. Reed, who at all times showed understanding and appreciation of the methodology of the study. His assistance was invaluable, both as moderator in the meetings and for helpful discussion of the content of the report on many occasions. Our Study Group was composed of experienced individuals, all of whom have had wide interest in the subject of the peaceful atom. The members of the group were: F. Aley Allan, Corbin Allardice, Caryl P. Haskins, Walter J. Levy, Stacy May, Bruce Mercer, the late Morehead Patterson, Isidor I. Rabi, Oscar M. Ruebhausen, J. Robert Schaetzel, Herbert Scoville, Jr., Oliver Townsend, Robert B. von Mehren, Henry M. Wriston, and Eugene M. Zuckert.

In addition to the regular members, the group profited from the valuable participation in one or more sessions of Howard M. Cohen, John F. Floberg, Raymond Freeman, Paul F. Genachte, Samuel A. Goudsmit, Spurgeon Keeny, the late John Kotselas, Jerome D. Luntz, Francis R. McCune, Ben T. Moore, and Philip Mullenbach.

I am grateful to Robert B. von Mehren for serving as rapporteur of these sessions.

Our five group meetings, and numerous other discussions at the Council with members of the group served as important stimuli and testing grounds for ideas. But the group has no responsibility for this book. The analyses, conclusions and proposals are solely the author's.

Caryl P. Haskins, who in addition to Philip D. Reed read the complete text, provided especially helpful detailed criticism. And I hope that the expectations of Philip E. Mosely, Principal Research Fellow of the Council on Foreign Relations, who encouraged me to assume this task, have in some measure been fulfilled.

William Diebold, Jr., of the Council staff, provided essential guidance all during the progress of the study. Numerous conversations with him, especially on policy matters, were important to the development of many of the concepts presented.

The Council on Foreign Relations has acknowledged the generous assistance which has been provided by the RAND Corporation in order to make possible the completion of this study through helping to make available the services of the author and through secretarial and research facilities of its staff. RAND, of course, bears no responsibility for the author's conclusions or recommendations.

During the course of this study I was privileged to observe peripherally some of the European problems while engaged in tasks for the Institut de la Communauté Européenne pour les Etudes Universitaires and as a consultant to the Secretary-General of the Organisation for Economic Cooperation and Development. Although these organizations also bear no responsibility for the analyses and content of this study, some of the observations made during my association with them are undoubtedly reflected here.

To RAND, which permitted me to spend a good fraction of my time for several years on the Council study, I am happy to express my gratitude. And to family, friends, and secretaries from Washington to Paris to Puerto Di Andraitx, who felt the indirect tribulations (possibly more so than the author) of a fomenting manuscript, I can offer no greater consolation than the thought that it is finally completed.

Arnold Kramish

March 1963

Contents

Part I

THE GIFT OF PLUTO

Chapter 1

The Strategy of the
Peaceful Atom

History will remember the moment, a moment of great psychological significance for the world, when on December 8, 1953, President Eisenhower presented his Atoms for Peace plan before the General Assembly of the United Nations.[1] (Whether history will decide that the word "plan" was too generous a description is still open to question.) The President's proposal was all that remained of "Candor," a more general operation which was to reveal in far greater detail than ever before the facts of life concerning the frightening destructive power of the world's growing stockpiles of nuclear weapons.[2] Operation Candor had aborted into Operation Wheaties at a series of high-level breakfast table conferences. The President evidently believed that means must be found to metamorphose nuclear stockpiles of destruction into cornucopias of beneficent applications. During its brief existence Wheaties became the operational expression of that belief.

In due course, Wheaties received its grand expression before the United Nations. It was a magnificent presentation; the immediate response exceeded all expectation. Even by television, viewers shared much of the emotional rapport exhibited by the assembled delegates, including those of the Soviet bloc, in their ovation to President Eisenhower. Through the sheer momentum of the President's statement atomic programs have multiplied everywhere,

[1] Dwight D. Eisenhower, "The Atom for Progress and Peace," Dept. of State Publication 5403 (Washington: GPO, 1954).
[2] Robert J. Donovan, *Eisenhower: The Inside Story* (New York: Harper, 1956), Ch. 13.

regional authorities and an international agency have been established, a proliferation of unrelated international atomic assistance treaties has been negotiated, and a broad base of technical knowledge and understanding has been laid. But this base can serve world-wide military as well as peaceful uses of atomic energy, unless more direction than now exists, or is evident, can be given to the Atoms for Peace program.

The strategy of peace is yet an elementary art, relatively untested. For broad guidance certain extensions of demonstrated military axioms are probably valid. In particular, the validity of Napoleon's maxim, *"On ne manoeuvre qu'autour d'un point fixe,"* has already been put to test at least twice in atomic diplomacy. The first application was the Eisenhower Atoms for Peace proposal which fixed a point, i.e., created a situation which forced the Soviet Union to act. It presented a program in which the Russians could not refuse to cooperate without severely damaging their best interests. But this superb tactical maneuver had little instrumental force behind it. In the brief, critical period when Soviet policy was most uncertain, hesitant, and probably most pliant, the American tacticians failed to press their initial advantage.

In a similar maneuver, but with excellent preparation and psychological "softening," the Soviet Union in the spring of 1958 fixed an action point in announcing a unilateral cessation of atomic testing, thereby forcing the United States to take a corresponding action. But the score is not quite even; in the first instance, the response could have been only as symbolic as the President's initial action. In the second instance, the response went beyond the limits of symbolism, resulting in a *de facto* situation which for the United States could have been equivalent in the long run to partial disarmament without any guarantees or indication of similar concessions by the Soviet Union.

Breakfast is now over; the world, temporarily satiated by a glut of conventional fuels, is no longer inspired or moved by the atom as a source of power, and is ready for the next repast. Is there anything of a technical or political nature hidden in the peaceful atom which can be unearthed and employed as a *point fixe* in a new attack on securing a stable peace?

Fixed Points for New Departures

If the role of the peaceful atom in this task is not yet clear, perhaps it is at least possible to formulate a few guiding principles. They would declare, first, that the benign application of atomic energy, no matter how widespread or for what noble purposes, does not in itself secure the peace. On the contrary, peaceful applications, *if pursued in isolation,* will increase rather than diminish stocks of nuclear materials available for waging war. But attempts to deal with the formidable problems which attend the peaceful applications, the problems of health particularly, can provide avenues of approach toward the resolution of the broader problems. The specter of nuclear annihilation has haunted the world for some time now, and it is abundantly evident that attempts to exorcise that spirit by grandiose but nebulous disarmament proposals are doomed to failure from the start. Without concrete agreement on the first and subsequent steps, such proposals are nothing more than expressions of a troubled conscience on the part of statesmen and scientists.

Two courses must be followed to obtain the maximum contribution of the atom: (1) the slow, step-by-step creation of moderately ambitious atomic-assistance mechanisms to serve as stepping stones toward a measure of control; and (2) the coupling of nuclear science to other sciences directly relevant to the immediate welfare and aspirations of people. These lines of action must be broadly defined; they must allow the introduction of political and technical ideas which some observers will consider naïve, impractical, futuristic, while others regard them as the ultimate and ideal solution. It is not possible to restrict or define the scope of responsible thought in an area as yet so faintly charted.

Other approaches would relate to the role of the Soviet Union, which for the time being has abandoned the peaceful atom as a major element in the pursuance of policy. Not having accepted, except in a symbolic manner, any of the armament control measures suggested by the West, and having suggested no reasonable alternatives, the Soviet Union remains the major target for some sort of policy rapport. In considering the role the peaceful atom might play in achieving that rapport, we must no longer assume that the Soviets are unsophisticated in the atomic arts or in atomic diplomacy, or that, because of their present neglect of the benign atom as a political weapon, they are sitting back waiting for the United States to come forward with *the* plan.

Remnants of the philosophy of the Atomic Energy Act of 1946 are still with us, a philosophy reflecting a belief in an impregnable atomic monopoly. The prohibitions in the Act against international cooperative programs of either a peaceful or a military nature were absolute. It permitted no transfers of fissionable materials, of restricted atomic data, or presumably even of talent. Many circumstances, including the Soviet atomic and thermonuclear explosions, and particularly the domestic and world-wide response to President Eisenhower's speech, led in 1954 to a revision of the Act. Even though many of the provisions of the revised Act are considered by some (especially by the nuclear industry) to be unnecessarily restrictive, it allowed wide discretion in the extension of the peaceful atom to the international arena.

Thus, it has been possible for the United States to *allocate* 65,000 kilograms of fissionable materials for research and power reactors abroad. The quantity allocated is enough to produce many thousands of nuclear bombs. When foreign demand for atomic power absorbs the entire 65,000 kilograms, the material will correspond to a significant diminution of this country's nuclear weapons potential. Indeed, if the energy predictions made at the time of the Suez crisis had proved correct, the United States at least, would now be in the process of fulfilling the second of the President's proposals, ". . . to diminish the potential destructive power of the world's atomic stockpiles."

If the flow of materials is only a trickle, the cascade of information released subsequent to the 1954 Act has veritably flooded the world—flooded in the sense that the volume and nature of the information, for at least a decade, will far exceed the abilities of most nations to make use of it. The critics who have pointed out inequities and inconsistencies in the technical information policies of the U.S. Atomic Energy Commission have chosen on the whole to ignore the vast amount of data already distributed, and that which still is being turned out.

Much of the release of new data by all countries has been the result of the need to make a good show at international conferences which multiply year by year, taxing the travel budgets of governments and private companies and reducing the productive capacities of technical staffs. Those massive, gluttonous Geneva Conferences of 1955 and 1958 are credited with "freeing," in turn, the subjects of fission and fusion. Now, a third Geneva Conference is being planned, but the sponsoring nations will have to dig deeply and invent madly in order to find something new and spectacular to free at its meetings.

Mechanisms of Atomic Assistance

Tête-à-tête meetings among governments have produced more interesting results than those of international conferences—bilateral agreements, providing for the supply of substantial amounts of material and technical and financial assistance. The United States has made about fifty such agreements. Most of them involve assistance in the development of atomic research programs, but about a third are commitments to furnish the more substantial assistance required to set up atomic power reactors. The U.S.S.R. has concluded similar, if not so philanthropic, arrangements. A small number of bilateral agreements has been negotiated by the United Kingdom and other nations.

One U.S. bilateral agreement is unique in that it involves several nations, controversial in that it involves too few. One of the points of attack on the bilateral treaty concluded with the European Atomic Energy Community (Euratom) was the privilege accorded Euratom of self-inspection of the use of sensitive materials provided by the United States, a privilege not granted other recipients of bilateral assistance. This provision of the agreement was interpreted by some as an abandonment of the long-range goal of universally applied safeguards under an international agency. But it could have been viewed in the opposite light—as a step toward testing the multilateral application of safeguards, taken before the larger international body for this purpose had acquired the political or physical ability to apply them.

As the political scion of the European Coal and Steel Community (created by the three Benelux countries, France, Germany and Italy), nourished mightily by the Suez crisis, Euratom could not have been expected to be much less controversial than its sister organizations. The European Defense Community died before Euratom appeared on the scene; the Common Market is growing in strength, stubbornly but surely. Having survived crises which involved much more than safeguards, Euratom is now about as strong (or weak) as any *national* organization dedicated to the furtherance of the peaceful atom in a world of military preponderance.

Less ambitious, at least as regards the production of atomic power, and less political in its aims, is the European Nuclear Energy Agency (ENEA), an instrumentality of the eighteen Western European nations that composed the Organization for European Economic Cooperation (OEEC). Although the United States is a full member of OEEC's successor, the Organization for Economic Cooperation and Development (OECD), it has not joined ENEA. However, it has negotiated bilateral treaties with individual members and cooperates fully in the Agency's joint projects, which have been numerous and fruitful. In the main the members are concerned with the difficult administrative problems common to all atomic nations and with the establishment of common research and development centers. The one major project of ENEA which will have direct economic impact on atomic power in Europe is the joint atomic fuel reprocessing center, Eurochemic.

As members of the OECD, the six nations of Euratom participate individually and collectively in ENEA's projects; but political and economic differences still prohibit full integration or coalition of the two geographically enmeshed programs. The United States has a joint research and development program with Euratom, but has no such arrangement with ENEA. This is only one of the instances which could be cited in which the Western world's research efforts are not fully coordinated or exploited to the maximum.

The whole peculiar structure—with a strong base of individual bilateral treaties upon which rests a tenuous fabric of agreements among groups of nations—is enveloped by a nebulous haze, the International Atomic Energy Agency (IAEA). Though it embodies the mechanism President Eisenhower called for to implement his proposals of December 8, 1953, the IAEA is unable to play the role envisioned because of East-West differences. Meanwhile, the

Agency struggles to survive, producing needed documentation, organizing small but useful conferences on specialized nuclear subjects, and trying to strengthen its usefulness to members who fall into the category of developing nations. In these activities the IAEA is attempting to justify its existence, regardless of the difficulties among the major powers in its membership.

The Challenge

All these mechanisms, ranging from bilateral agreements to the IAEA, represent significant accomplishments even though their relationships, one to the other, and their ultimate roles are not clear. In promoting the peaceful uses of atomic energy the efforts of the United States have been unstinting. But, as in most of our foreign aid programs, the only connecting thread of policy is financial and material assistance, which we hope will have some sort of beneficial result. Alas, as we have seen in fields other than the international atom, it often does not.

The United States is not the only originator of atomic-assistance mechanisms; the United Kingdom, Canada, France, and the U.S.S.R. all have them. But at present the core problem is U.S.-U.S.S.R. relations. This is a problem which must be attacked on all fronts—by strengthening Western purpose and capabilities; by devoting increased attention and effort to the political, economic and social problems of the developing nations; and, when appropriate, by direct negotiation.

The physical facts that the military atom can be diverted to peaceful ends and that the benign atom can also be used with harmful intent lead one to believe that the latter, the peaceful atom, must be useful in some way as a tool in the resolution of international conflicts. Certainly the problem goes beyond nuclear physics; it is rooted in a philosophy developed decades before the bomb burst over Hiroshima. Further analysis, or sheer frustration, may determine that the peaceful atom should best be omitted from future international negotiations. But such decision should be based at least upon some understanding of what benefits the atom can bring and how it complicates our world in so doing.

Chapter 2

Recipe for a Bomb

While he dwelt in Hades, Pluto was lord of all that descended to the bowels of the earth and all that emerged from the earth. At his pleasure he visited the realms of day carrying the cornucopia, symbol of inexhaustible riches.

The man-made element, plutonium, bears more than a cognate relationship to the god of the nether world, for it too possesses much the same potential, as did fabled Pluto, for destruction or beneficence. The enormous latent power of plutonium was first tapped at Alamogordo on July 16, 1945, and a few weeks later over Nagasaki. Since then, plutonium has become a coveted commodity for stockpiles of atomic bombs and, temporarily, somewhat of a nuisance for nuclear power programs.

Confronted in almost every other issue of popular magazines and Sunday supplements with visions of the bright new world of peaceful atomic energy, the reader is rarely given a glimpse of the formidable hurdles which must first be leapt. Some are economic or technical obstacles which only time and a well-planned development program will remove. And almost all have political aspects. Foremost among the hurdles is one that forms a connecting link between peaceful and military programs; that is, how to handle the font of atomic energy, the fissionable materials themselves.

The exact relations of atomic materials to atomic bombs and reactors were befogged for some time by security considerations, and later by lack of understanding—even among many persons who were sophisticated in the nuclear arts. Since these relations are highly pertinent to the attainment of a nuclear weapons capability by any country and also to the future industrial applications of nuclear energy, they must be looked at first. Formulation of peaceful atomic policy, now complicated primarily by fears of the diversion of nuclear materials to military uses, would be rendered vastly more simple if plutonium were not the Janus-faced substance it is.

The Basic Materials

Uranium is the basic and only source of fission energy which can be extracted from the earth; other atomic energy materials, like plutonium, must be created from uranium or from another natural source, thorium. But in its pristine state, thorium is not usable as a source of power.

In relation to other minerals uranium deposits are fairly common in the earth's crust; in fact, uranium is about as abundant as zinc or lead. The supplies available to the United States from domestic sources and from Canada and Africa are entirely sufficient; in fact, they greatly exceed present requirements.[1] The U.S.S.R. taps the sizable resources of its satellites, particularly those of East Germany and Czechoslovakia; in addition, it has domestic deposits of unknown extent. The United Kingdom gets uranium from the same foreign sources as does the United States, and also from very significant deposits now being developed in Australia. Allocations among the United States, the United Kingdom, and Canada are handled by a Combined Policy Committee, dating from World War II, which represents the first and longest-existing attempt at international cooperation in the field of atomic energy. France, the fourth atomic power, has modest domestic deposits and has had available uranium from its former colonies of Madagascar and Gabon.

Some countries, such as South Africa and Portugal, which lack atomic energy programs of significant size are blessed with large-scale, commercially exploitable, uranium deposits. It is unlikely that these countries will ever be able to absorb all the production of domestic uranium-mining enterprises; hence, if guaranteed markets are not provided by the major users, a free market in uranium may result, with many suppliers.

[1] "Uranium: Producers Face Period of Over-production," *Nuclear Engineering,* February 1960, pp. 49-52.

Fortunately, perhaps, nature provides very small *proportions* of uranium-235, the particular form, or isotope, of uranium which, when assembled in sufficient quantity, will split and thereby give off large quantities of energy. This splitting, or more properly fissioning, is accomplished by the multiplication and cascading of a neutral nuclear particle, the neutron, which is the instrument in the fission of the uranium atom. If the fissioning of the assembled quantity is accomplished in a very brief period, such as a hundredth of a millionth of a second, an atomic explosion will result. Should the assembly be so constructed that the time scale is much longer, the chain reaction can be controlled and the liberated heat can be harnessed for application, as in the production of electricity. Such an assembly, termed an atomic (or nuclear) reactor, is the heart of a nuclear power plant.

In natural deposits uranium-235 is found in the company of a much greater quantity of another isotope, uranium-238, a substance which is less fissionable than U-235. Indeed, it does not fission at all unless the neutron energies are raised very high. For many purposes it is possible to use the natural mixture of U-235 and U-238; for other applications, including the manufacture of atomic bombs, it is necessary to separate the two components. Most nuclear reactors use partially separated, i.e., enriched, uranium. Enrichment can be effected in several ways, hitherto requiring great inputs of energy and large, technically complex installations. In most countries the value of the energy obtained from the separation of U-235 would not cover fixed charges on the capital investment plus the operating costs, chiefly for power.[2]

Clearly, under such circumstances it would be an uneconomic venture and a drain on most nations' resources to engage in an effort to separate uranium-235 *solely for nuclear power purposes.*[3] But if nuclear weapons are wanted, particularly a diversity of them, and when cheap conventional power is available to operate the

[2] One of the three great uranium-235 production facilities in the United States burns 800 tons of coal per hour. This plant, at Paducah, Kentucky, consumes four times as much electrical power as the rest of the state combined! (U.S. AEC Press Release S-18-60, September 20, 1960).

[3] The three isotope-producing facilities in the United States consume 900 million kilowatt hours of energy per week. This is some 7 per cent of the nation's total electrical power production.

separation plants, and a nation can marshal the appropriate technical and industrial resources to construct them, then the uranium-235 path may be followed.

When uranium is "cooked" in a nuclear reactor, a number of interesting side reactions occur. Some of the uranium-238 present will capture neutrons and, instead of splitting, will be rapidly transformed to an entirely new element, plutonium. The major form of this element is plutonium-239, which, like uranium-235, is subject to fission. Plutonium is relatively more available as nuclear power material because, unlike uranium-235 which is not chemically distinct, plutonium can be separated by chemical means from the parent uranium.

Similarly, thorium can be inserted in a nuclear reactor, and through nuclear transformation it will become uranium-233, which is fissionable like plutonium-239 and uranium-235. To date, there has been relatively little emphasis on the production of uranium-233 and consequently only limited exploitation of thorium resources. India, Brazil, and Canada boast major reserves of thorium. Less extensive deposits are found in South Africa, Southeast Asia, Australia, Madagascar, and the United States. Production of uranium-233 demands an already well-developed atomic energy program, and to date the few nations which have had such a program have had access to adequate uranium reserves. But in a nation like India, which is so generously endowed with thorium, the natural direction of the atomic energy program will be toward eventual utilization of that resource. For the time being, however, uranium-235 and plutonium-239 dominate the nuclear scene.

The natural and "artificial" nuclear materials also have legal distinctions. Plutonium and uranium enriched in the isotope 235 or 233 are among those materials which the Atomic Energy Act defines as "special nuclear material." These materials are subject to more strict legal restrictions than "source material" which includes uranium and thorium.

The Diffusion Process and Other Technologies

What, then, does distinguish the two major special materials? How are they related economically and politically? Uranium-235 is now produced by only three nations, the United States, the

United Kingdom and Soviet Russia, which control this commodity as "supplier" or "donor" nations. France, now building a small plant, will undoubtedly take her place as the fourth U-235 producer, as she has taken fourth place in the production of atomic bombs. France has adopted essentially the same technology as the other three powers. This is the diffusion process by which U-235 and U-238 in a gaseous compound are pumped through acres of barriers with holes of exceedingly small diameter, through which the U-235 compound (being lighter) diffuses the more rapidly.

France's uranium-235 program and its atomic bomb program are examples of stubborn, intense, research efforts. Serious experimental and theoretical work on U-235 separation has been conducted since 1956, initially in conjunction with Euratom's Syndicate for the Construction of a European Isotope-Separation Plant. But certainly the major effort has been conducted as a national enterprise, independent of the ultimate participation of Euratom. The results of the experiments were presented at the Second International Conference on Peaceful Uses of Atomic Energy in September 1958, somewhat to the embarrassment of the United States which still kept similar data highly classified. The chairman of the session at which the French data were presented was an American scientist with intimate knowledge of U.S. processes who admitted that he was impressed by the technical elements of the French presentation.

The French plant at Pierrelatte in Provence will be modest in comparison with those of the U.S.S.R. and the U.S. The capital cost, of about a billion dollars,[4] will be comparable, considering inflation, to that of the first U.S. plant at Oak Ridge, Tennessee, which, however, has since been expanded many fold. The building of Pierrelatte proceeds even though France could obtain large quantities of fissionable materials in varying degrees of enrichment from Britain and the United States. Since materials obtained under bilateral agreements would be restricted as to use and would have to be accounted for, France would rather invest substantially to obtain an independent supply of uranium-235. The high cost of the French uranium, three or four times that of equivalent material obtainable under a U.S. bilateral agree-

[4] L'Usine où la France Choisit son Destin," *Candide* (Paris), July 11-18, 1962, p. 7.

ment, is an interesting indication of what the French are willing to pay in order to be absolutely free of any conditions imposed by a bilateral agreement.[5] The price of complete nuclear independence—self-sufficiency in both fissionable materials—is high indeed, but who can predict when a nation will come to consider nuclear self-sufficiency a bargain in terms of physical or political survival, or simply of national pride?

Lack of money and electrical power are not the only obstacles encountered by a nation which decides to build a U-235 diffusion plant. The engineering technology required is deemed so important by the United States that it still retains a very high order of classification on the diffusion process, as do the United Kingdom and the U.S.S.R. Each evidently believes that its process contains elements which make it superior to those of other countries. Or secrecy may reflect unwillingness to reveal inferiority. Nevertheless, the French have shown that they can succeed without knowledge of the other technologies and that it is possible to be independent, albeit not rich, in U-235 resources.

Other technologies of producing uranium-235 are available to nations aspiring to be members of the atomic club. There are at least two promising methods which eliminate the need for the complex barrier construction. One of these is the separation of isotopes by fast flow through a nozzle.[6] Another method, which has received extensive publicity, separates the U-235 and U-238 components by numerous centrifuges, in a manner somewhat analogous to a cream separator.[7] German scientists, who had gone a long way in developing the centrifuge process during World War II,[8] recently revised and developed it to the point where evidently the U.S. Atomic Energy Commission became alarmed and asked

[5] The Belgian Foreign Minister told a special Parliamentary Committee the cost of enriched uranium from a European plant would be three to four times the U.S. price. (*Applied Atomics*, London, No. 91, June 26, 1957).

[6] Myron Levoy, "Uranium Isotope Separation by Nozzles," *Nucleonics*, April 1960, pp. 68-118.

[7] *Nucleonics Week*, May 19, 1960, p. 1; same July 7, 1960, p. 2.

[8] Walther Bothe and Siegfried Flü (senior authors), *Fiat Review of German Science 1939-1946, Nuclear Physics and Cosmic Rays*, Part II, Section 7.4.2.1 Ultrazentrifuge (Wiesbaden, Germany: Office of Military Government for Germany, Field Information Agencies Technical—British, French, U.S., printed under the supervision of Dieterich'sche Verlagsbuchhandlung. Inhaber W. Klemm, 1948).

West Germany to classify the technology.[9] This unique step has some far-reaching implications. It alerted countries interested in developing atomic power to the fact that for them there might be a better U-235 production method than the diffusion process which they hold in awe. Moreover, there is great doubt that the centrifuge technology could have been hidden, anyway, since it is well developed in the Netherlands and in Brazil, where incidentally some of the German machines are being used. On September 1, 1960, only a few weeks after the approach to the West German government, the AEC released for public use one of the basic patents for the advanced isotopes-separation centrifuge.[10] Even during negotiations to keep centrifuging under wraps, AEC press releases heralded the availability of more patents.[11] And to complicate matters still further, a report appeared (TID-5753), prepared for the AEC by a German scientist who had worked on centrifuges for the Russians. Earlier, in June 1960, the basic German patent had been published.[12]

Being a member of Euratom, West Germany has certain moral obligations toward that organization. Must she keep this development, which has important peaceful implications, secret from her treaty partners? The U.S. request to West Germany reflected a deep concern that U-235 technology would spread to other coun-

[9] "West Germans Agree To Put Secrecy Lid on Gas Centrifuging." *Nucleonics Week,* August 4, 1960, p. 1. The story burst forth in the popular press some two months or more after it was common knowledge in the technical community. See *The New York Times,* October 11, 1960, p. 1; October 12, 1960, p. 1; October 13, 1960, p. 20; *New York Herald Tribune* (Paris edition), October 13, 1960, p. 3; October 15-16, 1960, p. 1; *The Times* (London), October 16, 1960; October 19, 1960.

[10] U.S. AEC Press Release No. IN-130, September 1, 1960. See also Patent No. 2,936,110, Method of Centrifuge Operation, issued May 10, 1960, to Karl Cohen.

[11] U.S. AEC Press Release No. IN-144, October 19, 1960, "Abstracts of 57 Patents Released for Public Use," pp. 8-11: Patent No. 2,947,471, Centrifuge End Cap, issued August 2, 1960, to J. W. Beams and L. B. Snoddy (deceased); Patent No. 2,947,472, Centrifuge Apparatus, issued August 2, 1960, to C. Skarstrom, H. C. Urey and K. Cohen; Patent No. 2,948,572. Centrifuges, issued August 9, 1960, to J. W. Beams and L. B. Snoddy (deceased); Patent No. 2,949,045, Housings and Mountings for Centrifuges, issued August 16, 1960, to F. C. Rushing.

[12] "Advances in Gas-centrifuge Enrichment Bring Big Problems," *Nucleonics,* September 1960, pp. 17-18.

tries, enabling them to build atomic bombs. But this is difficult to comprehend since it is much simpler to make an "elementary" atomic bomb, using the plutonium technology already known by all the world in minute detail.

The Consequences of Plutonium-239

Nevil Shute's absorbing (albeit somewhat technically inaccurate) novel *On the Beach* postulated an impetuous Albania dropping an atomic bomb on Naples. From some unknown source a bomb was next detonated over Tel Aviv. The chain of events then involved Egypt, England, the United States—with a final grand crescendo of Russians and Chinese annihilating each other, and the world, with cobalt bombs. Shute's novel and similar accounts have often been used to illustrate the instabilities of a world with a large number of nations capable of producing atomic bombs. Until France joined the nuclear club, the condition was dubbed "The Fourth Country Problem." It is now properly referred to as "The Nth Country Problem"—and the ultimate value of N is beyond the ken of any nuclear prophet.

After much governmental analysis and soul-searching, concern over the Nth country has now formally become basic in U.S. policy toward the sharing of nuclear materials and knowledge. In discussing a cooperative agreement with France before the Joint Committee on Atomic Energy, the Special Assistant to the Secretary of State for Atomic Energy and Disarmament made that concern clear:

We are not proposing, I would like to emphasize, assistance to France in the weapons field. We have borne in mind throughout our discussions with France our basic policy of not aiding fourth powers to attain a weapons capability.[13]

But, after a nation reaches a certain point of advanced weapons development, Public Law 85-479, approved by the President on July 2, 1958, does allow certain cooperative efforts and transfer

[13] *Agreements for Cooperation for Mutual Defense Purposes,* Hearings before Joint Committee on Atomic Energy, 86th Congress, 1st sess., June 11-July 2, 1959 (Washington: GPO, 1959), p. 45.

of non-nuclear parts of weapons. The principle was expressed by the congressional Joint Committee on Atomic Energy:

> With regard to the words "substantial progress" in the second proviso of subsection 91c (4) it is intended that the cooperating nation must have achieved considerably more than a mere theoretical knowledge of atomic weapons design, of the testings of a limited number of atomic weapons. It is intended that the cooperating nation must have achieved a capability on its own of fabricating a variety of atomic weapons, and constructed and operated the necessary facilities, including weapons research and development laboratories, weapons manufacturing facilities, a weapon-testing station, and trained personnel to operate each of these facilities.[14]

The United Kingdom has demonstrated "substantial progress," but the point at which other countries will meet this requirement is decidedly moot. Changing political and defense requirements will effect changes in laws, altering Nth country expectations drastically. It may even be necessary in some political considerations not to await "substantial progress" but, as Beaton and Maddox have pointed out, to treat "those (such as Canada, India and Germany) who can build nuclear weapons as if they had done so."[15]

It is beyond the scope of this study of the peaceful atom to discuss the military validity of this or other hypotheses that range from liberally salting the earth with Nth countries to denying all forms of atomic aid and cooperation, alliances notwithstanding. We are confronted with the stark reality that as a direct consequence of the Atoms for Peace program the United States, aided and abetted by the United Kingdom and Soviet Russia, has given the world an uncontrolled technology—the technology of plutonium—with which any nation, with time and sacrifice, can make atomic bombs. It is true that alternate technologies exist, but they remain less known, more difficult, or untested.

If plutonium were not created automatically in almost any conceivable atomic power plant and if its production for military purposes were not still strongly affecting the programing of adjunct

[14] *Amendments for Cooperation for Mutual Defense*, Senate Report No. 513, 86th Congress, 1st sess., July 14, 1959 (Washington: GPO, 1959), p. 11.
[15] Leonard Beaton and John Maddox, *The Spread of Nuclear Weapons* (New York: Praeger, 1962), p. 200.

peaceful application, then the pursuit of atoms-for-peace would be a joyful simplicity. Only economic and technological problems would remain, and even they would be rendered far less complex. On the other hand, it is the common danger, the common hope, residing in plutonium that can and should be used in the formulation of new policies for the resolution of the world's nuclear dilemmas. Policies ignoring or by-passing plutonium are illusory.

Illusions abound in this adolescent age of the atom, and the most curious of them relate to "atomic secrecy." No individual, least of all those busy, eminent men who constantly cry out against secrecy, could possibly assimilate and evaluate the vast, comprehensive, and varied amount of literature *in the public domain* that deals with both peaceful and military applications of nuclear energy. Volumes of secret information will never bridge the wide gap of misunderstanding among governments, scientists, and the public; more and better volumes interpreting nonsecret data might do so.

Fabrication of a Bomb

To understand the possible role of the atom in attaining peace, it is also necessary to comprehend its relations to war. To that end this chapter will raid the coffers where the so-called atomic secrets, which actually are public information, are kept and will present the reader with a recipe for the bomb.

When a nation embarks upon a weapons program, its initial problem will be to obtain sufficient fissionable materials of the requisite quality. If such materials are to be obtained solely through a treaty arrangement which has tied up atomic aid with inspection rights, the nation must use all of the materials generated under that arrangement for peaceful purposes. If it diverts some of the special materials to weapons, then the nation has entered into a clandestine operation. The bomb figures given in this chapter would then have to be modified by the percentage of successful diversion. (See Chapter 5.)

A nation might also develop part of its atomic industry on a clandestine basis, manufacturing special materials without any treaty encumbrance. Concealed from the Western world, this is presumably the mode which the Chinese People's Republic has chosen; how much does even Russia contribute to, or know about, the Chinese program?

A third type of weapons manufacture is carried out on a completely open basis, using domestic resources without treaty encumbrances. In this fashion, more or less, France has been engaged in her atomic bomb program. The plutonium in the French bombs has been produced openly in a weapons program whose facilities are not subject to control by any bilateral or multilateral treaty. If a nation clandestinely or openly enters into plutonium production apart from its peaceful endeavors, there is no current force, through treaty or sense of moral obligation, which would in any way inhibit using that material for weapons. (Even before the first bomb demonstration, a military program can be used for political effect.)

In contemplating a bomb program, the manufacturer must determine the quantity of material required per bomb, the total number of bombs effective for his particular aims, and the total cost. The first factor is easy to estimate, whereas the other two numbers are likely to be grossly underestimated.

For his calculations, the released data on the physics of "fast" power reactors will be of immense aid to the designer. He knows that a fast reactor is very much like a bomb, and he can check his data against that given in U.S. and British papers presented at the Second International Conference for the Peaceful Uses of Atomic Energy in 1958.[16] These papers tell him, for example, that the critical mass of the sphere of uranium-235 (93.5 per cent enrichment) will weigh 48.8 kilograms. General knowledge of fission and reference to the same sources will tell him that a critical mass of plutonium weighs only 16.45 kilograms.

But the designer also knows from paragraph 12.13 of the famous Smyth report that a heavy reflector is needed in the bomb to reduce the critical size and to perform other important functions in order

[16] W. B. Loewenstein and D. Okrent, *Physics of Fast Power Reactors*, P/637, UN Conference on Peaceful Uses of Atomic Energy (Geneva: 1958), v. 12, pp. 16-37. See also R. T. Ackroyd and J. D. McCullen, *Albedo Calculation Methods*, P/16, same, pp. 38-47.

to make the explosion more efficient.[17] Returning to the earlier sources of information, he finds that when uranium-235 has a heavy reflector its critical mass is only 16.25 kilograms, while under the same circumstances the critical mass of plutonium is 5.79 kilograms.[18]

Very roughly, then, we can say that 16 kilograms of U-235, or 6 kilograms of plutonium, will be required to manufacture some sort of an atomic device until the Nth country aspirant improves his technology by one means or another. But, due to the present (and probably persistent) difficulties of obtaining the uranium isotopes, the Nth country candidate will initially concentrate upon plutonium which, more likely than not, will be obtained through the operation of a power-producing nuclear plant.

To obtain a very crude approximation of how much plutonium is produced in an atomic power station let us postulate a plant with an electrical output of 150,000 kilowatts, which is roughly in the range of the plants being installed today. Let us also assume that the efficiency of the plant is about 20 per cent, that it operates about 300 days per year, and that the design is such that about eight-tenths of a plutonium atom is produced for every U-235 atom burned. This plant will produce the material for one plutonium bomb every ten days, or thirty bombs within the course of a year. Clearly, then, even a modest atomic power plant is capable of producing the fissionable material for a significant number of atomic bombs *as a by-product of its operation*. And if the power adjunct is not required, the same amount of plutonium can be produced with less complication in a single-purpose reactor.

But the plutonium is still in the reactor; it must be extracted,

[17] H. D. Smyth, *A General Account of the Development of Methods of Using Atomic Energy for Military Purposes under the Auspices of the United States Government* (Washington: GPO, 1945), para. 12.13. This classic work and the officially sponsored history of the Manhattan Project, *The New World, 1939-1946*, by Richard G. Hewlett and Oscar E. Anderson, Jr. (Pennsylvania State University Press, 1962), would be invaluable for defining directions and pitfalls for Nth countries.

[18] This corresponds to the thirteen pounds of fissionable material which President Truman told the Platform Committee of the 1956 Democratic Convention in Chicago was carried in one of the first bombs. See Fletcher Knebel and Charles W. Bailey, II, *No High Ground* (New York: Harper, 1960), p. 63.

purified, and appropriately fabricated. Now the handling of plutonium is not simple, for it is an extremely toxic substance. The
human body can absorb only a few millionths of a gram of plutonium without serious danger. Hence, elaborate and costly health
and safety techniques must be incorporated into every stage of the
process. Also involved are metallurgic studies of plutonium which
normally would not be necessary in a program designed merely
for the production of atomic power. All of this entails additional
investment in plant and personnel. It should be noted, however,
that when plutonium is burned as a power-reactor fuel (i.e., for
peaceful purposes), most of the health and safety precautions
needed in a weapons program are required.

Having obtained in proper form the material for the core of the
bomb, would-be producers have to explore and adapt other technologies of conventional explosives and electronics. Although the
general principles are well known, their technical application is
difficult.[19] Most of the techniques can be developed independently
of the acquisition of proper amounts of nuclear materials, since
they do not involve nuclear reactions. Diligent, world-wide search
of atomic energy literature, patents, and so forth, will provide the
investigator with much of the information he requires to plan his
non-nuclear experimental program.[20] Clues to the maximum size
and weight of the Nagasaki "Fat Man" bomb were abundant in
nonofficial literature even before its characteristics were officially
released by the AEC the eve of the nineteenth anniversary of Pearl
Harbor.[21]

[19] For example, see E. W. Titterton, *Facing the Atomic Future* (London:
MacMillan & Co., 1956), "How the Atomic Bomb Works," pp. 222-225. Also,
Nuclear Explosions and Their Effects (New Delhi: The Publications Division,
Government of India, 1958), "Fission Explosions and Critical Size: Implosion,"
pp. A-1 to A-11.

[20] For example, U.S. Patent No. 2,899,557, entitled "Apparatus for Producing
Shadowgraphs" and assigned to the U.S. Atomic Energy Commission, describes
an apparatus for recording phenomena which occur in times of a millionth of
a second or less ". . . in an implosion device comprising a metallic sphere subjected to the implosive force of a surrounding sphere by explosive material
simultaneously detonated at a plurality of points. . . . Such devices may include,
for example, a high explosive sphere comprising a ton or more of material."

[21] John W. Finney, "First Atom Bomb Photos Released After 15 Years," *The
New York Times,* December 7, 1960, p. 1.

Until the nuclear material is actually inserted in the bomb, essential bomb-development research can quite easily be carried out secretly. Since they do not involve facilities or personnel who might ordinarily be identified with an atomic energy program, the concealment of this sole indicator of interest in nuclear weapons could probably be maintained up to the very moment the nation is ready to insert the nuclear component and to test the bomb. This fact underscores the emphasis that an effective control scheme must put on the use of fissionable material.

Testing and Other Problems

Now comes the critical question. Is it necessary to test an atomic bomb? Here one is faced with the inescapable fact that the first primitive bomb tests by the United States, Britain and France—and probably by the U.S.S.R. also—did not fail. The U-235 bomb was first tested over Hiroshima. Experience gives us no reason to expect that a nation's first atomic device, based upon a simple and tried design, will fail. If a nation is reasonably confident that it has the recipe for the Nagasaki bomb, and feels confident of the results of preliminary testing of non-nuclear components, we can be reasonably sure that its device will explode, provided, of course, that some technican does not make a simple mistake. It may not, for one reason or another, give the precise yield expected, but nevertheless when detonated it will certainly be an atomic explosion. Only by dabbling in advance nuclear designs, seeking to increase efficiencies, adapting warheads, etc., does one incur substantial risk of failure.

A test ban will not prevent an exchange of blueprints, or the bombs themselves, among nations, thereby eliminating the need to test; and a test ban has no obvious relationship to further arms control measures. There are certain advantages in a well-negotiated, well-designed test cessation agreement, but such an agreement would not be an absolute panacea for the Nth country problem and other ills.

Are there any other technical or political conditions which will inhibit or prevent the emergence of Nth powers? The earliest mechanism sought to make use of the fact that plutonium is created in different grades, with differing costs and energy values. Even as plutonium-239 is being created in nuclear reactors, some of it is being destroyed—a small fraction by fissioning, and a smaller amount by conversion into a different isotope, plutonium-240. When the plutonium is separated after creation and irradiation in a nuclear reactor, the two isotopes cannot be chemically distinguished. What results is a veritable mélange composed mainly of plutonium-239 and -240 isotopes. Actually, other isotopes such as plutonium-241 and -242 will also be present in small amounts. Important though they are to the reactor designer, it is the presence of plutonium-240 which presents a major complication in the utilization of plutonium for bombs or for power.

On December 30, 1944, Major General Leslie R. Groves, wartime head of the atomic bomb project, reported to General Marshall: "Our previous hopes that an implosion (compression) type of bomb might be developed in the late Spring have now been dissipated by scientific difficulties which we have not as yet been able to solve."[22] One of these difficulties was the unavoidable presence of plutonium-240 in the bomb materials, which contributed to an undesirable phenomenon called "predetonation."

The detonation of an atomic bomb is an exercise in skillful precision timing, particularly in providing neutrons to start the chain reaction at just the right moment. Nature does her best to upset the timing by placing beyond the control of man a few scattered neutrons which may start a chain reaction a fraction of a millionth of a second before the bomb designer would like it to start.[23] This predetonation reduces the explosive yield of a bomb by amounts that depend upon when it occurs.[24] The stray neutrons which can lead to predetonation originate from cosmic rays, from impurities in the bomb materials, and from plutonium-240. The latter is an extremely impatient isotope which fissions spontaneously, without the aid of the neutron required by plutonium-239. In the act of fissioning, the 240 isotope emits several neutrons. Thus the greater

[22] Dept. of State, *Foreign Relations of the United States, Diplomatic Papers, The Conferences at Malta and Yalta, 1945* (Washington: GPO, 1955), p. 384.

[23] H. D. Smyth, cited, para. 12.16.

[24] Phillip Morrison, "The Physics of the Bomb," in J. L. Crammer and R. E. Peierls, eds. *Atomic Energy* (Baltimore: Penguin Books, 1950), pp. 101-125.

the plutonium-240 content, the greater will be the number of un-controllable neutrons flying about, and the greater will be the probability of predetonation.

Plutonium-240 can be thought of, then, as a denaturing ingredient affecting the bomb-grade of plutonium. Indeed, this is the mysterious denaturant suggested in the 1947 Acheson-Lilienthal report on the international control of atomic energy. The technicians participating in that report believed that the deliberate addition of large quantities of plutonium-240 to the world's stocks of plutonium would make the material unsuitable for weapons, but quite satisfactory for peaceful applications. But many plutonium bombs have since been burst, and meanwhile the addition of denaturants to bomb materials has received no further consideration in disarmament discussions. Hence it appears that, while plutonium-240 in certain amounts may be detrimental to particular bomb designs, it can be tolerated in others.

While denaturing is no longer considered effective, plutonium-240 still complicates the peaceful and military programs because of difficulties in pricing (discussed in the next chapter). It consequently has some importance, if not in prohibiting bomb manufacture, at least in encouraging or discouraging a bomb program.

The foregoing paragraphs have shown that it is neither simple nor impossible for a nation to become capable of producing primitive, low-order atomic weapons. However, a precautionary note must be sounded. The Nth country threat can be used as a political weapon in the hope of obtaining agreement on certain disarmament measures. However, in unrealistically overstating the ease with which smaller nations might obtain nuclear weapons, Nth country strategists might bring about more instabilities than solutions. For example, statements backed by apparent authority to the effect that a certain small nation might achieve a nuclear weapon capability, say within five years, can be used by political factions in that country in demanding the achievement of that capability. If the nation really has the necessary technical ability and resources, it may enter the ranks of Nth countries at an earlier date. But if, lacking both ability and resources, it enters upon a nuclear program as a result of political pressures, the results might be disastrous. The nation might dissipate scarce resources of men and materials which could have been devoted to much better advantage in a peaceful atomic energy program or, even more fruitfully, to non-nuclear technical development programs with greater long-range potential.

Further caution must be exercised in evaluating an Nth country's claim of weapons capability, especially if accompanying evidence does not confirm published representations. For example, on December 16, 1959, the Indian government issued the following statement:

> The position is that our atomic energy work has reached the stage when we could, without any external assistance, produce atomic weapons if we so wished.
>
> It is, however, contrary to our policy to do so. There is no question of India being abreast of the leading atomic powers in knowledge of atomic weapons or the resources to make them. No work has been done in India on atomic weapons, nor is proposed to be done.[25]

One cannot quarrel with the fact that a great deal of information necessary for the manufacture of a primitive atomic bomb is publicly available. However, at this stage India lacks most of the facilities and many of the subtle technological skills which are needed to utilize that information. Certainly the statement that India is abreast of the "leading atomic powers" in knowledge or resources is far from correct. There is no doubt, however, that some day India and other Nth countries will be capable of stockpiling small numbers of primitive nuclear weapons—if only by virtue of their constantly improving technological skills and production facilities engaged primarily in peaceful pursuits.

The purpose of this chapter is to emphasize as strongly as possible the inevitable points of contact between the peaceful and military applications of atomic energy. Whether or not the world will be able to minimize the dangers inherent in the further diffusion of nuclear weapons will depend to a major extent upon whether agreements can be reached on the control and application of peaceful atomic energy. Moreover, if significant accord cannot be attained on the peaceful applications, it is probable that the desired accord in the military sphere will never be achieved.

Some have already surrendered. Among the conclusions of the report transmitted to the Joint Committee on Atomic Energy in October 1960 was the following:

[25] *The Times* (London), December 17, 1959, p. 8.

C. The possibility of any significant near-term contribution by atomic power to the arms limitation objective must, therefore, now be written off. In the absence of lessened tensions and effective safeguards, achievement of widespread atomic power could in fact make the arms limitation problem more difficult.[26]

With the second sentence, one must wholeheartedly agree. If the first is the final word, the report will stand as the epitaph on a potential contribution to arms limitation which might have been effective had it been more imaginatively and vigorously promoted.

[26] Robert McKinney, *Review of the International Atomic Policies and Programs of the United States,* v. 1, Report to the Joint Committee on Atomic Energy, 86th Cong., 2d sess. (Washington: GPO, 1960), p. 78F.

Chapter 3

Plutonium for Peace

Having glimpsed the destructive nature of plutonium, the by-product which almost inevitably accompanies atomic power operations, we must now also give Pluto's gift its proper credit for potential usefulness in benign applications of nuclear science. The most active programs directed toward the use of plutonium for power are being conducted in the United States and the Soviet Union. It may well be that the most effective political and technical coup in Atoms for Peace will be scored by the nation first able to announce a demonstrated economic application of plutonium.

Plutonium merits primary emphasis in a study of the interaction of peaceful and military atomic energy programs, not because it is a superior material for either program, but because it is one of the main factors complicating the search for peace. One of the manifest objectives of this search is the elimination or control of fissionable materials. (On the materials of fusion, see Chapter 6.) Elimination is not an inviting alternative. The controls required to assure the elimination of existing supplies of fissionable materials and the prevention of future production would be as complex, costly, and difficult as the controls required to assure the benign use of these materials. Symbolically, the physical elimination of weapon stockpiles would mean that the world had abandoned hope of tapping the benefits of nuclear power and that, even though humanity were able to accomplish this massive disarmament step, it was not confident it could guarantee the security of these materials for benign purposes indefinitely. It is likely, then, that the conversion of stockpiles to peaceful uses will be regarded as more reasonable than their destruction.

Plutonium also complicates this alternative. The stockpiles, representing aggregate international investments of many tens of billions of dollars, consist principally of uranium-235 and plutonium. The technology of using uranium-235 for power will be well developed. If the power technology of plutonium is significantly less developed, conversion of the stockpiles will be complicated.

Technological Problems of Plutonium

Moreover, for some time to come the ability of power systems using uranium-235 to compete economically with conventional systems will depend on the value assigned to the plutonium generated in producing power. It will always be possible to assign a substantial military credit to the by-product plutonium, thus reducing the share of the total cost to be assigned to the power produced. But if military diversion is ended and plutonium has no peaceful value or a very low one, peaceful nuclear power may be too expensive.

The behavior of plutonium in bombs is complex, and the varied composition of plutonium likewise has a pronounced effect on the technical and economic aspects of its peaceful utilization. Therefore, the element's physical characteristics are important parameters underlying national policy in an era when plutonium will be plentiful and widespread. A salient fact is that the 240-isotope, bothersome for bombs, is not necessarily detrimental to the operation of a power reactor. This disparate behavior in its military and peaceful applications has important political and economic implications.

In a uranium-fueled reactor, the plutonium which is inevitably formed affects the economics of power production. For when the reactor fuel is reprocessed, it will contain an amount of plutonium which is roughly proportionate to the amount of time that the fuel has been used and to the power at which it has been operated. But if there is no military application for plutonium, the crutch which makes the power-cost calculations attractive vanishes. As the amount of plutonium increases, its *quality as a weapons material* is progressively reduced, regardless of the benign or military purpose of the parent reactor.

The credit value of the plutonium depends on its quality when it is extracted from the reactor and on the use to which it will be put. If the value of pure plutonium is high, it would be desirable to process nuclear fuels often, before the build-up of the plutonium-240 content begins. Relatively pure plutonium would then be extracted and credited against power costs. But frequent refueling increases operating costs. If fueling can be made infrequent, operating costs will decrease, but *down* go the quality of the plutonium and its value as a by-product. The nuclear power station operator therefore has to seek optimum operating conditions based upon his ability to stretch out refueling times and his prognostication of the market value of the plutonium produced.

This equation can be drastically affected by political factors. Consider France, for instance. Its need for plutonium weapons is immediate and demanding. Plutonium-burning atomic power plants have not yet been practically demonstrated, so plutonium in the short run is valueless for power purposes to France. The French government can, however, arbitrarily assign a high military value to plutonium of the quality it requires, while building a weapons stockpile to the point where it would be effective politically and as a *force de frappe*. On this kind of cost accounting atomic energy in France today could be considered to be economically competitive with conventional fuels. Almost the same situation is found in Britain where many of the projected atomic power stations, initially designated for industrial purposes only, were rescheduled in 1958 to permit the removal of military-grade plutonium. Under present circumstances, it would be impossible to compare the operating costs of the dual-purpose reactors with the costs of those devoted wholly to peaceful purposes, even were such costs available.

Future developments may put plutonium production on a sounder economic basis, independent of its military value and quality. In a *plutonium-fueled* reactor plutonium-240 would be, in a sense, a dilutant. Most nuclear reactors which have operated to date depend upon the action of slowed-down or "thermalized" neutrons in causing the fission of uranium-235 or plutonium-239. But plutonium-240 is much less sensitive to the proddings of thermal neutrons than is plutonium-239. Therefore, in a thermal-type reactor system plutonium-240 might as well be considered excess material without significant energy value. In thermal systems, also, the build-up of useless isotopes similar to plutonium-240 is aggravated.

But in the fast reactor, another type of nuclear power system which is presently under development, the energy value of plutonium-240 is about the same as that of plutonium-239. In the fast reactor, which is almost a compromise between a thermal reactor and the bomb, the unslowed neutrons fission both types of plutonium with equal ease. Because the physics of a fast reactor are somewhat akin to the physics of a bomb, the central core of the reactor, composed of almost pure U-235 or plutonium, is very compact and has a high density of power. This fact gives rise to most of the metallurgical and heat-transfer problems which place the fast power reactor in the "advanced" category. Perhaps the promise of being able to utilize unwanted plutonium-240 is sufficient reason for pursuing the development of fast reactors. In addition, a more widely recognized virtue of fast reactors is that they contribute neutrons greatly in excess of the numbers required to keep the nuclear fires going. These neutrons can be captured in "blankets" of uranium or thorium. The result is *that more fissionable material can be created than is burnt.* This is called "breeding," a process which promises a manifold multiplication of our nuclear resources.

Breeding is the reason the British embarked upon their fast reactor program. Because of a shortage of nuclear fuel in 1951 they stopped construction of a third plutonium-producing reactor, fearing that sufficient uranium would not be available to manufacture its fuel charge. They decided to attempt the breeding of nuclear fuel in fast reactors, hoping to build a system which would be self-supporting in its fuel requirements and perhaps even to enter into the manufacture of uranium-233 from thorium. In 1951, despite the scarcity of enriched uranium, the military demands for all of the plutonium produced were so urgent that it was decided to build a fast reactor with a U-235 core near the remote northern tip of Scotland at Dounreay. By 1956 the U-235 supply picture had become much rosier; nevertheless, Britain went on with the Dounreay experiment. One compelling reason was that the British had to have a long-range use of plutonium in order to justify, economically, their very large program of thermal nuclear power plants, irrespective of a military market for plutonium.

The first large fast reactor, the Enrico Fermi power plant near

Detroit, was to have come into operation in 1960 and is now due in 1963. It was delayed by difficulties related to some rather earthy domestic politics. Arguing that the reactor would endanger the health of the densely populated community, labor unions obtained a court order stopping construction of the plant as it neared completion.[1] Regardless of the merits of the contentions of the opposed parties (and each had cogent arguments), the plant's potential contribution to the peaceful application of atomic energy should not be overlooked.

The Fermi reactor is to be fueled by uranium-235, but the knowledge gained thereby will be helpful in using plutonium in similar systems, But, all in all, what is presently known about plutonium-fueled systems is negligible compared to the data gathered in the very extensive uranium-fueled reactor programs.

Price Problems

Even if all of the technical problems of using plutonium are solved, the contrast between the military and the power values of the substance will cloud the international picture. The recent comprehensive study by Mullenbach provides excellent illustrations of the confusing history of pricing.[2] Here we shall use a simple exercise to illustrate some of the complexities in the pricing system of the U.S. Atomic Energy Commission. Should the reader become lost, the lesson will nevertheless have been taught.

The buy-back, or fair price, schedule guarantees U.S. power reactor operators a fixed price for "weapons-grade"plutonium ranging from $30 to $45 per gram, depending upon the plutonium-240 content. (Presumably this scale reflects the costs of producing the various grades of plutonium, and also their utility in weapons of various designs.) The $45 price is for essentially pure plutonium; for plutonium which is "dirty" above 8.6 per cent, the base price of $30 per gram is paid. These prices were in effect until July 1, 1962. After that, for one year only, the price was set at $30 per gram, *regardless* of the plutonium-240 content. Beyond June 30, 1963, there had been no price commitment. The price reduction may be based on

---

[1] *New York Times,* June 11, 1960, p. 1; June 14, 1960, p. 17; "AEC, PRDC Ask Supreme Court to Review Permit Validity," *Nucleonics,* September 1960, p. 20.

[2] Philip Mullenbach, *Civilian Nuclear Power: Economic Issues and Policy Formation* (New York: The Twentieth Century Fund, 1963).

the anticipation (1) of an over-supply of plutonium, owing to the ever-increasing number of nuclear power reactors which are coming into operation, or (2) of improvements in nuclear weapons technology. These prices are really credits allowed the operators of nuclear power plants in the United States, for by law all fissionable materials produced in any type of plant are government property from the moment each atom comes into existence. While domestic users cannot really own these fissionable fuels, they can lease them advantageously without putting up large amounts of initial capital. Foreign users, on the other hand, can buy but not lease. (However, some of them can finance their purchases through the Export-Import Bank.)

As for plutonium produced abroad in an installation covered by a bilateral agreement, the United States has first option to purchase. It has *guaranteed* the purchase of plutonium only in the case of three reactors operated under the Euratom arrangement. Further, since the United States has committed itself not to use foreign plutonium (except British) for weapons, a different scale of values is applied to these foreign atoms, which are by definition benign, even though they are physically identical with their cousins eligible for military service.

The price scale is arrived at by multiplying the uranium-235 price by the approximate ratios of the constants which describe, for the nuclear engineer, the differing behavior of the materials in a reactor system. The resulting price for the plutonium of foreign origin is about $12 per gram, more or less, depending on the content of higher isotopes like plutonium-240 in relation to pure uranium-235.[3] The latter was priced at $17 per gram until July 1, 1961, when the falling price of natural uranium and a drop in the cost of separation in diffusion plants finally forced a 20 per cent reduction in the price of the highly enriched product.[4] A year later the price plunged an additional 8 to 12 per cent. It is U.S. policy to give

[3] Robert McKinney, *Review of the International Atomic Policies and Programs of the United States*, v. 4, Report to the Joint Committee on Atomic Energy, 86th Cong., 2d Sess. (Washington: GPO, 1960), pp. 1099-1100.

[4] U.S. AEC Press Release D-138, May 29, 1961, "AEC to Revise Charges for Enriched and Depleted Uranium." The price cut meant a reduction of a twentieth of a cent or less, per kilowatt-hour of atomic electric power (see David P. Herron, "AEC's New Prices for Uranium ... How Will They Affect Power Costs?" *Nucleonics*, August 1961, pp. 48-49).

both foreign and domestic users the benefit of such reductions. Further, a new policy elaborated late in 1961 sought to assure foreign operators of the continued availability of U-235 fuels throughout the approximate lifetime of the power plant.[5] Contracts can be written for fuel supplies up to a period of twenty-five years, subject to cancellation rights *on the part of the purchaser* with five years' notice. Whether or not prospective users will regard this as a sufficiently reliable international fuel supply remains to be seen. Undoubtedly an internationally controlled supply of fuel, with similar long-range assurances, would be preferred by some buyers.

This price structure means that the *energy* value of plutonium, when uranium-235 is in abundant supply, is considerably less than its *weapons* value. Presumably, the International Atomic Energy Agency, if it starts to stockpile plutonium, will have to pay other supplying nations at least as much as does the United States. For example, in the U.S.-Euratom demonstration program, IAEA is given an initial option on any plutonium in excess of Euratom's peaceful needs. If the option is not exercised, the United States will purchase the plutonium at the fuel-value price *in effect at the time of the purchase.* Beyond June 30, 1963, the $12 fuel-value price is not guaranteed; the 1961 price reduction on natural and pure uranium makes even that figure inflated by several dollars.

Thus, designers must now base future plant economies on a price of plutonium for fuel of less than $12 per gram, actually at about $9.50.[6] It is also pertinent to note that here is a disarmament cost we can calculate, for when weapon cores are refabricated into fuel rods, each gram of weapons plutonium, assuming that the present scale of prices is maintained, will diminish at least $20 in value.

The energy value of plutonium as at present calculated presupposes a world-wide availability of uranium-235 at U.S. production cost; this certainly is not the present situation. In the United Kingdom, uranium-235 production is small and expensive. To the Brit-

[5] Robert E. Wilson, "USAEC Policies Relative to Foreign Reactors," presentation at the 2d Joint Conference on Nuclear Power, U.S.-Japan Atomic Industrial Forums, Tokyo (released by U.S. AEC Press Release S-27-61, December 5, 1961).

[6] U.S. AEC, *Civilian Nuclear Power . . . a Report to the President—1962.* (Washington: Author, 1962), p. 58.

ish, therefore, the nuclear energy value of plutonium must be large. The British are competitive in atomic power with the United States and for nondomestic purposes, at least, guarantee a plutonium buy-back price which is roughly equivalent to ours. The net effect is that Britain is obtaining bargain-price plutonium. If need be she could afford to raise her buy-back price for plutonium produced by countries receiving bilateral aid so as to make her competitive position more favorable.

The peculiar effect which military requirements, and particularly the separate military price schedules, have upon the economics of associated programs is illustrated by the British-American agreement of May 1959 for the exchange of nuclear materials. Then, as now, the United States had pressing military requirements for plutonium, while the United Kingdom suffered a dearth of uranium-235 for both civilian and military programs.[7] Accordingly, an agreement was reached whereby the United States would exchange 1.76 grams of uranium-235 for every gram of plutonium supplied by the British.

From Britain's point of view this is a bargain. The cost of U-235 domestically produced in Britain is undoubtedly higher than the cost of plutonium, which is the reverse of the situation in the United States. By obtaining in trade with the United States 1.76 grams of U-235 for every gram of her plutonium Britain has bartered well.

Britain's plutonium is produced in stations which also produce civilian power. Two of these, Calder Hall and Chapel Cross, are intended primarily as plutonium producers. The first section of Chapel Cross came into operation in June 1959, and the last section of Calder Hall only a few months previously; one reactor has been operating since the middle of 1956. The British have unequivocally stated that the function of the Calder Hall station was plutonium production. Hence, when the power produced was not in demand, it was dumped; the reactor continued to operate in order to maximize production of plutonium. Under these conditions the value of the power produced probably does not enter strongly into

[7] Apparently Britain's demands for U-235 became somewhat less urgent during 1962. (*AIF Memo* [a monthly publication of the Atomic Industrial Forum, New York], July 1962, p. 16.)

the British government's calculation of the plutonium costs at Calder. However, as reactors which are largely power-producing come into operation in Britain and as their plutonium by-product is used for weapons locally or transferred to the United States, British calculations of its value for military uses and for power must be drastically altered.

For France the situation is vastly more complicated. If the United States did not supply enriched uranium, and France were to calculate plutonium values on the basis of potential uranium-235 costs locally, they would be astoundingly high. (For countries without a uranium-235 factory, the value of plutonium is actually infinite!) In this case the reasonable course would be to abandon the U.S. formula and to calculate plutonium values in relation to the local costs of the almost universally available natural uranium—that is, on the basis of the energy value of that uranium when used in the local technological context.

Thus, in assessing the value of a nuclear fuel, many complex, often conflicting, factors must be taken into account. Is the plutonium to be used in bomb production or as reactor fuel—or for both? If used for military purposes, what grade will be satisfactory for the design contemplated? If used as a nuclear power fuel, what technology will be appropriate? And there will always be the temptation to reduce atomic power costs by assigning large credits to the plutonium by-product, credits which would only be justified by intent to fabricate the material into its more diabolical form. This type of cost rationalization would not in itself be sufficient to trigger a weapons program, but it could form an important element in the argumentation for such a program.

The Central Issue

Sometimes befuddlement on how to apply foreign policies, power policies, and other considerations, combine in such an exquisitely classical manner that a single case suffices to illustrate all the problems. Such a case is the battle over the New Production Reactor (NPR) in the United States. While the history of the NPR is also instructive and interesting on the merits of private versus public power, only its foreign policy aspects will be discussed here.[8]

The case begins at the 1958 Geneva Conference on the Peaceful Uses of Atomic Energy where the Russians startled the world of the atom by unveiling what was to be the world's largest atomic power plant somewhere in Siberia. A superficial glance at the meager description of technical characteristics supplied by the Russians was enough to convince technicians in the rest of the world that this was a plant primarily for the production of plutonium for military purposes. The power side of the plant operated at very low efficiency and in no way represented a contribution to the art of developing economic atomic power plants for peaceful purposes. Quite properly the plant was belittled in the technical press (politely, of course!), and after a few months the Russians no longer boasted of it. The plant had vanished whence it came. Meanwhile, the U.S. plutonium-producing reactors at Hanford were deteriorating and nearing the end of their useful lives. It was necessary to add new facilities. A gigantic plutonium plant, the NPR was authorized in 1959 and construction was begun. Like any other reactor, the NPR would throw off a lot of waste heat, and it seemed appropriate to tap this waste heat for power and feed it into the Pacific Northwest grid. Superficially, this was a laudable aim, producing something useful from a waste product. But the economics of this scheme could never be clarified for the public, because this was a military plant mostly shrouded into secrecy. Also entering the picture was the specter of public power. On these points a bitter battle was fought by the AEC, the Congress, the unions, the utilities, and others, in the summer of 1961.

Regardless of which factions in this battle had the logic of economics on their sides, the real damage was done in presenting this venture as something which would advance the peaceful atom and the prestige of the United States. The NPR is a military plant. Its technology and economics are classified; were they unclassified, it

[8] "Technical and Economic Studies of Generating Electrical Energy with New Plutonium Production Reactor Released Today," U.S. Joint Committee on Atomic Energy, Press Release No. 309, March 28, 1961; *Congressional Record*, v. 107, no. 117, July 13, 1961, pp. 11554-11583; same, v. 107, no. 120, July 18, 1961, pp. 11919-11955.

is not the type of plant which we would be happy to see being built in the U.S.S.R.—and it would be unwise to export its technology to most countries.

But the most effective act of undermining the spirit of the Atoms for Peace philosophy and the oft-stated policy of the United States of continuously striving for an effective arms control arrangement was the contention of NPR supporters that, should any future arms control arrangement seem to be floundering, NPR could swiftly provide plutonium for arms again. Any arms control program which permits the existence of a NPR reactor anywhere after plutonium production for military purposes has been cut off is not arms control at all; and if the United States insisted on the retention of a NPR reactor under the guise of a civilian power plant, it would have to allow other nations similar privileges. Our goals in the area of arms control must not be impaired by using them as political levers in decisions which are not related to arms control.

The necessity of clearly defining those goals and separating them from other confusing policy issues is evident. Simplicity of action has its virtues, and subsequent chapters will argue this with regard to small reactors, food preservation, and other peaceful uses. The implication seems to be that, while the legitimate military interests in various peaceful atomic energy activities must be given full expression, there is also a need for a sharp separation from military policy of those aspects of atomic energy which the world is observing with mixed hopes as something which might contribute to peace.

Disparities in the values of nuclear materials from one country to another could have detrimental effects on the peaceful applications of the atom and the role it is expected to play in securing the peace. Fortunately, the passage of time, the experience with our own rapidly adjusting price schedule, and the approach of sufficient special materials for weapons, all seem to be bringing U.S. prices at least to a natural and sensible level. Another perturbation would be the unlikely event that a weapons limitation agreement is reached. Then, excess stocks of fissionable materials would develop and their prices could be expected to fall. This is a calculable cost of disarmament, equivalent in financial terms to losing many tens of tons of gold from Fort Knox for each ton of fissionable material devoted to peaceful use. Furthermore, irrespective of weapons limitation, advanced technology could easily cause shifts in demands for the various types of fissionable material with corresponding shifts in relative values.

Certainly the shifting spectrum of fuel prices has affected domestic atomic power incentives in the United States. The presence of so many other complicating factors has made it hard to say what effect these shifts have had on international policies. But if in the past we have not been reluctant to make wide price concessions for defense reasons, should we not be prepared to be similarly flexible when that would strengthen the possibilities of arms control and enhance the world-wide peaceful utilization of fissionable materials? Solution of the technological problem of the utilization of plutonium would have more than economic significance. Only that solution could give full substance to the hope that those primordial materials which man has so recently re-created might "serve the needs rather than the fears of mankind."[9]

[9] Eisenhower's Atoms for Peace speech.

Chapter 4

The Peaceful Hazards

Not long ago outside a clock factory in Lanarkshire, little William Gilchrist and two playmates discovered an intriguing canister of ashes. Unfortunately for William and his friends, the ash contained radioactive materials discarded by the factory. Master Gilchrist's experiences for the next few days resembled adventures in a science fiction melodrama. Rushed to London, the three boys were lowered to the bottom of lead-lined pits while above them were suspended an array of Geiger counters with their neon lights flashing wildly. Indeed, the boys had become radioactive, but after a few thorough scrubbings they were dismissed. Returning home, they became heroes and the envy of their school friends.[1]

A world traveler, finding a bargain in a Swiss wrist watch in Singapore, brought it back to the United States. The wayfarer happened to be employed in an organization where radiation was likely to be encountered and, because his film badges seemed to have received an unusual amount of radiation, his watch was checked by the Atomic Energy Commission. The watch was found to contain radioactive strontium-90 in the luminescent markings. (The use of strontium-90 for such purposes is not licensed in the United States but evidently is permitted in some foreign countries.) As a result, the AEC warned that all similar watches imported during a certain period should be checked for radiation.[2] The radiation level of the watch was such that several years of continuous exposure of the skin, but a much briefer exposure of a sensitive organism

---

[1] *The Times* (London), April 3, 1959, p. 6.
[2] *The New York Times*, December 18, 1959, p. 9.

The Peaceful Hazards | 41

like the eye, could have produced serious damage, according to the AEC. Fortunately, strontium-90 was misapplied on only a limited number of watches. A large proportion of those which were considered dangerous have been recovered, but some owners are still wearing their watches unaware of the small radiation source they carry with them.

During 1960 it was found that certain high-quality jewelry was composed of an alloy of ruthenium material which was weakly radioactive.[3] In this case the Atomic Energy Commission ordered that all fabricators' stocks should be disposed of in accordance with AEC regulations on radioactive material but decided that, because the hazard to the wearers was so small, there was no need to recover the jewelry already sold.

These occurrences represent a very small fraction of the incidents in the past decades involving accidental release or dissemination of radioactive products. With the vastly increased use of radioisotopes in industry, agriculture, and medicine, similar incidents are bound to occur. Proper precautions will minimize their frequency; nevertheless, there will always be a chance that weakly radioactive materials will be encountered in unexpected circumstances. For the most part, only a few individuals at a time will experience the hazards, such as they may be. But some incidents may result in the release of larger quantities of radioactive materials, thereby endangering populated areas.

For example, a release of radioactivity occurred at a British plutonium production site (Windscale) in 1957 while the reactor was shut down during a routine maintenance operation. The danger to the countryside was virtually nil, but the milk in the area was found to be so radioactive that its distribution was temporarily suspended. Despite the economic losses sustained (for which the farmers were later compensated) and the contamination of food supplies, the demeanor of the population was not greatly disturbed.

It was the release of short-lived iodine-131 rather than bone-seeking strontium-90 which led to the temporary ban on milk distribution in the vicinity of Windscale, and even this could have been

[3] "AEC Concludes Investigation of Ruthenium Use by Jewelry Industry," U.S. AEC Press Release No. C-169. August 30, 1960.

prevented by a better arrangement of filter screens.[4] The main damage sustained was to the reactor itself. In fact, this was so great that it was never started up again. The major consequences of reactor accidents, even those of a less serious character, have been loss of expensive facilities and increased operating costs. Only in a very few instances has there been loss of life.

The Need for International Action

Accidental release of radioactive materials will become more frequent as the use of radioisotopes becomes more widespread and as reactors of all types, from small research devices to large power stations, become more numerous throughout the world. The technologically advanced nations will recognize the extent of the dangers and be prepared for them. But radioactive materials are being used now in a multitude of ways from the North Pole to Antarctica, from Indonesia to the Congo. Small nuclear reactors are plentiful; and the larger ones, too, are surely going to be distributed widely around the earth and in space. In many instances poorly trained technicians, inadequate safety equipment, or simple human error may release latent radioactivity.

The avoidance of atomic misfortunes is not merely a technological problem; it also provides an opportunity for international action. At present, no international mechanisms or standards exist for assuring the safety either of individuals or of whole populations when nuclear mishaps occur. This is, at the moment, a national problem, a national responsibility. Real wisdom accumulates only with experience. Sometimes the need for a major review of policy is suggested by a major accident. For the British, it was Windscale. For the United States, it was the death of three technicians at the National Testing Station in Idaho.[5]

Though there is no mechanism for international cooperation in

[4] Great Britain, "The Deposition of Strontium 89 and Strontium 90 on Agricultural Land and Their Entry into Milk after the Reactor Accident at Windscale in October, 1957" (London: HMSO, 1958). See also "Windscale Accident Fall-out Measured," *The Times* (London), August 17, 1960, p. 5.

[5] "AEC Makes Survey of All Reactor Operations," U.S. AEC Press Release No. D-12, January 12, 1961; "Three Killed by Blast in Atom Reactor," *The New York Times,* January 5, 1961, p. 1.

assessing reactor hazards, some nations will (or rather should) learn from the misfortunes of others. But they must assess their reactor hazards independently. For example, the first British-made power reactor constructed in earthquake-prone Japan had to have a resistance to horizontal seismic forces three times as large as the safety factor ordinarily specified in Japanese building codes.

Israel had to change the initial plans for the location of its first atomic reactor—a 5,000-kilowatt research installation for use by the Wietzmann Institute in Rehovot—for fear that radioactive materials released through an accident might drain into the country's existing source of water. Then other fears natural to that turbulent area arose. A nuclear accident is only a remote possibility, but suppose that the reactor were deliberately sabotaged or bombed? To avoid this danger the Israelis built their reactor some distance northwest of Rehovot at Nebi Rubin on the Mediterranean coast. Their reasoning ran somewhat as follows: The most likely aggressor would be Egypt. If Egypt could be made aware that contamination spread by air and sea currents along the seacoast would endanger its population, the reactor probably would not be bombed. Other factors evidently governed the siting of Israel's second reactor (see Chapter 5).

The Israeli reasoning suggests a serious situation to which even non-nuclear warfare might give rise. As research reactors and atomic power plants multiply, the risk increases that non-nuclear aggressive actions may result in the release of large quantities of dangerous radioactive materials. In warfare of any type a power plant is a primary target. A few conventional high-explosive bombs falling on a reactor, or penetrating storage tanks of waste materials, could cause the same type of radioactive hazard that would be produced by the explosion of a small atomic bomb.

Even were instruments and men perfect and accidents nonexistent, the world would still face the problem of disposing of the fantastically large amount of radioactivity which will be created in atomic operations. This problem must be solved, not only for the sake of populations now living but also for the safety of many subsequent generations. Like the fallout from tests of atomic bombs, it transcends national boundaries, thus requiring and providing an opportunity for coordinated, international action. And if solutions of the fallout problem (i.e., test moratoria) are to be coupled with conditions which presumably contribute to a stable peace, should not international efforts to achieve safer utilization of the peaceful atom also be part of a larger plan leading to national security as well as human safety?

Radiation and Modern Environmental Nuisances

Radiation has never respected political or geographical boundaries. Since the beginning of time the universe and the earth within it have been bathed continuously in a shower of cosmic radioactivity, a manifestation of the incomprehensible forces which created the universe and which still may be creative. Only in the waning years of the nineteenth century and the early years of the twentieth did men become aware of the shower of radioactivity from space and the related emanations from materials in the earth. Among those who pioneered this understanding were Pierre and Marie Curie, names immortalized in several scientific terms which are now common. Their most familiar memorial is the curie, a unit of radioactivity. A radioactive substance whose atoms undergo a nuclear change at the rate of 37 billion per second is said to possess a curie of activity. This is approximately the rate at which a gram of radium, discovered by the Curies, disintegrates.

A curie represents quite a large amount of radiation but by itself does not measure potential biological injury. The measurement of harm is a complex matter depending on the type of radiation encountered, the energy of the radiation, and physiological factors. Under certain circumstances a few millionths of a curie can be harmful; under others, temporary exposure to several curies of radiation may have little effect. Properly controlled, large or small doses of radiation may even be beneficial, as in cancer treatment through exposure to radioactive cobalt, or in treating angina pectoris.[6]

Most radioisotope uses involve only thousandths or millionths of a curie, i.e., millicuries or microcuries. Before nuclear reactors were invented only a very few curies of radioactivity had been tedi-

---

[6] "Radioactive Iodine Said to Aid Heart," *The New York Times,* February 12, 1961, p. 55.

ously produced from natural substances for medical and industrial purposes, but now with the advent of the nuclear reactor many millions of curies can be easily produced; indeed, they are unavoidably created as a result of the operation of the reactor itself. They are the waste products of the fission process.

The circumstances under which radioactive products might be released with harmful results are varied. Isotopes used in medicine and industry can be misplaced; a nuclear reactor can have an accident; a poorly designed capsule for the disposal of radioactive waste could rupture underground or on the ocean floor. Despite all precautions there will be accidental releases of radioactive material. Those who are unwilling to accept the slight risks involved must also be ready to forego the great benefits which peaceful applications of atomic energy can bring.

We accept without question the advantages of the industrial revolution which are largely due to the burning of fossil fuels and we do not loudly proclaim the disadvantages. For example, in Britain, where the use of coal gas is extensive, more than 870 deaths in 1958 were attributed to that commodity.[7] Our modern way of life, our modern comforts pollute our planet. As a by-product of their beneficial results, man's power plants, automobiles, and the like have released into the atmosphere about 360 billion tons of carbon dioxide during the past century. By the year 2000 another 1.5 trillion tons will have been added. The biological consequences of such pollution are likely to be severe; but, ignoring this presently controversial question, other catastrophes may be in prospect. The temperature of the earth's surface depends very much upon the carbon dioxide content of the mantle of air. As a result of intensifying this "greenhouse" effect, it is quite possible that the average temperature of the earth's surface will increase.[8] This would ultimately make certain areas less habitable and conceivably lead to melting of the icecaps and the inundation of many of the world's greatest coastal cities. All this in addition to the irritating (and probably

[7] Great Britain, *The Registrar General's Statistical Review of England and Wales for the Year 1958,* Part III (London: HMSO, 1960), p. 67.

[8] The experts still argue about this (*The New York Times,* January 30, 1961, p. 40), but the fact remains that the ultimate effects of industrial pollutants on this planet do include some major catastrophic possibilities.

quite damaging) effects of smog. If there are many uncertainties in such predictions, they are probably comparable to those involved in speculations on the effects on the world environment of the gradual addition of very small amounts of radioactivity.

It is commonly believed that very little is known about the effects of ionizing radiation. This is not so. More is known about the effects of ionizing radiation than is known about the biological effects of any of the innumerable environmental nuisances that man has created.[9]

We seem to accept the benefits of burning coal and oil without fear of possible readjustments which the use of these fuels entails. Now that great caution is being exercised in the release of man-created radioactivity into the environment, need we be afraid of the peaceful uses of a commodity which has vaster import than all the fuels civilized man has used until now?

Disposal Problems—Technical and Political

The quantities of radioactive effluents thus far disposed of are small when compared with the amounts which will be generated in an expanded nuclear power economy. Reactor operations produce about 1,000 gallons of high level waste (containing over one curie of radioactivity per gallon) for each ton of uranium processed. Each reactor load consists of a charge of many tens, or hundreds, of tons of uranium. And each gallon of waste contains an amount of strontium-90 perhaps a million times as great as that which it is estimated the human body can tolerate, to mention only one of the harmful radioisotopes present. Thus, the disposal problem is a choice between diluting radioactive wastes many, many trillionfold if there is any chance that they could find their way into the human body and, alternatively, safely imprisoning these vast quantities of harmful materials so that they are excluded from the biological cycle.

By 1980 the world nuclear power industry will have accumulated several millions of gallons of waste, which is but a small fraction of the wastes accumulated in the manufacture of weapons material.

[9] Merril Eisenbud, Professor of Industrial Medicine and Director of Environmental Radiation Laboratory at New York University Medical Center, "Educating the Public About Radiation," *Nucleonics*, June 1960, p. 83.

By the year 2000 the totals from peaceful activities may approach 100 million gallons or more. Then major responsibility for possible contamination will shift from the shoulders of the military to the sponsors of peaceful atomic energy programs. The disposal of these vast quantities will continue to present major technological and legal problems.[10] For over fifteen years the many millions of curies of radioactive wastes generated at the Hanford, Washington, plutonium production plants have been buried in huge underground tanks in isolated areas. Similar disposition has been made of at least 99 per cent of all the concentrated, highly radioactive waste products thus far created in the world's nuclear weapons manufacturing facilities. This method of disposal is not expensive and there is still a lot of room underground.[11] But since there are uncertainties about the long-range structural integrity of underground burial chambers, it is essential that their sites be selected so that if leakage does occur, it would not contaminate large areas and underground streams.

What are the alternative disposal methods? At present, large quantities of dilute radioactive wastes are daily pumped into the environment. For example, the British plutonium production center at Windscale discharges thousands of curies per month of radioactive waste into the Irish Sea. In Atlantic coastal areas only about 8,000 curies of *contained* radioactive material, mainly from research reactors and isotope laboratories, were deposited between 1951 and 1958. But these amounts will increase. Since most of the ocean disposal areas will lie outside the territorial waters of any country, it is important that international agreement be reached and registration procedures established so that particular areas of the ocean will not be loaded with radioactive matter beyond their safe capacities. The major difficulty in oceanic disposal is that once the material is dumped we have no real assurance that we are safely rid of it. Physical control may have been lost because of the uncertain time factor and our ignorance of the unknown processes which occur at

[10] "Waste Disposal," *Nuclear Engineering*, January 1960, p. 27.
[11] The cost of the radioactive waste-handling system attached to each plant should be no more than the cost of fly-ash and slag-handling equipment associated with a coal-fired plant.

the bottom of the sea.[12] For atomic power, international cooperation in oceanography stimulated during the International Geophysical Year has become an important field.

Regardless of technical evaluations, political factors and general
public misapprehension will continue to influence or restrict
waste disposal activities. Technical arguments mustered by French
government experts were unable to convince officials on the Riviera
and in Corsica that a low-level experiment in waste disposal would
not hurt the tourist business. Under present psychological conditions the politicians were probably right. They forced the government to yield on the issue[13] and France continues to have great difficulty in disposing of its radioactive wastes, each incident making
it harder to overcome popular objections. After the Mediterranean
incident the Commissariat Général à l'Energie Atomique proposed
to bury weakly radioactive materials in tunnels dug in the Jura
mountains, but it merely succeeded in bringing into a new area
what is rapidly becoming an old and familiar controversy.[14]

In the Western hemisphere a dispute arose in June 1959 when
the Mexican government protested the licensing of a U.S. firm to
dispose of radioactive wastes in the Gulf of Mexico, at equal distances from U.S. and Mexican shores. The U.S. Department of State
wrote in a statement to the AEC, "Our Embassy at Mexico City con-
curs in the Department's view that Mexico's reaction to granting
the license would be uniformly adverse and would cause harm to
our relations with Mexico, regardless of any explanations that
might be given."[15] A strong phrase, "regardless of any explanations
that might be given." In this instance the AEC denied the license.
On the surface, its decision perhaps seems of minor importance, but

[12] Roger Revelle and M. B. Schaefer, *Oceanic Research Needed for Safe Disposal of Radioactive Wastes at Sea*, P/2431 of 2d UN International Conference
on Peaceful Uses of Atomic Energy (Geneva: UN, 1958), v. 18, pp. 364-370.

[13] *The New York Times*, October 11, 1960, p. 4. Also Jonathan C. Randal,
"Paris Heeds Monaco Protest. Delays Dumping A-Waste," *The New York
Herald Tribune* (Paris edition), October 13, 1960, p. 3.

[14] Déchets radioactifs: nouvelle controverse," *Le Figaro* (Paris), December 1,
1960, p. 10.

[15] Letter of November 18, 1959, from Roy R. Rubottom, Jr., U.S. Department
of State, to the Honorable John A. McCone, U.S. Atomic Energy Commission.

it had interesting undertones which give some insight into the interaction of technical and political considerations. It hints that the latter, for better or for worse, may take precedence as the disposal problem becomes more and more acute.

The Commission denied the license on the ground that the integrity of the waste container after disposal at sea was questionable. One of the Commissioners, while concurring in the action, felt it necessary to point out that the findings were "... based on the eagerness of the Commission to allay all anxiety, however unreasonable, unfounded, and scientifically unsound, of the residents of those areas with regard to safety." He noted further:

... In the meanwhile, however, and because of the damage already done to the rate of development of the peaceful atom by sensational exaggerations in the press and over the air of the hazards of this newly available form of energy, it may well be that the nuclear progress of the United States can be best and most rapidly promoted by recognizing firstly that public knowledge of the subject will develop gradually and secondly by taking in this case extreme, even if not completely logical, measures to satisfy even unreasonable popular doubts concerning health and safety.[16]

Politically the Commission's action was probably correct; technically it might possibly be justified. Yet technical considerations were made to bear the burden of the decision. This raises the interesting question: If the proposed method of disposal could have been demonstrated to be absolutely harmless, how could these technical facts have been presented so as to convince the objecting parties, including residents of the Gulf area in the United States, as well as in Mexico?

Reactor wastes also raise a specter in relation to the Nth country problem. Radiological warfare would use radioactive material as an offensive weapon.[17] The use of waste fission products for pur-

[16] U.S. AEC Press Release No. C-121, June 23, 1960, "AEC Issues Decision in Houston Waste Disposal Case," pp. 37-39.

[17] Samuel Glasstone, ed., *The Effects of Atomic Weapons,* prepared by the U.S. Department of Defense and published by the U.S. Atomic Energy Commission, June 1957 (Washington: GPO, 1957), sec. 9.95-9.97. Also *Chemical-Biological-Radiological (CBR) Warfare and Its Disarmament Aspects,* a study prepared by the Subcommittee on Disarmament of the Senate Committee on Foreign Relations, Committee Print, 86th Cong., 2d sess. (Washington: GPO, 1960), pp. 16-18.

poses of destruction is extremely inefficient and cumbersome; atomic bombs are much more effective. Nevertheless the packaging and delivery of waste products from an atomic power reactor could constitute an extremely provocative weapon of small-scale destruction and high psychological impact. This weapon could be utilized by countries having no atomic bomb program, and it is even conceivable that wastes could be purloined for this purpose from remote dumping grounds by nations which have no major nuclear program at all, military or benign. Here is a strong argument for international registration and supervision of atomic burial sites.

Since the indiscriminate dissemination of radioactive waste, either through accident or by a deliberate act of warfare or sabotage, would seem to be a matter of concern to all nations, it should be one of the relatively simpler (although still difficult) tasks of international negotiation to conclude an agreement subjecting all large-scale disposal sites to international registration. If disposal sites have been selected which have no military or other "intelligence" significance, it does not seem that any nation could have any objection to revealing their location. Since the wastes have trivial military significance to those nations which already possess large stockpiles of nuclear weapons, it may be possible to arrange for inspection of the disposal sites—an arrangement which conceivably might prove a step toward working out more significant measures of international control.

Regardless of the nature of the international action which mutual concern calls for, it is evident that even in that mythical world where no nuclear weapons exist, civil defense organizations, local and national, must be prepared to handle radioactive emergencies caused by sabotage, war or chance.

Another possibility of long-range contamination arises very early in the chain of processing activities. When an ore-processing mill concentrates uranium, it dumps large quantities of waste into nearby rivers. These wastes contain radium and other radioactive products in far greater concentration than is normally found in the environment. Unless protective measures are adopted, inhabitants some distance downstream might drink water containing several times the concentration of radioactivity considered safe. Agricultural products grown on soils adjacent to the rivers would have higher than normal radioactivity.

Surveys of the U.S. Public Health Service in 1959 indicated that this situation had occurred at several uranium mills in Colorado. The water of the Animas River had been contaminated all the way into the state of New Mexico. Approximately 30,000 persons were using water which was contaminated in some instances as high as ten times the safe working level.[18] In addition to the radioactivity, toxic chemicals were present which had destroyed the bulk of fish and other aquatic life. As a result of the surveys the U.S. Atomic Energy Commission ordered a number of mills to take steps to control more thoroughly the concentration of radioactive and toxic materials sent downstream.

The dumping of radioactive products downstream into the territory of another nation, might cause serious international difficulties. Clearly there is a need for international agreement on safety levels in uranium and thorium mill operations. Levels of exposure from indiscriminate dumping could be equal to, or greater than, those encountered world-wide as the result of atomic bomb tests. It seems reasonable, therefore, that steps taken to curb such tests because of fall-out should be supplemented by attempts to limit widespread radioactive contamination from nonweapon sources.

Not only is radioactive pollution of this modest sphere we inhabit a problem, but, since we now have the capability to send devices into outer space and to other bodies in the solar system, we need also to be concerned about contamination elsewhere. Future space vehicles undoubtedly will use nuclear batteries, or may even be propelled by nuclear energy. While still close to earth, these may present special contamination dangers and, when in space, may give rise to difficulties thus far not envisioned. Recognizing this, the AEC toward the end of 1959 established an Aero-Space Nuclear Safety Board to consider space contamination problems. Initial considerations indicated:

... that the potential radiation exposures which might arise from the development of all aerospace nuclear power sources (as forecast for the

[18] *Radiation Protection Criteria and Standards: Their Basis and Use,* Summary Analysis of Hearings before the Joint Committee on Atomic Energy, 86th Cong., 2d sess., October 1960 (Washington: GPO, 1960), pp. 350-394.

next 20 years) can be held well within presently accepted limits for the population at large. This conclusion would remain valid even assuming a parallel effort elsewhere matching that of the United States.[19]

Speculative proposals have been made to rid the earth of radio-active effluents by projecting them into outer space. In the distant future waste disposal grounds could conceivably be found on desolate solar system bodies, but too little is known at the moment of return mechanisms, the effect of space contamination on future scientific investigations, and other relevant matters to evaluate this possibility. Not the least of the difficulties is to attain delivery of space projectiles with 100 per cent reliability. And even assuming this is accomplished, a vast reduction in the estimated present cost —perhaps $2 million per 100 pounds—of putting waste into space would have to be effected.[20] While disposal in space can hardly be considered an urgent matter at present, the contamination of space by nuclear components of rockets must be. "The use of nuclear rockets will raise serious international political problems since the possibility that a reactor could re-enter [the earth's atmosphere] and fall on foreign territory cannot be ignored."[21] Could an international collaborative effort directed toward minimizing the artificial contamination of space be linked with the control of missiles which can deliver nuclear warheads? A first approach might be made through international registration of all launchings involving a nuclear component, with world-wide studies of their effects.

The Possibilities of International Action

There are seemingly no limits to the possibilities of uncontrolled contamination. Common interests demand urgent international action. Further, many aspects of contamination relate to the more baffling questions of weapons manufacture and control. Satisfactory international resolution of the health and safety problem, provid-

[19] U.S. AEC Press Release S-26-60, December 15, 1960, p. 2.

[20] Estimate given in discussion on the disposal of radioactive waste sponsored by IAEA, Vienna, on September 20, 1960 (see *IAEA Bulletin,* Special Number, November 1960, p. 10).

[21] Public Affairs Press, *New Frontiers of the Kennedy Administration, The Texts of the Task Force Reports Prepared for the President* (Washington: Author, 1961), p. 7.

ing common standards and a mild form of inspection and enforcement, could carve a strong initial foothold on the trail leading toward a meaningful system of arms control. International cooperation and agreement on these important matters can be based only upon the initial establishment of "safe" levels. The initial establishment of safe levels and deliberations started some three decades ago have provided a good beginning.

The standards problem shows how bewildering, even to the specialists, the fantastic array of international bureaucratic agencies can be. Because fixing standards seemed an easy task, every organization which had any interest at all in atomic energy seized upon it, including the World Health Organization (WHO), the International Labor Organization (ILO), the United Nations Educational, Scientific and Cultural Organization (UNESCO), the International Commission of Radiological Unit (ICRU), the International Commission on Radiological Protection (ICRP), the International Congress of Radiology (ICR), the International Organization for Standardization (ISO), Euratom, OEEC, IAEA, and others. Nor is this list comprehensive since it does not include subordinate or separate national organizations.[22]

The ICRP, one of the older bodies, has great international stature. Established in 1928 to recommend permissible radiation dosages, it is composed of representatives from East and West who rarely enter upon philosophical discussions in their recommendations. The ICRP does not recommend standards for preventive measures, something which is largely within the province of the ILO. However, as the nuclear industry began to expand and as fallout became a dominant political issue, the ICRP in its 1958 report found it necessary to observe:

(58) Proper planning for nuclear power programs and other peaceful uses of atomic energy on a large scale requires a limitation of the exposure of the whole populations, partly by limiting the individual doses and partly by limiting the number of persons exposed.

(59) This limitation necessarily involves a compromise between dele-

[22] A good summary description of the work of international and national organizations is found in *Radiation Research in the Life Sciences. Current Projects in the United States and Throughout the World,* Committee on Government Operations, 86th Cong., 2d sess. (Washington: GPO, 1960).

terious effects and social benefits. Consideration of genetic effects plays a major role in its evaluation. The problem has been discussed extensively in recent years and suggestions have been made by different national bodies. The Commission is aware of the fact that a proper balance between risks and benefits cannot yet be made, since it requires a more quantitative appraisal of the probable biological damage and the probable benefits than is presently possible. Furthermore, it must be realized that the factors influencing the balancing of risks and benefits will vary from country to country and that the final decision rests with each country.[23]

The "balancing of risks and benefits" could differ drastically from country to country. An Nth country applicant in a hurry to obtain plutonium as quickly and cheaply as possible might take much greater risks than a nation entering a long-range, peaceful program. And, in some areas, life is a relatively cheap commodity.

Although not legally binding on member nations, the recommendations of the ICRP are usually adopted with minor variations by cooperating national bodies such as the U.S. National Committee on Radiation Protection (NCRP). Similarly, in the United States the consequent recommendations of the NCRP carry no legal implications as regards the statutory responsibilities of the AEC and the Public Health Service. As a means of centralizing responsibility for radiation protection, the Federal Radiation Council (FRC) was established in 1959.[24] But the eventual responsibility of the FRC, or what is more important, its authority has not been defined.

The division of political responsibility within a nation raises difficulties, but on the international level they are compounded. Various groups have instituted studies looking toward the formulation of standard radiation practices, standard glossaries, symbols, etc.

[23] *Radiation Protection: Recommendations of the International Commission on Radiological Protection*, Adopted September 9, 1958 (London: Pergamon Press, 1959), p. 14.

[24] By Public Law 86-373. With a working group composed of representatives from the appropriate government agencies, it has performed much important spade-work. For example, see "Background Material for the Development of Radiation Protection Standards," Staff report of the FRC, May 13, 1960. Also *Radiation Protection Criteria and Standards: Their Basis and Use*, Hearings before the Joint Committee on Atomic Energy, 86th Cong., 2d sess., May 24-26, 31, June 1-3, 1960 (Washington: GPO, 1960).

What is required now is an organization to coordinate organizations. The ILO, particularly, has put in a strong bid as the proper agency for this task. However, the IAEA has the greatest number of member nations and symbolically at least, represents the international peaceful effort in atomic energy. It seems essential, therefore, that all agencies and groups prescribing and enforcing radiation standards should closely coordinate their work with the IAEA. But again the paradox of cause and effect emerges. International agencies will not bow to the IAEA until it is strong; it will not become strong until they do bow.

Compensation, Liability and the Accident Rate

The establishment of international standards for protection against radiation is only part of the health problem created by an expanding nuclear economy. Should injury occur because of a radiation accident, will the victim be as equitably compensated as when he breaks a leg or loses an arm? The mysterious nature of radiation and the fact that the long-range effects of radiation damage to the human body are still largely unknown continue to demand greater compensation. One finds in various nations widely differing concepts of liability for accidents which are purely nonnuclear; the injection of the atom naturally complicates the matter.[25]

Disregarding emotional, mysterious, or political circumstances which often make statistics meaningless, the actuarial figures indicate that the probabilities of accidents are extremely small. For example, AEC studies appear to indicate that if a hundred large power reactors were operating in the United States, a citizen's chance of being killed in any year by a single reactor accident would be less than one in 50 million.[26] This should be contrasted with the chance of one in 5,000 to which the citizen exposes himself in exchange for the comfort and convenience of living in an auto-

[25] E. Blythe Stason, *Legal Problems of Liability and Financial Protection Connected with Radiation Injuries*, P/2352, 2d UN International Conference on Peaceful Uses of Atomic Energy (Geneva: UN, 1958), v. 11, pp. 6-16.
[26] U.S. AEC, *Theoretical Possibilities and Consequences of Major Accidents in Large Nuclear Power Plants*, WASH-740 (Washington: GPO, 1957), p. ix.

motive civilization. (Needless to say, these statistics and AEC philosophy regarding them are not always unchallenged.) [27]

When a catastrophe occurs, injuring persons and property beyond the immediate area of a reactor, the claims are likely to be numerous and costly. It is difficult to predict accurately the results of a catastrophic accident, since, fortunately, in the United States and elsewhere over a fifteen-year period there have been fantastically few accidents.[28] And the vast majority of those have not occurred in the operation of the larger reactors. Further, most of the accidents (about forty) were technical failures in components which did not result in radiation exposure or injury. Actually, the data can be used to support either of two opposing opinions on the safety of nuclear reactors. Either they can be used to show that since accidents occur with a finite frequency they *might* develop into something catastrophic, or to demonstrate that despite the frequency of accidents, no catastrophe has occurred and that, therefore, it is extremely unlikely.

In the history of the AEC most deaths and injuries have been the result of accidents which might have occurred in any large-scale industrial undertaking. During the twelve years ending in 1955, the U.S. atomic energy program suffered 184 fatalities. Of these only two were due to radiation injury, and both occurred during experiments with weapons systems which were not in any phase related to the peaceful utilization of atomic energy. Through January 1961 only three deaths had occurred as a result of reactor operations, all of them in a single accident (January 3, 1961) in which no dangerous radioactivity was dispersed outside the building housing the experimental device.[29] Still, the accident did demon-

---

[27] "Nuclear Mishaps Worry AFL-CIO," *The New York Times,* July 17, 1960, p. 4. Also, "Medical Supervision of Workers Exposed to Ionizing Radiations," presentation by Leo Goodman at the European Atomic Energy Community Symposium at Stresa-Ispra, Italy, May 4, 1961.

[28] U.S. AEC, *A Summary of Industrial Accidents in USAEC Facilities, 1945-1955* (with supplements updating informaiton through 1958), TID-5360 (Washington: GPO, 1956). Spencer Burkett, "Nuclear Accident Survey," *Nuclear Power,* October 1960, pp. 77-80.

[29] U.S. AEC, "Interim Report on the SL-1 (Stationary Low Power Reactor No. 1)," prepared by a Board of Investigation appointed by AEC General Manager A. R. Luedecke and attached to AEC Press Release No. D-33, February 2, 1961 (Washington: Author, January 27, 1961). Mimeographed.

strate that no reactor yet devised can be considered absolutely safe even, as in this case, after several years of reliable operation.

On the basis of 1955 statistics, it appears that the accident rate with nuclear reactors was only one-half the rate in major industries, as reported by the National Safety Council. The few misfortunes of later years, although more dramatically publicized than accidents in other industries do not significantly affect the statistical picture. For 1957 the injury rate in the coal industry was about 7 per cent. For construction activities in the U.S. atomic energy program, the rate was 4 per cent, while in actual reactor operations the rate was about 1.75 per cent.[30] These accident rates were exceeded slightly in the oil industry in 1957.

Many were the injuries, often long undiscovered, suffered by the early handlers of substances utilizing radioactivity for the beneficent purposes visualized by the Curies. It is significant that at present, when radioactive substances are so much more widespread, the rate of radiation injuries is probably lower than the unrecognized rate of injury during prefission years, when the dangers were not appreciated.

Studies of financial liability for nuclear accidents, taking into account the costs of evacuation of personnel and consequent restrictions on productive activities, indicate that damages might reach an upper limit of $7 billion. Clearly these are risks which private companies cannot cover by conventional means. Hence, in 1957 Congress enacted the Price-Anderson Amendment to the Atomic Energy Act of 1954 to provide government funds up to $500 million per accident for indemnities, in addition to the amounts furnished from private sources. Although the amendment applies only to accidents occurring within the United States, foreign as well as domestic suppliers are protected. Reactor licensees and suppliers are required to hold insurance policies ranging from $1 million to $60 million. This insurance is obtainable privately from insurance pools.

The situation of exporters supplying nuclear products abroad is complicated by differing concepts of legal liability and other legal

[30] U.S. AEC, Technical Information Service, *A Summary of Industrial Accidents in USAEC Facilities,* TID-5360, Supp. 2 (Washington: Author, September 1959), p. 2.

and psychological difficulties. Moreover, in the smaller countries a major nuclear accident could spill over from one into another, so that regional agreement is required. The participation of private industrial firms in local or foreign nuclear activities depends a great deal on a satisfactory resolution of the liability problem. A regional agreement on basic principles seems essential, but at the same time national states must be free to take action within their boundaries. Thus, how to combine uniformity with flexibility is the difficult problem facing the international groups that are attempting to devise agreements on liability.

Indemnity has thus far been the major preoccupation of several international nuclear organizations. Under the aegis of OEEC (now OECD) a convention was drafted suggesting that the maximum liability for an operator be fixed at $15 million.[31] This figure corresponds in general to that fixed in the U.K. Nuclear Installations Act of 1959, which requires private indemnification of £5 million in respect of one accident at a single site. As for broader coverage (i.e., job liability), the British philosophy is to regard any damage in excess of £5 million as a national disaster which would oblige the government to render assistance without a previously defined limit. Euratom, however, appears to regard the OECD and British private indemnification limits as low and hopes to supplement the OECD Convention with stronger provisions; indemnification in the range of $120 million is being considered. The International Atomic Energy Agency has held a number of meetings to consider a broad international liability convention similar to that of the OECD but expressed in more general language and with special provisions because of the Agency's wider geographical coverage.

The appearance of nuclear-powered ships on the high seas may well force the issue on reaching international liability agreements. Traditionally, the Belgian government has undertaken the circulation of draft maritime conventions for discussion and approval by the Comité Maritime International. Since nuclear propulsion systems in ships, like land-based reactors, will require govern-

[31] Organisation for European Economic Co-Operation, "Report to the Council of the Steering Committee for Nuclear Energy on Third Party Liability in the Field of Nuclear Energy" (Paris: Author, June 23, 1959), p. 1.

mental guarantees of indemnity for accidents, in addition to those obtained privately, the Comité has established a close working relationship with the International Atomic Energy Agency. If the IAEA can show that it has contributed significantly to international indemnity agreements applicable to both sea- and land-based reactors, it will have a strong case for arguing that it can engineer broader, atomic energy control measures.

No matter how or where they are used—whether for propulsion, for electrical power, for medical purposes—reactor systems and associated radioactive materials can be made safe; but they are not safe either inherently or necessarily. Indeed, they must be regarded as dangerous until they are demonstrated to be sufficiently safe. In the United States and the United Kingdom, at least, highly competent (and highly skeptical) committees of experts must approve the safety aspects of any reactor system before it can be built, and before it is allowed to operate. But with every country free to pass on the safety characteristics of its own reactors, and with competent inspectors still very scarce in the world, it should not be surprising that more frequent and perhaps more serious accidents may occur as reactors multiply.

The IAEA has a Panel on Safe Operation of Critical Assemblies and Research Reactors which has prepared a safety manual and assisted in the establishment of safety procedures for two or three small research reactors. Were this activity extended to the realm of *power* reactors (something which would require a full-time panel staff), it would give the IAEA its first important responsibility in the power field. Certainly, any government whose reactor system might accidentally spew radioactive materials over international boundaries should not only have the opportunity of using the services of an international safety panel but should also be considered under obligation to do so.

The adoption and enforcement by the members of the IAEA and other nations of safety measures fixed and inspected by an international body would involve large administrative expenses. But the stringent control measures responsible for the admirable safety record already achieved by a few safety-conscious powers, if incorporated in a multilateral agreement, would contribute much toward international control of nuclear materials. For radiation safety procedures, such as the control of wastes, extensive radiation monitoring, accounting for hazardous materials, and other safety concerns are intimately related to the measures which would be required in an international system of inspection of all nuclear activities.

Chapter 5

Is Control Possible?

In the Negev, Abraham dug a well and named his watering-place Beersheba, "the well of the Covenant." There is still plenty of water in the wells of Beersheba, and there is uranium, too, in the Negev. Together the two resources suggest atomic power, a suggestion which became obvious to Israel some time ago. It has been said that all Beersheba knew of the atomic reactor being built east of the city, and that passing Rusians were aware of it. But owing to the Israeli habit of secrecy, the rest of the world was generally unaware of the project. Then Washington was seized with another attack of "Nth country-itis," more violent than the affair of the German centrifuges (see Chapter 2).

Fearing Arab boycotts of French equipment suppliers and Arab commando raids, Israel apparently had some valid reasons for secrecy. Foolishly, Israeli authorities informed U.S. officials that the construction was to be a textile plant. Thus were conceived the fears that Israel was building an atomic weapons factory. But the furor in Washington forced confession that the plant was to be a reactor (Israel's second), intended only to "serve the needs of industry, agriculture, health and science." The political impact of the forced announcement was entirely negative.

Israel handled the matter badly, but it should be recognized that no nation is under legal or moral obligation to report or disclose any indigenous atomic energy operation, to place it under any form of international inspection, or to satisfy any other nation about its purpose. Many circumstances might justify secrecy, not least the danger of diversion or theft of fissionable materials and the possibility of sabotage. Israel is not unique in having these problems. The world is being peppered with reactors, large and small, many in countries less stable than Israel. It would not be surprising to hear of a reactor being looted of its shiny components, including the radioactive fuel elements which would be brandished about (how brief a life for the celebrator!) as symbols of a new freedom.

It has been the fashion recently to consider a nuclear reactor, or two, indispensable instruments toward the achievement of the goals of even the least developed of the emerging nations. Atop Mount Amba, a hill just outside Leopoldville, stands a modern university dedicated to the social and physical betterment of the Congolese people. The Congo need not feel excluded from the increasingly less elite community of very small atomic powers, for Lovanium University possesses a magnificent research reactor (containing ten kilograms of uranium enriched to 20 per cent in the 235-component) supplied under a U.S. bilateral agreement with Belgium. Shortly after the reactor was fueled the Belgian government was no longer in a position to guarantee the safety of the reactor and fuel as required in the bilateral agreements. Accordingly the Lovanium reactor was the first such institution to enjoy the uncertain distinction of being guarded by United Nations troops of equally uncertain status and tenure. Thus came the opportunity for the International Atomic Energy Agency to grasp the initiative for assuming safeguards responsibility in a very ticklish situation; and it did so for both the original fuel loading and a supplemental one.[1]

The radiation dangers which might arise from misuse of the Congo reactor or its components are limited. Also the form and content of its uranium-235 fuel are not at all suitable for creating an atomic bomb, if sold to or taken by another country in a period of chaos. But the reactor's exposed situation, plus the Israeli incident, show that we are already at the point where reluctance to permit international control and inspection, or unanticipated changes of government, or both may cause political complications.

Nuclear devices are products of a complex, well-developed tech-

[1] *International Agreements for Cooperation*, Hearings before the Subcommittee on Agreements for Cooperation of the Joint Committee on Atomic Energy, 87th Cong., 2d sess., June 25, 1962 (Washington: GPO, 1962), pp. 54-55.

nology; the preceding chapters have shown why their use should, ideally, be restricted to an equally well-developed political environment—but the development of the latter lags woefully. The Israel and Congo incidents will be but minor memories when that day arrives (glorious for the nuclear engineer, abhorrent for those with the political responsibility) when beyond any reasonable doubt atomic power has become more than marginally competitive with conventional power. Then, atomic plants will multiply. The major powers who now have exclusive control of the peaceful atom will still refuse to cooperate in establishing "safeguards," that misleading euphemism for inspection and control. The minor powers will seek to break down the monopoly, asserting their sovereign rights. In the same way they will reject international inspection and control. This is how the situation is developing today. Only if the major powers begin to sacrifice certain aspects of their autonomy in the control of nuclear matters will the noncommitted nations ever acquiesce in any significant control measures.

Current Control Agreements

The U.S. bilateral assistance pacts (some 44 agreements with 42 countries) call for accounting and inspection "whenever any significant assistance is provided in the form of nuclear facilities, source materials, special fissionable materials, or any other assistance which presents a potential for military use."[2] Most nations receiving this assistance seem to be happy with the inspection provisions, which apply only to the projects specifically covered by the agreement. Some countries receiving American help have substantial projects of their own not subject to inspection.

Only three bilateral agreements, those with Canada, Great Britain, and Euratom, do not accord the United States inspection rights. In these instances the United States accepts a pledge and frequent consultations as sufficient guarantees that materials transferred expressly for peaceful purposes will not be utilized in other ways. For Euratom there is perhaps a further safeguard, frequently

[2] Robert McKinney, *Review of the International Atomic Policies and Programs of the United States,* v. 3, Report to the Joint Committee on Atomic Energy, 86th Cong., 2d sess. (Washington: GPO, 1960), pp. 842-856.

expressed as follows: "The French will be watching the Germans, the Germans will be watching the French; the other four will be watching both." As regards Euratom, the United States relies on regional integrity and regional stability. Whether we would rely as fully on other regional groupings is a question that has not yet arisen since none have appeared with the stability and integrity of Euratom.

The drive toward complete nuclear independence, unhindered by external controls, is strong in some nations. In rendering assistance, a donor country has to weigh two alternatives. If the recipient is bent on possessing nuclear weapons, to deny it assistance in peaceful areas will delay its eventual entry as an Nth country. But, on the other hand, a nation that has had to struggle unaided to achieve weapon production is likely to drive a very difficult bargain when pressed to accede to control measures. Donor nations who fail to provide peaceful assistance when requested may suffer political lesions. On that ground they may decide to take the risk, reasoning that the initial facilities provided under bilateral agreement with or without rights of inspection may be insignificant when compared with the experience and knowledge necessary to conduct an independent program after the bilateral agreement has lapsed or been negated by a change of government.

A realistic, perhaps fatalistic, attitude characterizes the Soviet philosophy on control. The Russians constantly insist that atomic sharing "is rendered by us on terms of complete equality of sides without encroachment on any country's sovereignty."[3] But there are practical reasons for this generosity; the U.S.S.R. has extended aid mainly to nations in its own bloc where there are adequate political and military controls. About fourteen bilateral agreements have been made with a smaller number of states. Five nations outside the bloc, Egypt, Ghana, Iraq, Yugoslavia, and Indonesia, have been sold small research facilities. Most nations receiving Soviet aid also accept Soviet technicians, some of whom undoubtedly are well trained to detect signs of diversion of fissionable materials. To have emphasized control in its sharing program would have undermined a policy position that control over nuclear testing was

[3] Khrushchev interview with a representative of *Il Tempo,* March 24, 1958.

an entirely adequate solution to the Nth country problem. Further, the Soviet position is more attractive to many of the neutral nations than the American insistence on inspection.

A vivid Indian statement shows the bitterness some neutrals feel about control arrangements:

The provisions are such that this chain [of generation of nuclear materials] continues indefinitely. Thus, as far as fissionable materials are concerned, once it comes under an Agency project not only is it controlled but all of its future generations are controlled. It is as if not only the recipient of aid were to be placed under bondage but his children, his grandchildren and all succeeding generations for ever and ever.[4]

Dr. Bhabha was referring to safeguarding provisions proposed for IAEA administration, not ones that would be applied bilaterally by the United States. The United States has encouraged partners in bilateral agreements to request IAEA safeguards. The inspection of IAEA would be comparable to that which the United States itself requires, but it would seem less acceptable to the countries receiving aid.

After much debate, the IAEA has adopted a policy of inspection and control of a very limited extent. The safeguards approved by the Board of Governors of the IAEA on January 31, 1961, apply to an insignificantly small amount of materials which will be supplied by the Agency during 1961-63. The safeguards are adequate but are limited to reactors for research, testing, and furnishing power on a small scale, and to the fissionable materials used or produced in the reactors. A few nations, like Japan, have voluntarily agreed to permit the IAEA to inspect parts of their atomic programs. This, the first international agreement on inspection, is purely optional. It represents a small step toward broader agreements covering power reactors, facilities for the production of fissionable materials, and stockpiles, but by itself it does not contribute significantly to achieving meaningful, world-wide control.

Aside from objections of a political character, some nations will balk at paying the costs of IAEA inspection, which in some in-

[4] Dr. Homi J. Bhabha, Statement at the Conference on the Statute of the IAEA, United Nations, New York, 1956.

stances could make marginally attractive atomic power uneco-nomic. A study of a hypothetical IAEA-controlled program of monitoring ten reactor stations, with a total electrical output of 250 megawatts and with a single chemical processing facility, indi-cated a total annual cost of a little over $1 million for control and physical security.[5] This represents an increased cost for the elec-tricity produced by that complex of about ½ mill per kilowatt hour, something like 5 per cent. The study further assumed that errors in plutonium accounting would have a 95 per cent proba-bility of being detected. With a daily production of about 750 grams of plutonium, the accumulated error in a year could amount to as much as 12,000 grams of plutonium, just enough for two critical masses. The accumulation of so much plutonium over a period of a year would require very clever diversion at all the appropriate phases of materials processing. The longer the period during which diversion occurred, the greater would be the chances of detection. In larger systems, with the same possibility of detec-tion, correspondingly greater amounts could be diverted in briefer periods.

If this same modest 5 per cent margin of error is to be applied to mass production if and when arms control finally is effected, then we must consider the possibility that several thousands of bombs of the "Club" members must forever remain unaccounted for. This margin of error exceeds the total production, for some time to come, of all the possible Nth country aspirants.

In normal operations the material unaccounted for would not actually be lost. The percentage of uncertainty simply represents calibration errors in the analysis. In this situation continuing re-search and development directed toward improving analytical equipment, with particular attention to automation, would pay off in reducing "losses" and also the costs of control personnel, one of the main factors making inspection expensive. For example, the use of television monitoring from a central station and radiation monitoring by electronic devices should be investigated more fully. More intriguing would be the possibility of developing foolproof,

---

[5] "Inventory Control Study," U.S. AEC, Technical Information Service Ex-tension, Oak Ridge, Tennessee, September 1, 1956 (study by C. J. Anderson, *et al.*, Vitro Engineering Division, Vitro Corp. of America, New York, N.Y.).

sealed inspection units which could be examined periodically or which would signal observations to inspectors stationed some distance from the plant.

No atomic power plants or processing complexes have yet been designed with specific reference to international inspection. In such a design additional costs would be entailed, depending upon the degree of security desired. Control procedures and systems which are designed to minimize losses of material and costs of additional inspection personnel will generally also be most effective in preventing diversion. To attempt to reach 100 per cent protection against diversion, regardless of costs and the negative psychological and political aspects of complete control, is unrealistic. But these are technical problems, somehow resolvable within certain physical limits.

The Range of Control Possibilities

The political limits to what can be done are more troublesome. The range of possibilities is from no international control at all, which is approximately the present situation, to full international control over all nuclear activities, which is not necessarily the ideal situation. U.S. policy has sought a moderate course between the two extremes. The components of present policy seem to have been:

a)   education of other governments regarding their self-interest in an effective system of safeguards;

b)   agreement with the other donor nations on a common system of inspection and controls, consistent with the safeguarding provisions in the Statute of the International Atomic Energy Agency;

c)   development of a system of inspection and control within the IAEA, with the ultimate objective of transferring the administration of bilateral controls and safeguards to the Agency;

d)   implementation, meanwhile, of the safeguarding provisions in our bilateral agreements through the establishment of accountability, physical security measures, and periodic inspections, including the stationing of resident inspection teams in recipient nations.[6]

[6] From May 1957 to January 1, 1963, on the order of a hundred inspections were made in more than 20 countries.

e)   finally, minimizing the adverse political effects which might arise from the implementation of the safeguarding provisions.

Except for a few minor amendments, the Atomic Energy Act of 1954 restricts U.S. foreign activities in the atomic energy field to peaceful uses in the hope that eventually the military applications of atomic energy could be brought under effective international control. In 1954 the technology of atomic energy and the essential atomic energy materials were available to relatively few countries, with the United States having virtually a monopolistic position as a supplier of U-235. Both these facts seemed to mean that it might be feasible to direct the development of atomic energy throughout the world along exclusively peaceful lines. It was hoped, likewise, that the organization of the nascent industry within a system of control and inspection would provide useful experience for more comprehensive arms control eventually and, perhaps, for disarmament, and that it would also be the first step toward an international system of nuclear safeguards.

Practical difficulties in carrying out such a policy were recognized from the outset. First, there was the "double standard." The United States, the Soviet Union, and the United Kingdom were progressively basing their armament systems on nuclear weapons, but the United States was unwilling to make these weapons available to her allies. Second, the safeguard policy thrust the other supplying nations (the United Kingdom and Canada) into the uncomfortable position of inspecting activities in recipient countries to insure that they were abiding by their commitments to use atomic energy materials exclusively for peaceful uses.[7] Third, to be effective, the policy required the supplying nations to pursue identical policies, even in commercial competition.

In addition to the foregoing, a new view of weapons-sharing adds significantly to the difficulties in carrying out the U.S. policy on safeguards; in point of fact, this new view undermines the policy. The revised Atomic Energy Act of 1958 (Public Law 85-479; see Chapter 2) permits U.S. cooperation with foreign nations in cer-

---

[7] But, curiously, "the Canadians have imposed no effective safeguards" for the reactor they have built for India—one which could produce two critical masses of plutonium per year. See Leonard Beaton and John Maddox, *The Spread of Nuclear Weapons* (New York: Praeger, 1962), p. 138.

tain military applications of atomic energy; the United States now cooperates with allied nations in developing nuclear-powered submarines. The stalemate in U.S.-Soviet relations and growing disenchantment with the prospects for agreement on disarmament have weakened the assumption of earlier policy that atomic energy development could be oriented along exclusively peaceful lines. Moreover, the restricted nuclear weapons "club" has lost some of its significance now that the French have developed and exploded nuclear devices. Finally, the softening natural uranium market has made it more difficult to reach agreement with supplier nations on a common policy.

Hard evidence is accumulating, therefore, that our present safeguards policy cannot be successfully carried out. Moreover, political factors make it likely that further efforts to push the present policy not only will prove ineffective but also will involve great political and economic costs. The assumptions of U.S. policy on safeguards are simply not acceptable to many who are asked to accept them. Also, it contains convenient built-in opportunities for political criticism and active opposition. Concessions within the framework of an obsolete policy may be more damaging than helpful. Control, inspection, and the achievement of broad U.S. national objectives remain important; yet the safeguards policy must be radically changed, not by allowing it to collapse but through sensible, sometimes drastic, alterations.

As the world blindly groped for some means to initiate a chain reaction which would bring about control, or a stable balance in world armaments, it seized upon limited control of nuclear testing activities. For the greater part of the world's population, the elimination of weapons tests meant the elimination of fears of nuclear contamination. Some found other grounds for hope. First, they thought, the abandoning of tests was a means of preventing the emergence of Nth countries, and, secondly, it would increase international confidence in nuclear inspection. That the elimination of testing would prevent the appearance of Nth countries is improbable, as was shown in Chapter 2. That it would be a step toward more effective international control is by no means clear. Certainly most of the techniques of test detection have little to do, for example, with the techniques of monitoring a cutoff in the production of fissionable materials. And any monitoring of production requires far closer internal inspection than the Soviet Union has thus far indicated it could accept even for testing.

Are there any other possible techniques which would gradually evolve into a control system going to the heart of the matter, the materials and armaments themselves? Are there any international legal mechanisms which we could apply? In his *De jure belli et pacis*, Hugo Grotius considered, both philosophically and practically, the conduct of men and nations under the assumption that the laws of nature are unalterable. Unfortunately, several systems proposed by scientists and laymen alike in the past fifteen years for the control of atomic energy have violated, through wishful thinking, basic laws of nature. The awesome forces of the atom exist; they cannot be eliminated or altered; the best we can hope is that they can in some manner be controlled or monitored. It is doubtful that since 1625, when *De jure belli et pacis* was published, any fundamentally new precepts of international law have been discovered. Rather than promulgate fundamentally new laws for men and nations in this nuclear age, would it not be prudent to examine first what could be accomplished by applying existing rules of conduct?

One of Grotius' most significant contributions was his definition of "those things which have use both in war and out of war," i.e., conditional contraband. In addition to materials which have utility in both war and peace, there is a broader category which can have either good or bad uses. Since fissionable materials clearly fall in both categories, perhaps some of the international rules applicable to conditional contraband could be applied also to them. This approach is encouraged by the fact that in the effort to control fissionable materials, emphasis has been placed primarily on *international traffic*. This is natural; what a nation does internally with a commodity is clearly not as subject to control by an international body as are exports and imports. Many precedents could be cited of the successful control of commodities at the point at which they move across national borders. The beginnings of the decline of slavery can be traced to the eighteenth century sentiment and legislation against the *international* trade in slaves. Narcotics control perhaps offers a more appropriate parallel.

In his introduction to the first issue of the United Nations *Bulletin on Narcotics,* the first Secretary-General of the United Nations, Mr. Trygve Lie, stated:

The problem of narcotic drugs is in no sense a problem confined to one continent or civilization.

In themselves narcotic drugs are neither dangerous nor harmful. Indispensable to modern medicine, they are used the world over to alleviate pain and restore health. Thus used they bring a great benefit to mankind. But abused they cause havoc and misery. The social dangers of drug addiction are well known.

This dual nature of narcotic drugs has made it necessary to submit them to the most stringent international control. This control, functioning now under the auspices of the United Nations and expanding rapidly to the field of newly discovered synthetic drugs, ensures the limitation of their manufacture, trade and consumption to legitimate needs only.

This international control and the treaties on which it is based have, however, a wider significance than the limited field of narcotic drugs. If the principles on which these treaties and this control rest could be applied with equal success to wider fields of human endeavor, to other kinds of dangerous weapons, peace would be within our reach.[8]

The parallels with international control of atomic energy are clear enough, but no one within the U.N. or without has taken Mr. Lie's simple cue.

A Proposal for Phased Nuclear Arms Limitation

The aim of any atomic control plan must be to find a means of cutting off the production of fissionable materials for military purposes. In foreseeable circumstances nothing but violence will effect a sudden cutoff; hence, restriction must be approached and intensified gradually. My suggestion is that restriction be initiated by applying existing legal mechanisms to international traffic in nuclear materials. It may be an unreasonable or unrealistic suggestion, for a host of counter-arguments can be raised; but my hope is that at the minimum it would suggest viable alternatives to the increasing number of individuals seeking new solutions. What is

[8] "Statement by the Secretary-General," *Bulletin on Narcotics* (Lake Success, New York), no. 1, October 1949, p. 3.

required now is not a grand, comprehensive inspection scheme, thrust upon unwilling nations whose internal structures and philosophies do not permit its consideration, much less its acceptance. Control must be attacked in a series of moves, each at least somewhat mutually acceptable when made, each showing the way toward a more comprehensive action, and each predicated on the success of that preceding. These phases make up the proposal for nuclear arms limitation that I am putting forward. In sequence the four phases are:

I. Registration of Trade
II. Registration of Use
III. Restriction of Use
IV. Inspection

In Phase I, Registration of Trade, the stipulation would be *that all special nuclear materials which enter international traffic be registered with the International Atomic Energy Agency.* This would mean that all special materials would be subject to international registration, *except* those produced within the nation utilizing them and those imported before the agreement came into effect. This restriction would be needed, initially at least, to override the major security barrier: the possibility that the accumulation of sensitive materials might be estimated on the basis of total accumulated stocks of raw materials. Realistically, however, even full knowledge of previous data would provide only the roughest measurement of a nation's nuclear armament strength. Efficiencies of nuclear manufacturing processes and contemporary bomb designs vary so widely that the quantity of input materials now bears faint relationship to output.

The reporting of international traffic in *processed* special materials, such as enriched uranium-235 or plutonium, should not endanger any nation's security. Amounts of materials transferred in the various peaceful atomic programs are known if not formally reported, so there is no difficulty here. Some materials which are utilized beyond national boundaries for defense purposes, with the exception of uranium-235 for Britain, are neither sold nor lent. Possession of such critical components is retained by the original owner. The only known transfer of enriched fissionable materials for weapons purposes took place between the United States and the United Kingdom under the conditions of an agreement concluded in May 1959, which expired June 30, 1962 (see Chapter 3). The amounts transferred are secret. However, revelation of the amounts of enriched materials transferred after Phase I comes into effect would not reveal the total amounts of materials transferred under the treaty.

Our experience suggests that to put such a plan into effect, a few leading nations should declare that they will adopt it, regardless of what others do. Conditional proposals, to be adopted only if all nations agree, are unlikely to lead to action. Soviet acceptance of the IAEA concept—partial acceptance as it was—did not occur until the major Western nations had decided to go it alone. The Russians, in turn, used precisely the same technique in forcing an unnegotiated but effective cessation of nuclear testing. History will show that both of these unilateral moves were of the highest significance, and both the East and the West can be considered to have won a victory of sorts thus far in the international nuclear chess game. The next initially non-negotiated move, whether it be similar to the plan presented here or different, may well be decisive.

It should be relatively simple for the Western powers to formulate coordinated action, for in transfers of special materials, and particularly raw materials, a high-level international committee has been functioning for almost two decades. The logical move for the supplying nations is to declare that they will voluntarily report to the IAEA all future international exchanges or sales of nuclear materials. The IAEA would extend to all other nations, including those of the Soviet bloc, an invitation to volunteer the same information on the same basis. But it should be made clear that initial Western participation in the registration plan is not contingent upon the participation of the Russians or, indeed, upon preliminary discussions with them.

Considered separately, registration of atomic materials in transit perhaps is not highly significant; but as the first of several phases of effective atomic energy control, traffic registration could represent a preliminary attack on a remarkably tough problem. Were all parties, including the Soviets, eventually to enter into Phase I, and if it operated successfully, it would provide a foundation for further negotiation with the U.S.S.R. on the implementation of later, more meaningful phases. Successful operation of Phase I for, perhaps, two years should set the stage for proceeding to Phase II, Registration of Use.

In view of the Universal Declaration of Human Rights which proclaims the individual's "right to life, liberty and security of person," it seems within the province of the United Nations to enunciate the following principle: That nations and individuals engaged in nuclear research and development operations of any sort have an obligation to conduct these activities at minimum risk to other nations and to the individuals of all nations. Further, it is the common right of all nations and all persons to know of any such operations which possess a potential of harm or could conceivably be expanded to a stage dangerous to human life and security. At the minimum this obligation applies to operations based upon materials which, by entering international traffic, have thereby become the responsibility of more than one nation. To apply this principle the rule of Phase II would be *that in all aspects of an atomic energy program a country would be obliged to report periodically what amounts of imported fissionable material were used for what general purpose—whether that purpose be the production of atomic power or nuclear weapons.*

There are precedents in our society for a reporting procedure of this sort. The gambler declares his activities and secures a license by purchasing a special stamp; firearms registration is required in most states. Hundreds of registered alien agents, pursue their commercial or propaganda activities essentially unhampered, but law enforcement agencies maintain that registration is a useful adjunct to the regulation of potentially harmful activities. It keeps the spotlight on them. True, the number of unregistered and undeclared gamblers and agents of foreign governments is legion, but registration is nevertheless an integral part of a responsible policy of control.

The primary goal of the nuclear registration is to move toward responsible nuclear policies on the part of every nation. It is unlikely that the plan would contribute to a false sense of security. The number of nations and subdivisions of nations on this shrinking globe is small, and, whether we like it or not, each is closely watching the other. Without inspection inside a country there is no positive method of checking a false registration statement. But a nation making such a statement would have to undertake an extensive manipulation of facts about its peaceful and military programs, and, since the former is supposedly not secret anywhere, false apportionment of nuclear materials could eventually cause considerable embarrassment. For example, a nation could not blithely claim that all its imported raw materials were being utilized for its peaceful program if the scale of that program were entirely incommensurate. Moreover, under the rule of Phase I which would continue, two nations, not one, would be obliged to report each shipment.

No direct means exist for penalizing registration violations. The United Nations does not have the authority of a world government, and the difficulties of imposing sanctions are only too clear. The power which "world opinion" was presumed to have seems to have eroded in the course of the actions in Goa, in the Congo, and through Soviet resumption of nuclear testing. It is the contention of some that these events illustrate "world opinion" to be a chimera without any force whatsoever. Nevertheless, although "world opinion" cannot have a prophylactic effect, it does have long-range political consequences: a simple example would be the significant erosion in the Japanese Communist party after the resumption of nuclear tests by the Soviet Union in 1961. As moral force and statements of attitudes the resolutions of the United Nations can have strong impact, highly embarrassing at the very least. If we abandon the concept of the United Nations as a moral force, its utility can only erode and we will therefore effectively have abandoned the concept of an internationally enforced peace mechanism.

The need to make a public declaration of the proportionate effort it was devoting to peaceful and military atomic programs would itself be of more than minor significance to the internal and external policies of a nation.

In Phase III, Restriction of Use, the first elements of arms *limitations* appear. It would be agreed *that all special nuclear materials which enter international traffic be utilized solely for peaceful purposes. This restriction applies to all materials, whether raw or processed, and to all future generations of nuclear materials which are produced from the controlled materials.*

Phase IV, Inspection, would institute *internal inspection of all installations reported to be "peaceful."* Denial of inspection rights at sites which had been declared peaceful users in the earlier phases of registration would constitute an obvious evasion.

Further particulars of the implementation of Phases III and IV and their extension to more comprehensive arms limitation are simple to envisage. But they are perhaps not appropriate for consideration when the feasibility and utility of Phase I has been only postulated. Sacrifices of national sovereignty will appear in the later phases, notably when internal inspection begins. But presumably the world would not advance to these phases unless some degree of cooperation had been demonstrated earlier, for it is universally recognized that if the peaceful applications of atomic materials cannot be monitored, there is no hope of ever controlling the entire bulk of fissionable materials.

Some Objections and Advantages

The plan presented here for consideration has many facets and implications, each of which must be subjected to careful examination. I have proposed unilateral action as a first step. Unilateral action *per se* does not stimulate multilateral action unless both parties are benefited. The Soviets undoubtedly are subject to the same uneasiness as we are regarding the emergence of Nth countries, no matter how near or how distant. The Soviets, however, are faced with a unique Nth country situation, namely that of China. Undoubtedly the Soviet Union has been under increasing pressure from China to supply nuclear warheads, and all the available evidence indicates that the Soviet Union is as concerned about this as is the West. Indeed, for the Russians, China presents a more immediate political and geograpical problem.[9] Phase III, which would restrict the use of transferred material to peaceful purposes, would be very advantageous for the Soviet Union in its relations with China.

[9] A. Doak Barnett, "The Inclusion of Communist China in an Arms Control Program," *Daedalus*, Fall 1960, pp. 831-845.

It must be recognized, however, that Phase III would also prevent the United States from transferring nuclear materials for weapons purposes to the British, the French, or to any other allies. But the United Kingdom seems to have accumulated adequate U-235 supplies already, and France has developed her internal sources and production facilities. The defense of Europe is still a highly controversial subject; opinions range from internal demands for unilateral disarmament to insistence upon large-scale nuclear weapons systems independent of U.S. support. This matter will not be settled for a long time. Meanwhile, the possibility that the proposed plan in its distant phases might conflict with an as-yet-undetermined mutual security system is no reason for not testing it in its earlier stages. Inevitably, the later phases of this plan, or any other disarmament plan, involve mutual sacrifice of nuclear strategic positions. In either event, whether the earlier phases have been effective or ineffective, the lessons gained should materially aid in the achievement of a more stable security.

In all of its phases the plan demands concessions by the major, as well as the smaller, powers; more certainly by the former. It would involve the reporting and the control of shipments which the United States receives from Canada and South Africa, those which the U.S.S.R. gets from East Germany and other satellites, and those which Great Britain gets from Australia and other countries. Moreover, Phase IV would involve international inspection at all plants utilizing imported materials, whether for research purposes or production of power.

The Place of the IAEA

In examining the plan presented here, the matter of improving the position of the IAEA by giving it progressively more important authority is not an unimportant consideration. At present the IAEA is still weak, with no apparent direction. It is not the mechanism envisioned by President Eisenhower on December 8, 1953, for effecting a diminution of "the potential destructive power of the world's stockpiles" nor "a new channel for peaceful discussion." If the Agency's members want to develop it for that purpose, they must impart to it more vitality than is now evident.

In addition to serving as a clearing house for safeguards, the IAEA should have another role. It should assist in building up stockpiles of fissionable materials to supply nations who would use that material for peaceful purposes. I believe that means can be found of pursuing this course which will at the same time strengthen the Agency and repair a deficiency in present American bilateral control. Both uranium-235 and plutonium are involved.

Could an incentive be devised that would place plutonium under IAEA control? The United States has designated the Agency as an acceptable recipient of plutonium generated under certain bilateral agreements, but thus far the Agency has not exercised its options for lack of any clear notion of what to do with the material. It is suggested that the IAEA would gain a number of advantages if it began to exercise the plutonium options, thereby becoming a world, plutonium-for-peace bank. To do that, it is proposed that the IAEA establish an international rate at which 20 per cent U-235 would be exchanged for plutonium.[10] This would mean that some of the plutonium deposited with the IAEA would be used to pay for 20 per cent U-235, in much the same manner as the United States has received British plutonium in exchange for U-235 at an established ratio (see Chapter 3). Uranium-235 will be a very desirable commodity for many years to come as embryonic atomic energy programs develop. Thus, there will be a real incentive to exchange plutonium for it. The exchange would provide a large supply of U-235, independent of bilateral controls but subject to IAEA controls. The incentive for exchange would apply to plutonium generated in materials obtained outside of the bilateral agreements as well as within them. Since recipients of 20 per cent U-235 could include thorium in their nuclear reactors, thereby breeding U-233, another fissionable material, the plan must be extended to include U-233 and the establishment of an exchange ratio between it and 20 per cent U-235.

The IAEA should be invited to take an active part in a long-range program of studies of plutonium-burning reactors and experimental operation so that deposited plutonium may eventually

---

[10] This is the maximum enrichment of U-235 usually supplied under bilateral agreement.

prove useful as an atomic power source, being re-allocated on some basis to member nations. The plutonium deposited with the IAEA could be utilized to a large extent in these studies. It might also be desirable for the IAEA to participate in the operation of a central facility for the separation of plutonium to obtain experience in processing this material.

This course of action would be of advantage in the development of nuclear power in the participating nations. Initially, domestically held plutonium is almost worthless in starting an atomic power program, but exchange for U-235 would give them material of value and discourage the hoarding of plutonium for future contingencies. Later, if plutonium power schemes are developed, the material will have a different value and the rate of exchange may have to be altered. Nations that have taken advantage of the exchange of plutonium for U-235 may then be in a better technological position to burn plutonium efficiently than those that did not. But the proposal does not encourage nations *initially* to orient their programs toward plutonium production. If power is the desired product, it would be foolishly inefficient to burn U-235 to obtain plutonium which, in turn, is used to obtain U-235. For an extended initial period the amount of plutonium generated is a rough measure of the scope of a nation's atomic power program and its need for additional U-235 fuel. In this sense, therefore, this proposal initially relates to demand and supply automatically. It also avoids complex international monetary exchange problems.

The most important advantages of this proposal lie in the improved position of the IAEA that should result if it were adopted. The IAEA would have its own supplies of fissionable materials. It would also have a well-defined task of long-range research on a problem of enormous consequences, namely, the effective burning of plutonium or U-233 or both for power. Thus the Agency would be endowed with a prestige and mission which it would not have if it were merely a control agency. Meanwhile, a stockpile under international control would be accumulated, thus symbolizing and physically implementing an essential part of the Atoms for Peace program "to begin now and continue to make joint contributions from their stockpiles of normal uranium and fissionable materials to an International Atomic Energy Agency."[11] This, curiously, the Eisenhower administration never seriously considered.

Only actual contributions, not conditional offers of sale at disadvantageous prices, can launch the transitional phases of a meaningful international control program. The United States supports the greater proportion of the IAEA budget by the donation of dollars. Donations of fissionable materials, themselves, should also be considered essential support of IAEA operations. The IAEA has eight million dollars a year to accomplish its mighty goals. This is the cost of perhaps thirty critical masses of uranium-235, or the cost of one or two large missile tests.

The proposals advanced here are certainly not the panacea that most people are impatiently seeking. They do not stop arms production; they do not prevent surprise attack. But if we cannot at once find a neat and sudden way out of the present armaments dilemma, let us at least begin to establish a substructure, or a matrix, of nuclear behavior. We need a patient understanding of the slow manner in which legal processes become effective. It is impossible to locate the precise point along a given "disarmament path" at which an ultimate solution, if such exists, will appear.

[11] Dwight D. Eisenhower, "The Atom for Progress and Peace," Dept. of State Publication 5403 (Washington: GPO, 1954).

Part II

DEVELOPING TECHNOLOGIES

Chapter 6

Power

In his delightful satire "On the Feasibility of Coal-Driven Power Stations," the eminent nuclear physicist Otto Frisch postulates a civilization which had developed solely on the basis of atomic energy. Suddenly a new source of energy, coal, is discovered which seems to have certain advantages over nuclear fuels. But in his mythical atomic world the technological difficulties of utilizing coal appear to be most formidable. For example, the burning of coal releases large quantities of highly toxic gases like carbon monoxide and sulphur dioxide. So Professor Frisch concludes:

Here is a grave argument against the use of coal and in favor of fission reactors, which have proved their complete safety over a period of several thousand years. It will probably take decades before a control system of sufficient reliability can be evolved to allay the fears of those to whom the safety of our people is entrusted.[1]

Unfortunately, Professor Frisch did not extend his interesting analogy to the political realm—to the issue of public coal versus private coal, to the coal lobby, and to "Coal for Peace." Alas, no parable will guide us through the tangled web woven of the innumerable threads of atomic fact and fable during less than a decade of Atoms for Peace.

To return to this imperfect world, which has done very well indeed with conventional fuels, we find the energy situation not particularly desperate at present in areas already in a good technological position. Exploitable reserves of fuel coal appear to amount to 5,000 billion tons, an amount which at the present rate of use would last for about eighteen hundred years. But with the annual

[1] *Nuclear Engineering* (London), December 1956, pp. 368-369.

demand growing at six per cent or more, the limit will come much sooner. Exploitable reserves of the other fossil fuels (i.e., petroleum and natural gas) are estimated at less than 70 billion tons; at the present rate of utilization, they would be exhausted very much earlier than the coal reserves, probably about the end of the century.[2]

The world is growing more dependent upon oil, because of the ease of extracting, transporting, and using it, the availability of geographically and politically diversified sources of supply, and, above all, the increasingly attractive prices. But most of the recent international political difficulties concerning fuel have been related to oil. A crisis like the Suez affair which threatens to disrupt oil supplies draws attention to alternate energy resources. Since then, however, oil plenty and the discovery of the Saharan and Libyan deposits have made the memory of Suez fade away. And as memory fades, the somewhat grandiose plans projected for the development of atomic power lose their urgency.

The Economic Challenge of Fossil Fuels

If political stability can be maintained and if mutually satisfactory exploitation of the energy resources in North Africa, the Middle East and elsewhere can be achieved, there will be no urgent immediate need for atomic energy—and not even the most enthusiastic adherents of nuclear power would regret it. Assured, steady oil supplies will delay the installation of large-scale nuclear power plants, and at the same time allow unhurried, better-planned development of economical plants for the period when atomic energy enters serious competition.

When enthusiasm for atomic power was at its height, about 1955-56, the Russians were considered the principal competitors, but since that time their cutback in atomic power production has been, relatively, the world's deepest. In conventional fuels, on the other hand, they are now competing most vigorously. Their present rates of oil production and the indicated reserves are both increasing rapidly; the U.S.S.R. only recently has become an im-

---

[2] *International Science and Technology* (New York) February 1962, p. 24.

portant exporter of oil. It is claimed that in 1959 a half-dozen Soviet tankers left each day for foreign ports carrying export oil.[3]

When the entire system of Soviet pipelines is completed, there should be little economic incentive, or justification, for constructing atomic power facilities in Eastern Europe. The prestige of having atomic power units could be satisfied by the few plants now in construction or planned. Except for advanced research facilities, further construction of atomic power plants in the Soviet satellites may be virtually nil. This is a situation the Soviet Union probably would like to make permanent, for it guarantees a good market for surplus petroleum and at the same time minimizes Nth power capabilities in the satellite nations.

In the rest of the world the present oversupply of oil from the Near East, Canada, and South America will be made more acute by the increase in Soviet exports after the pipelines are completed. Even relatively small export sales can exert a downward pressure on prices. In 1960 Russian offers forced oil companies in India to slash their prices about 12.5 per cent, and price cuts in other areas followed. Italy made an agreement to import Soviet oil covering 15 to 20 per cent of its requirements. The pattern is being repeated elsewhere.

The strong Soviet bid for world oil markets is making the development of atomic energy less economic. But if the Middle East is to be regarded as an unreliable source of oil, the U.S.S.R. must be even more so. Apart from the instabilities created by power politics, it should be recalled that as late as 1955 the Soviet Union was a net energy importer. At present, Soviet energy requirements are increasing rapidly because of the growth of existing industrial areas, and the industrialization of more remote regions. But the indications are strong that surpluses will be available for some time to come and that they will be exported.

In these circumstances, for both the Soviet Union and the West, oil takes precedence over nuclear fuels as a political instrument in dealing with the uncommitted nations. For them conventional fuels are certainly of more immediate significance. The net effect

[3] "How Russia's Oil Pipelines Have Developed," *The Times* (London), June 8, 1959.

of the increased supply of oil, irrespective of the source, is to diminish sharply their expectation that atomic power has any meaning for them.

Although coal is being used less now, it will remain as a world-wide source of energy, since technological improvements in its transportation and utilization are to be expected. Coal is still Western Europe's main source of energy; and its competitive position is likely to remain strong. For example, at present less than two-thirds of a pound of coal can produce a kilowatt hour of electricity, whereas 1920-vintage plants required three pounds per kilowatt hour. Cheap transportation of coal by pipeline is now a reality, as is the technique for burning wet fuels. For example, crushed coal mixed with water is pumped from an eastern Ohio mine to a consuming plant over one hundred miles away. The liquid coal technique, using other types of suspensions, is being further developed by other countries interested in revitalizing the coal market.[4] Thus, in regard to handling, coal is taking on the character of a fluid, like petroleum. The prospect of large-scale coal hydration to obtain liquid fuels and essential chemicals is another indication that coal is destined to make a strong reappearance in the energy picture in the perhaps not-too-distant future. These technical developments will furnish important support for the sagging U.S. coal industry. Less radical improvements, emulating the mechanization already widespread in U.S. industry, would aid Europe's coal industry immensely.

The use of natural gas, often found with petroleum deposits, also is on the increase. Two major factors contributing to the growth of the gas industry are consumer demand for a clean fuel and the development of pipeline transportation. Technology is also continually improving methods of production and recovery which, in turn, directs attention to better methods of marketing the product. New developments in the liquefaction of methane make the bulk transportation of this commodity by ship a reasonable economic venture.[5]

[4] "A New Liquid Fuel for Industry," *International Management*, January 1962, p. 41. "Coal by Oil Line Studied in Canada," *The New York Times*, October 23, 1960, p. 89.
[5] Sir Harold Smith, "Importing Liquid Natural Gas to Britain," *The New Scientist* (London), February 12, 1959, pp. 338-341; "Methane Sails to Market," *The Economist* (London), February 12, 1959, pp. 707-708.

Thus, the technology of the conventional fuels has continuously improved while better nuclear technologies are being sought. This parallel progress obviously postpones the date when nuclear power will become economically competitive with fossil fuels. Comparative projections of the costs of nuclear power versus fossil fuels, which fail to take into account technical progress, are not valid.

Nations not blessed with domestic resources of conventional fuels must rely on imports, which involve bulk shipments by pipeline or tanker. Such shipments can easily be intercepted by an enemy. In the narrow perspective of the moment, Suez seemed to show that excessive dependence of any nation upon fossil fuels imported in bulk over long distances was a fatal mistake. What it really showed, in a very brief period of time, and to the detriment of grandiose atomic energy plans, was the ease with which economically advanced nations could find and use effectively alternative, diversified, sources of fossil fuels.

Europe is presently reassured not only by the increase in the available amounts of oil but also by the diversification of the sources. Whether or not diversification of the sources will provide sufficient security is yet to be seen; whether or not increasing dependence on a single energy commodity, oil, is in itself an invitation to future political crises cannot be foretold.[6] This is the gamble which Europe chooses to make by decreasing its reliance on domestic sources of coal and by approaching nuclear power on the terms suggested by the present uncritical situation.

Would accelerated programs for nuclear energy undertaken by Euratom and others have provided security of the energy supply in the long run? Europe has uranium, but the deposits (except in Eastern Europe) do not compare with those in Canada, the United States, Africa, and Australia. Thus, there is a transportation problem. But a small amount of uranium, even natural uranium, is equivalent as a source of energy to many, many times its weight in petroleum products. Except in Britain, most of the presently planned nuclear power systems envision the use of enriched uranium. Even Britain, which started to build a large number of stations fueled with natural uranium, is turning in its plans for the

[6] Harold Lubell, "Security of Supply and Energy Policy in Western Europe," *World Politics*, April 1961, pp. 400-422; same, "Middle East Crises and World Petroleum Movements," RM-2185 (Santa Monica, Calif. RAND Corp., 1958).

future toward enriched systems. At present the only major source for enriched material is the United States which, strongly allied with Western Europe, might be considered a reliable source of supply. Perhaps, however, Europeans will recall that the United States in November 1956 did not give Britain and France the assistance they wanted in getting extra oil until they withdrew their forces from the Suez Canal.[7] It seems inevitable that countries should seek a high degree of self-sufficiency in nuclear fuel; so as demand rises, separate isotope separation centers will almost certainly be built in Europe, and possibly elsewhere in the long term.

The desire for national self-sufficiency in all sources of energy, the development of a free market for uranium, and the falling price of the fuel still keep interest in the natural uranium reactor very much alive. Canada, with large surpluses of uranium and unable to support what in the mid-1950s was a booming industry, naturally emphasizes the development of systems using natural uranium, a type in which she has been pre-eminent. Late recognition that for a variety of reasons natural systems will prove attractive to some countries has forced the United States to consider this field also, despite its abundance of enriched materials.

Whatever the pace that politics and economics set, physical necessity will eventually bring the world to depend on new forms of energy. Known reserves of fossil fuels would last perhaps a millennium at the present rate of use. But this calculation neglects the fantastic rate of increase in the world's population and the fact that the requirements of each individual demand an increasing amount of energy. Obviously there is a limit to the population the earth can support, but if, in a hundred years or so, world population leveled off at three to four times the present figure, the seven billion souls then alive, all using more energy than now, would burn up the world's known fossil fuel reserves in less than fifty years.

Even if the population growth is slower, alternative sources of energy must be employed. Hydroelectric power is limited by physiographic factors. Solar energy will undoubtedly be used more extensively, particularly for heating purposes. And the develop-

[7] Richard P. Stebbins, *The United States in World Affairs, 1956* (New York: Harper, for the Council on Foreign Relations, 1957), p. 340.

ment of both solar and hydroelectric sources incurs high capital costs. Although the bulk of the demand for energy could be met by electricity generated through nuclear fission, are the attendant political headaches, the safety problem, and the other difficulties worth the gain? When, if ever, will atomic power be a paying proposition economically?

The Economics of Atomic Power

Nuclear power plants have some attractive features. The bulk of the fuel they require over a considerable period of time is so small that transport facilities and costs do not significantly influence location. Vagaries of the weather, the lack of rainfall or of sunshine, do not affect the operation of a nuclear power reactor. It can be designed without reference to water supply. It can be designed to be cooled by gases and other liquids, if necessary, and it is not affected by altitude, longitude, or latitude.

If they are not burdened with some of the disadvantages of fossil-fueled plants, contemporary plants nonetheless do not differ much in principle or appearance from their conventional counterparts. The fuel, nuclear or fossil, is burnt in a chamber, whence heat is extracted by one means or another to operate a steam turbine. The capital cost of the turbine section of a nuclear plant is independent of the nature of the fuel, and so it remains a fixed cost for systems of a given size. The size—and therefore the cost—of the "burner" section depends upon the fuel it uses and how effectively the heat can be extracted from that fuel. A reactor using natural uranium is bulky and has large associated capital costs, while the opposite is true for systems employing enriched fuels.

Here again, physics, nature, and politics clash: most of the countries that would balk at using enriched fuels can ill-afford the capital costs associated with a natural uranium reactor; and money is easier in the nations which have the enriched fuels to build the more compact, less expensive, nuclear power plants. But, if they invest less in the plant, they pay more for fueling it. Thus, whatever the system and the compensating factors, the sum total of essentially three basic costs—turbine, reactor and fuel costs—must be squeezed tediously closer toward the costs of the conventional plant it resembles. We are essentially forcing a twentieth-century marvel to use and compete with nineteenth-century techniques of energy conversion and, under these circumstances, nuclear power will ever be but narrowly competitive, at the most, with conventional systems. The answer to the economic question varies widely with the sources consulted.[8]

Those who remember the U.S. goal of two million kilowatts of electrical nuclear power by 1955 and who are seeing about 50 per cent of that goal reached by the end of 1963 had voiced some skepticism. Clearly, nuclear power is going to be economic later than was originally expected owing to the current surpluses of fossil fuels and the drop in the costs of conventional power. But the disappointments in nuclear power development have not been without profit, for meanwhile we have encountered and solved many unexpected technological problems. A British editorial sums up the situation quite clearly: "It would appear that nuclear energy has now grown up and whilst conservatism in the assessment of costs and potentials is still the key-note this stems now from a policy of caution rather than one of despair."[9] Experience has value.

With increased knowledge and, consequently, with greater confidence, the AEC had launched a ten-year reactor program which promises economic nuclear power by 1968 for areas with high power costs. The research program was varied and comprehensive.[10] Now the pendulum seems to be swinging toward the index of optimism, as reflected in a recent study of the U.S. Atomic Energy Commission. Significantly, however, the study emphasized that

. . . it became evident with the passage of time that our attention had probably for too long remained focused narrowly on short-term objectives. This restudy made it apparent that, for the long-term benefit of the country, and indeed of the whole world, it was time we placed relatively more emphasis on the longer-range and more difficult problem of breeder reactors, which can make use of *nearly all* of our uranium and thorium reserves, instead of the less than one per cent of the uranium and very

[8] "The Challenge of the 60's" (editorial), *Nucleonics*, January 1960, pp. 68-72.
[9] "On Second Thoughts" (editorial), *Nuclear Engineering*, July 1960, p. 287.
[10] "AEC Puts Together a Long-Range Power Reactor Program," *Nucleonics*, April 1960, pp. 71-82. U.S. AEC Press Release IN-166, December 27, 1960; S-16-60, September 5, 1960; S-9-60, June 8, 1960.

little of the thorium utilized in the present types of reactors. Only by the use of breeders would we really solve the problem of adequate energy supply for future generations.[11]

Installed kilowatts of nuclear energy are a meaningless measure in the nascent stages of nuclear power, and it is now clear that the somewhat emotional disparagement of U.S. programs in the mid-1950s was entirely unjustified. Later, kilowatt goals were drastically cut everywhere, here and abroad, as the difficulties and the proper role of nuclear energy became more and more apparent. As the situation now stands, the United States, spending at the rate of about $200 million a year,[12] has been developing a far broader spectrum of civilian nuclear reactor systems than any other nation. U.S. responsibility is to continue to develop its atomic power program in conjunction with others who can contribute.

As the outlook improves for the competition of nuclear systems with conventional plants, the solution of a number of problems will progress rapidly. For example, since we have not yet found out what to do with atomic wastes, some people argue that the development of nuclear power should be held at a low level. Actually, much thought has been given to waste disposal, but the industries that will build and use atomic power plants have not devoted a significant amount of their research and development resources to the problem. Once atomic power is demonstrated to be economically competitive, however, one can be assured that concerted efforts will be made to surmount secondary obstacles which would inhibit its wide-scale application. This holds true for socialistic as well as capitalistic systems. In the Soviet Union the reconsideration of power plant policy during the past several years has been carried out strictly on a ruble and kopek basis.

Moreover, whatever technical progress is made in reducing costs of nuclear power, a major economic factor for many areas will be the percentage of time the power is required, i.e., the load factor. The operating hours of local industries and the urban use of

[11] U.S. AEC, *Civilian Nuclear Power ... a Report to the President—1962* (Washington: Author, 1962), p. 1.

[12] For example, see U.S. AEC Press Release IN-165, December 27, 1960, "AEC Announces Results of Quarterly Survey of Civilian Reactor Costs, September 30, 1960."

electricity often cause much higher consumption of electric current during the day than in the evening. One means of taking care of the peak load economically, if local geography and water resources permit, would be to pump water into storage reservoirs during off-peak periods. Then during the day electricity would be drawn from hydroelectric generators driven by the water pumped and stored at a higher level during the night and from the nuclear power plant. Pumped storage facilities have been and are being constructed in connection with conventional thermal power systems in a few areas in the world. By taking advantage of high load factors in nuclear systems and coupling these with conventional hydroelectric systems, an extremely attractive over-all economic situation can develop.[13] In Sweden, studies of the storage of energy in the form of hot water under pressure in rock chambers appear to indicate economic savings similar to those obtained from water reservoir storage.[14] But in localities where the load factor must be low, and where there is no opportunity to use or store a continuous high base load, it will be long before further technological improvements justify the use of nuclear power.

Even with a low load factor, many areas would not require power plants of the large, central-station type. Small plants in the range of 10-30 megawatts, or medium-sized plants up to 60 megawatts, not only would serve the smaller urban and industrial centers, but also could be most useful in supplying power for mineral extraction and processing plants in isolated areas. But the investment per kilowatt required for small nuclear power plants is unacceptably high; consequently they appear attractive only for military use or in very unusual situations.[15] This explains why the major factor in developing the technology of small reactors has been the U.S. Army nuclear power program. Two major types of

[13] J. M. Kay and A. A. Fulton, *Combined Use of Nuclear Power and Pumped-Storage Hydro Stations*, P/1448, 2d UN International Conference on Peaceful Uses of Atomic Energy (Geneva: United Nations, 1958), v. 13, pp. 561-568.

[14] P. H. Margen, "Thermal Storage in Rock Chambers," *Nuclear Engineering*, June 1959, pp. 259-262.

[15] A good survey of interesting military applications is given in AEC reports numbered NYO-2937 through NYO-2948, "Study of Remote Military Power Applications," 12 reports on specific situations prepared for the AEC by Henry J. Kaiser Co., Oakland, Calif., January 1960 (revised July 1960).

reactors have already undergone extensive development, and at least five additional types are projected.[16] These include two semi-mobile plants whose components, when disassembled, can be transferred to a remote locale, reassembled, operated and, if necessary again, disassembled and transferred to still another site. Three types of fully mobile plants are also being studied. One is a trailer-mounted unit; the second, a plant which might serve both as a source of power for land vehicles and as an auxiliary power source. The third is a barge-mounted reactor.

The first locales are in the Arctic or subarctic where installations include an under-ice base in Greenland, a plant at McMurdo Sound in the Antarctic, and one at Fort Greely, Alaska. Each of these installations, it is true, is in some ways unique, but comparisons of their costs with costs of power produced by conventional fuels suggest that there must be less unusual situations throughout the world where small nuclear power plants would have at least a marginal advantage.

A joint AEC-industry study indicates that the costs of nuclear power from the McMurdo Sound project will be 56.4 mills per kilowatt hour compared to 97.5 mills for conventional power.[17] This factor of two in favor of nuclear power rises to as much as three at the new Marie Byrd Station some eight hundred miles southwest of McMurdo Sound, because of transportation costs.

The same type of plant in an isolated site elsewhere, say in Africa, might give a cost of 130 mills per kilowatt hour for a 1,000-kilowatt plant. A conventional plant at the same site would deliver power at, say, 38 mills per kilowatt hour.[18] This great disparity in costs creates a dim outlook for small nuclear plants in the less developed areas. But that outlook is still heavily weighted by the effect of using plants of military design for civilian purposes. "As such plants are developed and modified more in line with civilian

[16] "The Army Reactor Program," *Nucleonics*, February 1959, pp. 46-54.

[17] "Senate Committee to Appropriate Antarctic Reactor Funds," *Nucleonics Week*, June 9, 1960, p. 1; U.S. Congress, Joint Committee on Atomic Energy, "Use of Nuclear Power Reactors at Continental and Remote Military Sites," Press Release No. 266, April 4, 1960.

[18] U.S. AEC Press Release IN-137, September 30, 1960, "The Army Nuclear Power Program: Its Reactors and Their Application to the Less-Developed Areas of the World."

requirements, the high initial costs should drop somewhat to a point where they are more economically attractive as well as logistically desirable."[19] It is heartening, therefore, to find in the past few years a growing realization of the benefits of developing small nuclear power plants independently of the army program.[20] In 1959 an Atomic Energy Commission task force assigned to study the potential of the small nuclear power plant concluded:

> We believe that, despite optimistic studies of large plant economies, there is no fundamental reason why a large nuclear plant in the U.S. should approach competitiveness more rapidly than a small plant. This point of view is particularly strengthened when it is realized that small plants are appropriate for high cost fuel areas, whereas a large electrical requirement and high cost fuel are generally inconsistent assumptions in the U.S.[21]

If this is true for the United States, it is also true for other areas of the world where similar conditions are found.

If small standard atomic power plants could be developed and *mass-produced* for small industrial operations and isolated communities, the presently indicated capital cost could undoubtedly undergo a major reduction, though it might still be at least several times that of an equivalent conventional plant. But the atomic plant would be intended for areas where drastic *fuel* savings would reduce the over-all power costs.

An important future factor in the capital costs of small plants is the very real possibility (discussed later in this chapter) of the development of a reactor that generates electrical power more or less directly, eliminating intermediate equipment. The higher cost of a small nuclear power plant can be attributed to both the nuclear reactor and the generating equipment. In the present design of small atomic power plants, low temperatures and low pressures are used; hence, the generating equipment is large and

[19] Same, p. 14.

[20] U.S. AEC Press Release S-6-60, May 5, 1960, "Small Size Nuclear Power Plants," Remarks prepared by John A. McCone, Chairman, AEC, for delivery at American Public Power Association Convention, Shoreham Hotel, Washington, D.C.

[21] U.S. AEC, Technical Information Service, Oak Ridge, Tenn., *Task Force Evaluation Report—Small-Sized Nuclear Power Program*, TID-8508 (October 1959), p. 5.

costly. Eliminate the latter, and the capital cost would drop sharply. All in all, so many possibilities exist for a further lowering of the present barrier of high capital cost that it would be entirely premature to dismiss small atomic power plants for civilian use.

Still, whether large or small, the atomic power plant that can be built today or within the next decade holds limited promise for nations already industrialized. Yet only they, and possibly two or three other nations, can build, finance, and fuel them. The "have not"countries, for the most part, are already discouraged about the prospects of atomic power, and it is hardly necessary at this juncture to depress them further. But should they wish to gain nuclear experience, they might well look more closely at applications not involving the generation of electricity. The experience thereby gained will have much applicability in the nuclear power-generating arts.

Reactors for Heat

Not every industrial process depends upon the operation of electricity-driven machines. A great many operations simply require heat. For example, over 80 per cent of the total energy used in the paper and pulp industry is provided by low-pressure steam, and only 20 per cent is in the form of electricity. Large-scale chemical processing, such as conversion of hydrocarbons, production of calcium carbide, and manufacture of soda ash, all require exceedingly large quantities of heat. At least 80 per cent of the energy requirement of a highly industralized nation is nonelectrical. In the United States the proportion seems to be increasing. "If heat reactors look promising for the U.S., they look even more promising for foreign countries."[22]

One of the evident, perhaps unfortunate, characteristics of the formative years of nuclear research and policy making has been the orientation toward electrical power. Most workers in the field are aware of the alternative possibilities for the application of nuclear fission energy, but the bringing of nonpower concepts to even rudimentary engineering stages has been slow. Undoubtedly many of those responsible for decisions in this field view nonpower

[22] "Heat Reactor Prospects Abroad," *Nucleonics,* February 1958, pp. 70-71.

applications as advanced concepts, to be considered in later stages of the technical development of nuclear power. In the minds of others, the all-purpose usefulness of electrical power is the key factor; with them alternative applications of atomic energy meet considerable incomprehension and sales resistance.

The northern countries, as might be expected, have taken the lead in the design and construction of heat-producing reactors. The reactor in Halden, Norway, will provide process steam for a paper factory. Sweden has two heat-producing plants to provide winter comfort for small communities. One of them, reactor ADAM, serves the 70,000 inhabitants of Västerås near Stockholm. Aside from its interest as a community heating plant, ADAM provides a novel experiment in burying a reactor in rock, in order to minimize accident risks. Another underground reactor will provide both heat and electricity for a new suburb, Fersta, just south of Stockholm.

In Chapter 4 it was shown how nuclear power systems could reduce atmospheric pollution from conventional power systems. For areas where atmospheric pollution would persist because of other factors (for example, the discharge of chemical wastes), the imaginative suggestion has been made that an extremely high capacity reactor producing heat at low temperatures could generate enough energy to blow a hole through the inversion layer which traps atmospheric pollution.[23] Another experiment would place a reactor on the ocean floor, to modify coastal currents and thereby the weather.[24]

A most attractive operation would be the production of pure water through evaporation processes using nuclear heat. For this operation the reactor could provide useful energy around the clock, thus guaranteeing a very high load factor, in contrast to many situations where electrical demand varies widely throughout the day or the season. Because of the relative simplicity of the

[23] Statement of David B. Hall of the Los Alamos Scientific Laboratory, *Frontiers in Atomic Energy Research*, Hearings before the Subcommittee on Research and Development of the Joint Committee on Atomic Energy, 86th Cong., 2d sess., March 22-25, 1960 (Washington: GPO, 1960), p. 169.

[24] Harris B. Stewart, Jr., "Man Begins to Explore 'Inner Space,'" *The New York Times Magazine*, May 7, 1961, pp. 52-80.

processes, builders could draw upon existing reactor designs and proven fuel element technology. This evidently has occurred in Norway and Sweden. The advantage of these plants is not limited to the experience derived from building and operating them and to the energy they supply; they can also be used as efficient producers of isotopes. And as they produce plutonium from natural uranium, they entail the same responsibility for safeguards as power reactors.

Another use of heat-producing reactors is in the chemical industry. Nitric acid is, perhaps, the most widely used chemical commodity; about 75 per cent of the annual output is employed in the fertilizer industry. Production in the United States is approximately three million tons per year with a net worth of $300 million. The nitric acid industry consumes a significant portion of the nation's fossil fuel resources, about 10 per cent as much as is used in producing electrical power.

Reactors used as chemical producers, i.e., "chemonuclear reactors," can take many forms. One process, already well demonstrated, uses the direct impact of fission products on a mixture of nitrogen and hydrogen to produce nitrogen dioxide, which can be easily converted by chemical means into other chemicals, principally fertilizer. Three 100-megawatt plants constructed each year could satisfy the U.S. demand for fertilizer, now increasing at an annual rate of 60 to 75 per cent.

Some of the applications of heat generated by nuclear processes, as in acetylene production or nitrogen fixation, would require high-temperature reactors, thus encountering many of the problems met in designing an efficient, high-temperature, electrical-conversion system. However, in these energy-tapping concepts, many of the technical barriers to the production of nuclear power are diminished, or are simply nonexistent, since most of the nonpower applications, such as central heating, oil refining, and coal carbonization, require *low-temperature* reactors. In their operation the troublesome problems of materials, characteristic of high-temperature, highly efficient nuclear power reactors, do not arise. Some low-temperature installations which involve a fairly direct utilization of fission energy would require relatively low investment in capital equipment for the intermediate and final conversion stages characteristic of nuclear power plants. Thus, it would seem to be wiser, in terms of convenience and economy, for an emerging country to attempt to gather its nuclear experience by operating a low-temperature reactor system, which in many applications would be quite useful. Even if it were not, on the whole, more economical than conventional processes, this type of operation might be the cheapest way to buy nuclear experience.

Direct Power Production

The electronic and ionic revolution is producing techniques which will drastically reduce the costs of producing power from both conventional and atomic fuels. These techniques are generally referred to as the "direct" generation of electricity. While the generation of electricity in some of these new techniques is more direct than in others, the term "direct" has come to signify a system in which moving parts are drastically reduced or eliminated. The over-all effect is to reduce or eliminate the costs of providing intermediate steam generation and turbine equipment.

At least five different direct systems are being studied,[25] but the discovery of entirely new processes which may be more efficient than the present ones cannot be ruled out. One possibility is thermoelectrical generation based on principles discovered more than a century ago but rendered interesting only recently through the development of unique semiconductor materials. Another is thermionic generation using phenomena observed by Thomas Edison in 1883. A third is the fuel cell, again with origins that can be traced back more than a century. Magnetohydrodynamic generation, which substitutes a stream of hot gas for the wire coils in the Michael Faraday dynamo of 1831, is also being studied. And finally

---

[25] Karl G. Hernqvist, "Thermionic Converters," *Nucleonics,* July 1959, pp. 49-52; Richard J. Rosa, "Magnetohydrodynamic Power Generation Using Nuclear Fuel," Research Report 87 (Everett, Mass.: Avco-Everett Research Laboratory, a division of Avco Corp., March 1960). Also, G. M. Grover, "Los Alamos Plasma Thermocouple," *Nucleonics,* July 1959, pp. 54-55; B. C. Lindley, "The Direct Generation of Electricity—1," *Nuclear Power,* June 1960, pp. 100-103; "The Direct Generation of Electricity—2," *Nuclear Power,* July 1960, pp. 80-83.

there is the possibility of direct collection of the electrical energy of the atom as it is split.[26]

As we are beginning to learn how to extract electricity directly from the charged particles of fission, it is curious that we are also learning for the first time how to obtain electricity from a simple flame. A flame, after all, is simply an ionized gas, and ionization is intimately related to electricity. But harnessing the flame is a complex process which involves directing it and containing it by means of magnetic fields. This is the science of magnetohydrodynamics, which will have great significance for both conventional and nuclear power generating processes.

Some of the various direct generation phenomena have been successfully demonstrated on a minute scale in reactor systems. It is quite probable that in the future one or all of them will render obsolete present-day concepts of both conventional and nuclear power plants.

The development of the fuel cell in which the process of electrolysis is reversed, two gases or chemical reactants combining to produce electricity directly, may have some unique and interesting atomic energy connotations. For example, the power from a nuclear plant could be used during off-peak-demand periods to electrolyze hydrogen and oxygen which would then be stored and utilized in fuel cells during peak-demand periods.[27] This would give the reactor the high load factor which is essential for economical operation.

Since fuel cells may eventually be used for small power units in vehicles and perhaps even in homes, another interesting possibility is a central-station reactor producing fuels other than hydrogen and oxygen (including, perhaps, oil and coal gasification products) for distribution to fuel cell units in the vicinity. Fuel cells of the future may well operate most efficiently on synthetic fuel rather

[26] Theoretical and experimental work on this concept of a "fission cell" has been pioneered by Dr. George Safonov. It was by means of the Safonov experiment that a very small amount of electricity was probably first directly generated from the fission process at the Argonne National Laboratory on September 12, 1958.

[27] K. M. Towers, "Energy Storage," *Nuclear Engineering*, February 1958, pp. 47-51; "Direct Conversion with Fuel Cells?" (Technical Advances), *Nucleonics*, July 1958, p. 110.

than on natural hydrocarbons.[28] It may prove possible to produce synthetic fuels by nuclear techniques; thus atomic energy may amplify the enormous changes which fuel cells are destined to make.

As these concepts mature, their investigation involves some exceedingly intriguing physics amenable to international collaborative research. Since they may represent the next important step beyond the present families of nuclear reactors, they should be of special interest to nations and international bodies that are already making substantial investments in nuclear power plants. For Euratom, the new direct systems would seem to provide an especially important field for research. Many talented scientists in several European laboratories have had much experience in investigating the classic electrical phenomenology inherent in the new systems. The research reactors necessary for the investigation are already in existence in several places on the continent. Here indeed is an exciting possibility for a joint U.S.-European research program.

New Fuels, Fusion, and the Future

Presently available nuclear techniques, and even the magic of direct conversion, cannot possibly satisfy long-range energy demands, for the economical operation of all these systems depends on the extraction of uranium minerals from comparatively rich ore deposits. But to meet future demands we must mine lower-grade ores and we must also develop advanced techniques for breeding fissionable material from the now useless uranium-238 and thorium-232.[29] When we reach that stage, the rocks of the world literally could be processed for fuel. It has been shown that all granite contains extremely small but extractable amounts of fertile materials. Using these materials to meet energy demands at some twenty times the present rate would require the mining of some ten million tons of rock per day. This sounds like a formi-

[28] K. R. Williams, "The Fuel Cell for Transport?" *The New Scientist* (London), August 4, 1960, pp. 338-340.

[29] W. K. Ergen and E. L. Zebroski, "Breeding—How Soon a Necessity?" *Nucleonics*, February 1960, pp. 60-87; A. M. Weinberg, "Energy as an Ultimate Raw Material," presented before the Southeastern Section of the American Physical Society, New Orleans, April 10, 1959; A. M. Weinberg, "Power Breeding As a National Objective" (editorial), *Nucleonics*, August 1958, pp. 75-76.

dable amount, but the present world output of coal and lignite is about six million tons per day. Thus we may anticipate that the mining of fertile material will eventually approximate the present scale of the coal industry.

Moreover, if current *thermonuclear* research is successful, we may be able to burn the waters of the oceans as well as the rocks of the earth for our power. The deuterium present in a gallon of water could eventually yield 10,000 kilowatt-hours of energy at a minuscule fuel cost.

After the 1955 Geneva Conference on the Peaceful Uses of Atomic Energy a rumor gathered momentum in the industry that the then secret work on fusion processes was developing to a state where nuclear fission power reactors would soon be obsolete. The rumor reached its climax in July 1957 when an article in *Fortune* proclaimed, "There is now a slight but sobering possibility that the uranium-power age may be over almost before it has begun."[30] But the destruction of secrecy barriers about fusion at the Second Geneva Conference in 1958 brought the sobering consensus that power from this source was at least twenty years away. In fact the pessimistic conclusion of a technological optimist was " . . . that an economic exploitation of controlled thermonuclear reactions may not turn out to be possible before the end of the 20th century."[31]

But perhaps *Fortune* was right. Twenty years, after all, is not so long; it represents the lower limit for the amortization of a power plant. For the United States, and for other areas where in the same time-span fission power is not likely to compete economically with conventional power, perhaps the correct attitude should be "wait and see." This risk, however, would probably not be warranted. First of all, the time span for achieving fusion power may be quite long. Second, although the nuclear power systems now in existence may be uneconomic, they are convenient and necessary in specialized applications. Third, atomic power is becoming an economic

[30] Francis Bello, "Fusion Power: The Trail Gets Hotter," *Fortune,* July 1957, p. 135.

[31] Edward Teller, *Peaceful Uses of Fusion*, P/2410, 2d United Nations International Conference on the Peaceful Uses of Atomic Energy (Geneva: September 1958), v. 31, p. 32.

reality in high fuel-cost areas. Fourth, the primary contribution of a fusion reactor may well be the production of abundant and cheap fissionable materials rather than the production of electricity directly. The fissionable materials so produced could then be utilized in fission reactors of present types to produce power. Hence, it will be necessary to have satisfactorily developed the latter type of reactor when the fusion age dawns.

The production of power by fusion demands a technique somewhat the inverse of that used in splitting the atom. The fusing or combining certain light-weight nuclei, like heavy hydrogen and tritium, releases large amounts of energy, just as does the splitting of uranium-235. The extremely high temperatures that are required to make these nuclei combine produce a "fourth state of matter," *plasma.* In the past several years the realization has come that the properties of plasma, also important in magnetohydrodynamic research, are less understood than was formerly believed, so that the search for thermonuclear power is largely an attempt to obtain this understanding

Comparison of some of the major research programs now under way in various countries is interesting. The total operating costs of thermonuclear research in European countries in 1958 and 1959 were $6.7 million and $12.9 million, respectively. Scientific staffs numbered 216 in 1958 and 320 in 1959. The comparative costs for the U.S. Atomic Energy Commission fusion program were $28.7 million in 1958 and $38 million in 1959. The personnel employed in these years was 288 and 347, respectively. The most striking aspect of these comparisons is that, while the staff totals for the United States are not much larger than in Europe, the expenditures for the U.S. program are three or four times as large. This difference is largely accounted for by the construction in the United States of several large-scale pieces of experimental apparatus which have no counterparts in Europe.

Since thermonuclear research (in the Western world at least) is a completely open subject, it would appear that both scientific staffs and appropriations could be utilized with greater efficiency, not merely by the exchange of information on results achieved, but also through over-all planning and exchange of scientists of appropriate talents to work on the highly specialized pieces of experimental equipment, wherever they may be situated.

The United States gives wholehearted encouragement to the various European efforts in fusion research. Since economic competition in this field will not emerge for many decades, it would seem that the common good and progress would be accelerated by close cooperation and exchange among all the Western programs. And further, if a satisfactory *quid pro quo* could be formulated, the exchange of personnel and information with appropriate Soviet laboratories does not seem to be out of order.

Although the new technical frontiers will first be conquered and exploited by the technologically advanced nations, they do hold much promise for the less advanced. The pity is that no single, permanent organization exists, so constituted and so developed as to be able to predict authoritatively the impact of the new technologies on emerging economic areas. The direction and pace of these developments might be drastically altered if such predictions were available.

Some day, somehow, as the less advanced areas emerge, their energy requirements will multiply phenomenally. So will ours. And if we achieve the techniques of either breeding or harnessing thermonuclear energy, future generations will not be discouraged if we have not achieved both. For either will provide the world with billions of years of energy. Since, as some predict, the solar system probably will not last that long, mankind's energy problem would then have been solved. The real questions at the moment would then seem to be: (1) What responsibility does the present generation bear for the development of atomic energy for the benefit of succeeding generations? (2) Will the development of atomic energy make it impossible for a good fraction of succeeding generations to exist, in the kind of world which we hope for?

Chapter 7

Propulsion

For most people nuclear power is a mysterious force which, rightly or wrongly, is prejudged to be beyond one's comprehension. Atomic radiation, whether beneficently or maleficently applied, cannot be seen or otherwise sensed. The immobile atomic power plant looks like any other electric power station, and the electrical current which it produces has no special identity. But, somehow, anything in motion always seems psychologically to possess a close identity with the forces that move it. Thus, it is with the atomic locomotive, ship, plane, or rocket. And it is this imprecise association that renders economic and technical comparisons of nuclear with conventional propulsion very difficult, if not impossible. Like Sputnik, an atomic airplane would represent a tremendous political advantage for the first nation to fly it. But does the atomic airplane represent for aviation or for a nation's economic, technological, and strategic position the same type of breakthrough as did Sputnik?

Propulsion at first seemed to be the only practical peaceful application of nuclear fission. A Committee on Postwar Policy, appointed about a year before the atomic bomb was first tested, made the following recommendation in regard to nuclear propulsion:

The Government should initiate and push, as an urgent project, research and development studies to provide power from nuclear sources for the propulsion of naval vessels. It might be advisable to authorize the initiation of these studies at once, without waiting for the postwar period, in order to utilize scientific personnel already familiar with pile theory and operation. The development of fission piles solely for the production of power for ordinary commercial use does not appear economically sound nor advisable from the point of view of preserving national resources.[1]

Sea-Going Vessels

Obviously, the long-range prospects for economic nuclear power were then somewhat dimmer than they are now. But for the stubborn persistence of a Navy captain, even this minimum application of nuclear power would not have been investigated so soon. On May 31, 1953, a land-based prototype of a submarine power plant demonstrated the world's first practical utilization of atomic power, an event which might have occurred much later had majority opinion been followed. Subsequent generations of this reactor, installed in nuclear submarines like the *Nautilus* and in the Shippingport, Pennsylvania, atomic power plant, gave the United States a significant lead in the development of one family of nuclear power plants, the pressurized-water type. "The Navy Reactor program is the only part of the U.S. reactor effort that has consistently had a sense of purpose and direction. As a consequence, its achievements have been phenomenal, and the U.S. is unquestionably leading the world here."[2] This lead, in its civilian aspects, is now being challenged.

On and under the sea the dozens of descendants of the *Nautilus* —the nuclear surface ships, the *Enterprise,* the *Savannah,* the *Long Beach,* and the *Bainbridge*—give dramatic proof that the power of the atom can be harnessed. The power can be tapped for periods up to five years (eventually perhaps up to ten years) without refuelling. Here is a new force of great stategic importance which affects drastically the planning of the U.S. Navy.[3] But maritime power is not measured solely by naval power, nor should the atom be considered a military monopoly.

Years of official apathy led a trade journal to cry "Wanted: Nuclear Clipper Ships—Now,"[4] but in the United States the propul-

[1] Richard C. Tolman, "Report of Committee on Postwar Policy, December 28, 1944," *Atomic Power and Private Enterprise,* Joint Committee on Atomic Energy, 82d Cong., 2d sess., December 1952 (Washington: GPO, 1952), p. 168.

[2] "Army and Space Reactors," (Editorial) *Nucleonics,* May 1960, p. 76.

[3] Plans which fluctuate wildly however. Contrast "Atom Fleet Plan Gaining New Life" (*The New York Times,* January 15, 1961, p. 4) with "Navy Says Costs Bar Atom Fleet" (*The New York Times,* April 10, 1961, p. 1).

[4] Editorial, *Nucleonics,* April 1959, p. 85.

sion of merchant vessels continued to receive far less attention than electrical power plants. Yet the practical advantages of the latter had not been demonstrated as forcefully as had propulsion by means of the cruising fleet of nuclear submarines. Elsewhere in the world, interest in ship propulsion often exceeded local enthusiasm for land-based nuclear power.

At Hamburg, Germany, a research institute is devoted exclusively to the application of nuclear energy in shipbuilding and ship navigation. The institute's research reactor was the first in Europe dedicated solely to marine propulsion.[5] A unique feature of the German program will be the construction of a ship which could be fitted successively with several different nuclear cores, so that each can be tested without the expense of building a separate hull for it. Needless to say, the principles which are tested aboard ship are also applicable to land-based reactors. Although the German program has some unique elements, by no means does it represent the only serious effort in this field. Belgium, Britain, Denmark, Italy, France, Japan, the Netherlands, Norway, Sweden, and the Euratom organization are all proceeding with plans for maritime propulsion, and all of them will be watching the experience of the United States with the first nuclear surface ship.[6]

On May 22, 1819, the *S.S. Savannah* set out from her namesake port in Georgia to capture the distinction of being the first steam-propelled vessel to complete an Atlantic voyage. Actually the *Savannah*, a converted sailing ship, was forced to use sails in rough weather and so did not make the full voyage under steam. History has kindly given the *Savannah's* name to another vessel which represents just as significant a forward step in transportation.

One hundred and forty years later the *N.S. Savannah* ("N.S." for nuclear ship) was launched. Nothing in her external appearance distinguishes the *Savannah* as a nuclear cargo ship. In her "innards," however, is a nuclear reactor quite similar to that which

[5] C. E. Steiner, "Prospects for Nuclear Powered Ships," *Nuclear Power*, January 1960, pp. 108-110.

[6] "Marine Propulsion Projects," *Nuclear Engineering*, May 1959, pp. 193-199; "Ship Propulsion Conference," Same, January 1960, pp. 14-18; J. S. Burkett, "Nuclear Merchant Ship Survey," *Nuclear Power*, August 1960, pp. 78-82; "New Research in Nuclear Marine Propulsion," *Bulletin from the European Community*, No. 49, October 1961, p. 9.

drives the nuclear submarine, the *Nautilus*. The reactor is fueled by 15,500 pounds of uranium, of which about 670 pounds is U-235. Incorporated in the design, of course, are all the safety devices and the shielding necessary to assure protection of cargo and crew. The cost of the *Savannah* is just about double that of a similar ship using conventional power. Like the cost of almost any nuclear application, this must be considered as part of the expense of gaining experience in the development of economic propulsion units.

There is no assurance that the pressurized-water reactor, which has been so extensively developed for submarines, and for the *Savannah,* is the ideal power source for surface ships. A 1960 study by the Danish Association for Industrial Development of Atomic Energy considered the cost of constructing three such ships and operating them from Kuwait around the Cape of Good Hope to Britain.[7] For a nuclear tanker the cost of transporting a ton of oil was about 50 per cent higher than the cost for diesel tankers. It is impossible, however, in such studies to predict for periods of emergency the cost of the fuel consumed by a conventional tanker, or the value of its cargo. Also, special circumstances other than fuel emergencies may justify nuclear surface ships.

The Soviets, for instance, had scored an impressive "first" in the nuclear propulsion field. Their icebreaker, the *Lenin,* in addition to applying atomic power to its special purpose, bears the distinction of being the world's first nuclear-powered surface ship. The *Lenin's* rating is respectable: 44 thousand shaft horsepower, over twice that of the *N.S. Savannah*. Like the *Savannah* it is driven by nuclear reactors resembling those in the *Nautilus*. The special purpose of the *Lenin* undoubtedly weighs heavily in its favor when costs and utility are being compared. The *Lenin* will be able to cruise the desolate northern sea routes for at least a year without refueling.[8] Canada, the other great arctic nation, sporadically has seriously considered emulating the *Lenin*. Plying the ice-bound arctic waters for many months at a time without

[7] "Nuclear Tanker Cost," *The New Scientist* (London), v. 8, no. 193, July 28, 1960, pp. 267-268.

[8] By now the *Lenin* has completed four or five round trips across the northern coast of Siberia. Apparently its utility is such that at least one more nuclear icebreaker will be built (*Nucleonics Week,* June 21, 1962, p. 5).

refueling, the nuclear icebreaker makes very good sense. It provides, also, the ideal way to test the safety characteristics of nuclear surface ships, for its isolated route minimizes the hazards of collision or operating accidents. Although the U.S. fleet of eleven icebreakers is inadequate and approaching obsolescence, there appears to be little official enthusiasm for atomic-powered replacements. It is thus quite possible that the United States will soon find itself in a subordinate role in the Arctic, an area rapidly gaining in significance.

A curious anachronism appears in the possible application of atomic energy to whaling, an industry dating from prehistoric times. The main product of whaling activities has been oil extracted from blubber; the highly nutritious, lean whale meat has always been a minor by-product. Japanese, Norwegians, Icelanders, and Faroese, among others, for many years have utilized whale meat to minimize protein deficiencies. Bacterial decomposition now makes the greater proportion of the Antarctic catch unfit for human consumption. Properly preserved, it would find a ready market. Nuclear technology can add largely to the supply and tap a new Antarctic resource.

Whaling operations are focused on a central factory ship which, operating for long periods in remote areas, has serious fueling problems. A solution would appear to be a nuclear-powered factory ship.[9] But a detailed examination of this idea shows that nuclear propulsion would not be economically feasible in whaling, unless certain other attributes of atomic energy could also be exploited. In Chapter 9 the sterilization of food by means of radiation treatment is discussed. The same reactor which provides the motive power for the whaler could possibly be used also for the irradiation and preservation of lean whale meat. When the problem is re-examined in terms of what might be accomplished by both functions—the saving of fuel oil and the production of an edible product—the economic aspects begin to look more favorable.

Whether or not the nuclear whaler is a realistic enterprise, the important concept that it embodies might be extended to a nu-

---

[9] George K. Brokaw, *et al.,* "A Nuclear Whaler," *Nuclear Engineering,* November 1958, pp. 471-476.

clear vessel processing excess foods in a producing area and transporting them with little or no refrigeration to a consuming area. Such a vessel might handle diversified cargoes between widely separated areas in the course of the several years it would travel without refueling. Food would be processed in ports by using nuclear power in canning or otherwise preparing food by conventional means, and by using also, whenever feasible, the preservative effects of radiation.

Another form of adjustment between population and food supply is emigration. For a half century, Japanese have emigrated to South and Central America; at present, the rate is about ten thousand per year. Plans of the Emigration Section of the Japanese Foreign Office call for successive increases in this figure to thirty thousand per year. The long voyage (forty days) is accomplished by five small, crowded ships. To relieve this situation, an industrial group has proposed the construction of a Japanese nuclear-powered emigrant ship with a capacity of two thousand emigrants.[10] With a shaft horsepower of 40 thousand, the single ship would be able to transport, with greater comfort and in less time, more than the combined capacity of the present fleet.

The whaler, the emigrant ship, and the food-processing vessel illustrate some rather unusual uses to which, with a little imagination, nuclear power can be put. In these and other uses nuclear-powered ships have some unique features. The most significant is that nuclear fuel does not demand frequent replacement. The first merchant ship, the *N.S. Savannah,* will burn about 150 pounds of nuclear fuel in the approximate three-year loading period. Fuel bunker space is accordingly eliminated so that the payload could be relatively constant. Operating under comparable conditions, a conventional oil-fired ship of the same size and speed would burn in three years about 80 thousand tons of fuel oil. The ratio of oil to nuclear fuel is one million to one!

With a constant fuel load, the nuclear-powered vessel would possess an almost constant draft. This feature may raise difficulties in some ports. At the Port of Lisbon, for example, oil-burning

[10] Seiichi Takeuchi, *et al., A Nuclear Powered Emigrant Ship,* P/1319, 2d UN International Conference on Peaceful Uses of Atomic Energy (Geneva: UN, 1958), v. 3, pp. 167-188.

ships have a navigational advantage in arriving lightened, having burnt a heavy load of fuel during the voyage. But this difficulty is perhaps trivial compared to the probable reluctance of many nations to allow nuclear ships even within territorial limits, much less to enter a crowded, strategic port. The Danes, for example, refused to let the *U.S.S. Skate* into Copenhagen harbor after its historic subpolar transit. On the other hand, the Norwegians were not reluctant to let the *Skate* visit Bergen; the *Triton* has docked at Bremerhaven, and other nuclear submarines at non-U.S. ports.

The successful operation of the enlarging nuclear submarine fleet has increased confidence in the safety of mobile nuclear power plants. An accident to a nuclear surface ship, nevertheless, would result in a more dangerous release of radioactive materials than would the equivalent accident in a nuclear submarine. Underwater, at sea, there is greater localization, initially, of escaped fission products. A disaster occurring above the surface, particularly in a port, might deposit deadly fission products in inhabited areas like the fallout from atomic bombs, but in a far more limited area. Considering the total amount of traffic, ship collisions or accidents are extremely rare, despite impressions etched by dramatic events like the sinking of the *Andrea Doria* and the collision of the *Constitution* in New York harbor. Of course, when even a very rare incident is coupled with a disaster of great magnitude, statistics are not very comforting either to the public or to the insurance companies. The determination of liability in this instance would be most tricky. The political disaster that such an event would represent provides the greatest incentive to provide propulsion units with maximum safety features.

While the possibility of the release of radioactive by-products through shipside accident or by collision may be remote, the release of the radioactive wastes from the nuclear furnaces will be an ever-present problem. These wastes cannot be discharged in estuaries or harbors, or indeed within a reasonable distance offshore. Ships will have to be equipped with tanks to contain the radioactive wastes until they can be discharged at approved locations on the high seas. The National Academy of Sciences and the National Research Council of the United States released in July 1959 a report by a committee of oceanographers examining the problems that would arise if there were three hundred nuclear-powered ships in operation by 1975. A fleet of this size would release almost one million curies (equivalent in radioactivity to about a ton of radium) of radioactive wastes every year. The responsibility for proper disposal of this extremely large amount of radioactivity will rest upon the many nations which at that time are likely to have nuclear ships in operation. Clearly, here is another promising opportunity for international collaboration in the field of nuclear energy: an international organization to set standards for the radioactivity monitoring program which will be necessary in every port of call, and for registering waste disposal in appropriate ocean areas. Only one international organization, the IAEA, now includes all the nations which are likely to have nuclear fleets by 1975. Disposal of radioactivity in man's environment, whether it be the atmosphere or the vast ocean depths, will always raise important practical and political problems. The IAEA could perform a great service by offering itself as the forum for their discussion and, hopefully, their resolution.

Mobile units which roam the world's oceans give rise to an interesting and perplexing aspect of international inspection. Diversion of fissionable materials could occur during a voyage or at unreported stops. Presumably, the main accounting will have to be done by inspectors at port areas but, through the use of secret port facilities and the alteration of records *en route,* a rather clever diversion scheme probably could be devised. To further complicate matters, if a nation were really intent upon deceiving the rest of the world, it might produce atomic bombs—a grandiose but not impossible project—in a mobile surface and undersurface fleet never stationary anywhere at sea. This suggestion, however, should be regarded as a challenging but not hopeless exercise by those who are devoting some thought to a nuclear inspection system.

The subpolar transit of the *Nautilus* and *Skate* suggests another peaceful use of nuclear propulsion: subsurface cargo ships. The surface of the sea, the classical road of mankind, is after all a rather unreasonable medium of transportation when the air or the subsurface of the ocean is available. A surface vessel is subject to the whim of tides and weather and has to cope with the poor hydrodynamical characteristics of the air-water interface. Below the surface there is calm, and the envelope of water adapts kindly to well-designed, fish-like shapes which seek to go fast. Under water or under ice, submarine cargo ships would be capable of operating at perhaps forty knots, compared to normal surface speeds of about sixteen knots for a modern large cargo vessel. All of this seems very attractive—until the cost is considered. The costs of a submarine cargo vessel would be between three and thirty times that of a surface vessel doing the same job more slowly. Obviously, only special circumstances, or additional applications, would justify serious consideration of such costs.

In the Air, on Land, and in Space

Problems of size and weight have hindered the development of nuclear-powered aircraft. In a surface ship and even in a submarine there is a relatively large space and weight accommodation; an aircraft must necessarily reduce these characteristics to the minimum. And even when a compact power plant has been achieved, the massive shielding required for the protection of passengers, cargo, and equipment presents another weight dilemma. Moreover, weird, or at least unexpected, problems are likely to be encountered. For example, neutron bombardment on the plane's structural elements could cause metal fatigue—a condition so vividly disastrous to the first British Comet aircraft (although in that case the origin of the fatigue was not nuclear). Also, ionization of the air surrounding a nuclear aircraft could make radiocommunication to and from it difficult.

Do nuclear aircraft have any practical utility, assuming the various technical barriers to have been overcome? Possibly in a military sense, although this has been vigorously debated. The primary virtue of a nuclear plane is its ability to stay aloft for long periods, which no ordinary passenger is inclined to do, unless his purpose is obscure. Nuclear planes have been thought of as television and other communication relays; but it now appears that earth-circling satellites could do the same job as effectively, and less expensively, since once permanently aloft they require no propulsive fuel.

To be able to land and take off many times successively without refueling is a possible advantage of nuclear planes for civilian air transport. Most airfields would not have to be equipped with fuel and fueling facilities, an attractive prospect for many remote areas where fuel is expensive or difficult to obtain. But consider the non-technical, the political, consequences of cargo- and passenger-carrying nuclear aircraft. If letting a nuclear submarine into Copenhagen harbor arouses great fears, would not permitting a nuclear aircraft to land at Kastrup airport amplify that fear? Public opinion, supported by statistically minded actuaries, will prevent overflights by civilian nuclear planes for a long, long time, irrespective of the technical advantages or liabilities.

Chemically-fueled jet passenger aircraft perform spectacularly and there is every reason to expect faster and larger aircraft to be thus propelled in the future. The glamour of nuclear flight does not in any sense justify the nuclear aircraft program; its development, effectively halted in March 1961 after incurring costs totalling $1 billion, had to be based purely upon military considerations.

Regardless of technical feasibility or impossibility, the nuclear locomotive and that long-fabled atomic automobile make little sense so long as conventional fuels are plentiful. Indeed, one could argue that one of the long-range reasons for using nuclear power where it is most efficient is to free conventional fuels for uses in which they are highly efficient and necessary, as for the propulsion of small vehicles and aircraft.

One of the more exotic applications of atomic energy will be its use in rocket technology to furnish power for greater space payloads.[11] Various chemical propellants are entirely sufficient to put a 50-pound instrumented satellite or a far heavier five-ton spaceship into orbit. However, to put man into what is truly outer space, to provide him with scientific instrumentation and living requirements for a long journey, the nuclear device is the only foreseeable source of power. A nuclear rocket can provide specific impulses several times more powerful than can be obtained from chemical combustion.[12] In addition to increased payload capacity,

[11] "Nuclear Rockets" (several reports on nuclear energy for rocket propulsion), *Nucleonics*, July 1958, pp. 62-75.
[12] The specific impulse is the amount of thrust given to a rocket per pound of fuel consumed per second. It is a measure of efficiency or adequacy of the rocket engine and thus might be compared to the way in which miles per gallon measures the efficiency of one's automobile.

nuclear power affords a long-term source of energy for distant space travel—energy which can be applied in quantity time after time, whenever it becomes necessary for the rocket to escape the gravitational field of another planet.

Nuclear propulsion is an obvious necessity in the long run if we are to put heavy payloads into space and into orbit. The U.S. project which investigates these prospects was initiated in 1955 but its target dates have been repeatedly put off because of technical difficulties and uncertainties of policy. A nonmobile unit has undergone some testing, but it will be at least 1967 before a flight test is a reality. The first evidences of strong presidential support for nuclear rocketry finally emerged about the middle of 1961, and it is to be expected that emphasis on this mode of space propulsion will increase.

Some interesting by-products have appeared from the solution of the problem of providing power within missiles for the operation of instruments. Solar cells have been used successfully for this purpose. However, in areas of space where solar power is weak or not available, alternative sources must be sought. Power plants at ratings up to 60 kilowatts using radioisotopes, or actually small nuclear reactors, have been developed.[13] Some are now encircling the earth,[14] providing power for buoys in mid-ocean, and serve as the basis of operation of an unmanned weather station in the Antarctic.[15] These small plants, termed "SNAP" units (for Systems for Nuclear Auxiliary Power), have significant earthbound application in furnishing reliable, long-term power for extremely isolated or inaccessible situations—for example, to operate automatic equipment to signal atmospheric, hydrographic, seismic or other characteristics. A high-powered SNAP unit appears to be the most reasonable power source for the communications satellites which

[13] U.S. AEC, "Chairman McCone, AEC, Announces Development of Small Nuclear Electric Power Device," Press Release B-7, January 16, 1959; Same, "Reactor Core Designed for Direct Conversion Reactor Tested Successfully at AEC Facility," Press Release IN-122, August 17, 1960.

[14] In a TRANSIT satellite launched on June 29, 1961. See also "SNAP Fact Sheet" distributed under cover of U.S. AEC Press Release D-169 of June 29, 1961.

[15] U.S. AEC Press Release E-34, February 8, 1962, "First Atomic-Powered Weather Station in Antarctic Begins Operations."

are circling the earth, providing links for world-wide communications of all sorts, including television.

International Cooperation

In all of the nuclear propulsion fields there is the opportunity for international cooperation to establish standards for operating nuclear vessels, aircraft, or rockets and to set the limits of liability. The rocket problem is particularly thorny because of the need to provide for safety in launching and re-entry, the disposition of highly radioactive engines on earth or in space, and the solution of many other problems.

Europe is seeking to qualify for membership in the "space club." But rocket manufacturing and testing demand budgets even greater than atomic energy development—therefore, many countries thus far have been content with asking for a small amount of space for their instruments on a U.S. rocket. Except for British and French emphasis on certain military vehicles, a European space program has been slow in developing.

Quite recently, however, two joint organizations have been formed to promote peaceful space research. These are the European Launcher Development Organisation (ELDO) and the European Space Research Organisation (ESRO). The membership of ELDO is essentially that of Euratom with the addition of Britain. In effect, ELDO is composed of those European nations which have the capability of constructing and launching large space research vehicles. ESRO members are essentially the same nations which participate in the European Organisation for Nuclear Research at Geneva. The larger body of membership in ESRO will use the vehicles provided by ELDO to conduct its space research.

The members of ELDO are technologically and financially capable of making significant contributions to a nuclear rocket program, and a U.S. collaborative effort with ELDO would certainly seem to be a natural step. Cooperation on the small auxiliary power units, like SNAP, might be possible within an even broader framework of nations like ESRO, for these units do not require the possession of vehicle and launching facilities for their development. The United States has existing nuclear agreements with Britain and Euratom, and it would probably be possible to arrange a joint nuclear rocket research program without extensive new legislation. The experience gained thereby would prove to be not unrelated to the resolution of the broader problems.

Chapter 8

Into Plowshares

Of all the peaceful applications of atomic energy there is none so intimately related to nuclear weapons as Project Plowshare. Indeed, Plowshare involves the application of weapons, or weapon-like devices, to nonmilitary endeavors. Although the Russians for some time had hinted at an application like Plowshare and others have advocated these techniques at least since 1951,[1] U.S. interest was first manifested in 1957. Then, toward the end of 1957 and in 1958, the question of suspending nuclear tests mushroomed. The confluence of the two developments was perhaps unfortunate, for it tended to identify Plowshare primarily as a means for continuing tests for the sake of testing. Certainly, this was the attitude adopted by the Russians. In the United States, the assignment of primary responsibility for Plowshare by the AEC to a group other than its Division of Military Application might have more forcefully emphasized its benign potential. That simple administrative change was not made until the middle of 1961.[2] This history and the feeling on the part of many that Project Plowshare was initially designed merely as a political mechanism together tended to veil its very real technical merits.

[1] Camille Rougeron, *Les Applications d'explosion thermonucléaire* (Paris: Editions Berger-Levrault, 1956). Arnold Kramish, *Atomic Energy in the Soviet Union* (Stanford, California: Stanford University Press, 1959), pp. 142-153.

[2] To a new Division of Nuclear Explosions (U.S. AEC Press Release D-198, August 11, 1961).

New Uses for Atomic Explosions

When a nuclear weapon or device is detonated three outstanding phenomena occur: the blast effect, the thermal effect, and nuclear radiation. Each has its own particular military application, and each will also be useful in the peaceful exploitation of nuclear explosions.[3] Since Plowshare is still in its early stages, some initial weird concepts undoubtedly will prove impractical while other useful applications remain to be conceived.

Prior to World War II conventional high explosives had been used more for peaceful projects than for military purposes. World War II approximately evened the score. In excavations the utility of explosives like TNT derives from blast pressures on detonation. For small-scale work involving tens or hundreds of pounds of explosives, nuclear explosives offer no competition because of costs and attendant disadvantages, but where big bangs are required, atomic explosives begin to look attractive.

Consider, for example, the construction of a second Isthmian Canal.[4] The volume of shipping through the Panama Canal is already straining its capacity and is increasing so fast that by the year 2000 at the latest two canals will be required. There is also the question whether the United States will lose the use of the Panama Canal, through political instability in the region.[5] The original cost of the Panama Canal was about $367 million; to develop its capacity or to provide an alternate route would now cost about $4.5 billion. Farther north, in Mexico, a canal across the Isthmus of Tehuantepec which would reduce distances between Atlantic and Pacific ports in the northern hemisphere by a thousand miles would cost about $8 billion.[6] Obviously, significant reduction of these astronomical sums would be welcome. Of the total construction costs, approximately half is for extremely difficult excavation. At an average cost of about $1 million per nuclear device, it has

[3] An excellent summary of Plowshare applications is to be found in *Annual Report to Congress of the Atomic Energy Commission for 1962* (Washington: GPO, January, 1963), pp. 241-67.

[4] William Beecher, "Big Ditch, II," *Wall Street Journal*, March 28, 1961, p. 1.

[5] C. L. Sulzberger, "The Case of the Vanishing Canal," *The New York Times*, November 20, 1961, p. 30.

[6] *The Times* (London), January 20, 1961, p. 10.

been estimated that nuclear excavation, using any of three different routes on the Panama Isthmus, would range in cost from $130 million to $190 million. Conventional excavation costs for the same routes would be approximately $2 billion. Even if the first estimate that the nuclear method will cost less than 10 per cent of the conventional methods is priced too low, the margin is so large that economic application of the new technique seems assured. With the large explosive yields available from atomic devices, the emergence of a new art, "geographical engineering," can be forecast.

The Isthmian canal project is receiving serious consideration by those who are concerned with providing new traffic facilities, but its actual implementation is probably distant. Another enterprise now dormant, Project Chariot, related to providing the northwest coast of Alaska with an adequate harbor so that important large-scale mineral deposits in that area, including coal, can be developed and marketed. There are also good possibilities for improving Alaskan fishing by providing a safe haven for the fleet. To that end, survey parties and technical teams had examined a site on the Chuckchee Sea (above the Bering Straits). It appears that approximately five million cubic yards of earth could be removed by simultaneously detonating two 200-kiloton devices imbedded seven hundred feet below the surface and three 20-kiloton devices imbedded at a depth of four hundred feet. These explosions would create a harbor about 250 yards wide and 950 yards long. Although there is more than reasonable assurance that the livelihood of local inhabitants would not have been endangered by this excavation, local opposition forced the deferring of Project Chariot. Since the proposed harbor would be only 150 miles from Siberia, the detonation might have had other interesting political repercussions.

Applications of the blast effect appear pedestrian when compared with more exotic effects of nuclear explosions. But the former either result in spectacular economic savings or make it possible to accomplish quite readily what conventional explosives could only do with difficulty. In surface mining, the removal of overburden, or other obstacles, could be facilitated by nuclear explosives. There remains the problem of loosening the ore. Taconite ore, perhaps the most obstinate of all, is extremely hard and abrasive and consequently very resistant to blasting and drilling. In this case the huge energies concentrated in nuclear explosive packages may well lead to highly improved extraction techniques.

In another application nuclear explosions might increase supplies of the competitive energy source, oil. One could enlarge the well radius and, by fracturing a large area, increase the permeability of the oil-bearing media so that more oil would flow into the well and thus be readily pumped out. A more imaginative application in the oil industry is the possibility of setting off a nuclear explosion in a shale formation. After many thousand tons had been pulverized, the shale would be ignited, thus providing heat to extract the oil which it contained. Actually the shale will burn at a lower temperature than the oil, which will settle in large amounts to the bottom of the excavation whence it can be pumped to the surface.

At one time it was contemplated that Canadian oil sands might be exploited by using the heat from a Plowshare device. By firing a device in the tar sands or directly below them, it seems possible to release the contained oil which would then be recovered. It has been estimated that the oil reserves in the Canadian sands dwarf the Middle East reserves by a factor of about three, but at present its extraction is not economically feasible. While there is some hope that Plowshare techniques would reduce costs of extraction, transportation costs from the remote area in Canada under consideration probably would make the oil too expensive. For reasons more clearly related to the "new atmosphere" after Premier Khrushchev's visit to the United States in September 1959 than to economics, the Canadian project was abandoned at that time. Nevertheless, there are probably similar deposits in areas of the world where oil is less plentiful than in Alberta, Canada. This technique might therefore prove attractive at some future date when political considerations permit Plowshare explosions.

Another kind of use of Plowshare techniques is in the proposal to form large reservoirs of geothermal heat by exploding a bomb in a deep underground cavern and then allowing a heat transfer agent like water or gas to flow into the cavity. The agent would transfer its energy into high-temperature steam which could be directed to turbines to provide power. Using cheap H-bombs, this scheme presents a means of tapping thermonuclear energy through a pulse technique rather than through sustained fusion reactions (see Chapter 6). While these subterranean plants would be characterized by very low fuel costs, their extremely high capital investments would probably require their being TVA-like government projects. These would be large installations of the order of 2 million kilowatts in electrical capacity, costing some $2 billion. Still, the over-all economics seem to promise competitive nuclear power and, unlike hydroelectric stations, the choice of locale is somewhat more flexible.[7]

Much pertinent experience could be drawn from the design and operation of existing power plants using naturally generated geothermal steam, although the temperatures involved in Plowshare heat extraction may be higher. Natural steam jets in southwest Tuscany provide Italy with some 150 thousand kilowatts of electrical energy. Other areas of the world like Wairakei-Rotorua in New Zealand and Tatio in Chile seem to possess similar geothermal potential. Some interesting studies have been initiated looking to the extraction of energy from hot lava beds.[8] The exploration of these geothermal techniques hints at another possibility for international cooperation, using the skills of those already versed in tapping geothermal power and those versed in volcanology to investigate this aspect of Plowshare.

The atomic bomb is a copious source of neutrons; in fact it is a potential breeder reactor, for it emits far more neutrons than are used up in the reaction. Hence, it has been proposed to surround an atomic bomb in a deep underground cavity with substances from which one wanted to manufacture large amounts of radioactive isotopes, through the capture of neutrons emitted by the bomb. One can even foresee that additional fissionable material could be manufactured in the underground cavity by providing

[7] George A. Hoffman, "Thermoelectric Powerplants Utilizing Contained Nuclear Explosions," RM-2490-1 (Santa Monica, Cal.: RAND Corp., February 18, 1960).

[8] Walter Sullivan, "Scientists Drill in Lava Lake," *The New York Times,* December 10, 1960, p. 25. See also George C. Kennedy and David T. Griggs, "Power Recovery from the Kilauea Iki Lava Pool," RM-2606-AEC (Santa Monica, Cal.: RAND Corp., December 12, 1960).

uranium or thorium to capture the bomb neutrons. The resulting material would then be mined and chemically processed to extract the plutonium or U-233. For this kind of Plowshare program to remain peaceful there would have to be a guarantee that its products also would be limited to nonmilitary applications.

In addition to the engineering, production, and power applications of Plowshare, nuclear explosions can be used as research tools.[9] Two new atomic elements, created by the first thermonuclear explosion in 1952, were identified in its debris. The enormous quantities of neutrons emitted in nuclear explosions give a pulsed source of neutrons many times more potent than those available through the use of nuclear reactors, the usual source. A pulsed reactor can be used to accomplish certain fundamental nuclear measurements, but a nuclear explosion would produce neutrons equivalent to those available from such a pulsed reactor for several thousand years. Much remains to be learned about the interaction of neutrons with matter and the nuclear explosion clearly provides the physicist with a unique tool.[10]

Nuclear explosions can also help us learn much about space and about the earth itself. One application would be in the investigation of the behavior of radiation belts and the propagation of electromagnetic radiation in space. On earth, atomic explosions can supplement the study of earthquakes from which we have learned so much of what we know about the globe. A well-designed program of world-wide, contained nuclear explosions could provide more precise information on earthquakes themselves, especially their relation to faulting. What is the state of matter at the core of the earth? This major geophysical question might be resolved. Seismologists, of course, will be able to list a host of other inquiries which they would like to pursue.[11]

[9] Gerald W. Johnson, "Peaceful Nuclear Explosions: Status and Promise," *Nucleonics,* July 1960, pp. 49-53.

[10] Donald J. Hughes, "Neutron Spectroscopy with Nuclear Explosions," *Nucleonics,* July 1960, pp. 54-58.

[11] David T. Griggs and Frank Press, "Probing the Earth with Nuclear Explosions," UCRL-6013, report by Radiation Laboratory, University of California, for the U.S. Atomic Energy Commission (Livermore, Cal.: Radiation Laboratory, University of California, September 1959).

Some Difficulties

Before any Plowshare applications are undertaken, much more accurate analysis will be required of the probable distribution of the resulting radioactive materials. This is especially necessary if radioactivity is likely to be vented into the atmosphere, or distributed through volumes of water, as in excavating an Isthmian canal or creating a harbor in Alaska. The radioactivity results from the presence of fission products in the bomb itself, and from the action of the bomb's neutrons on the surrounding materials, earth or water. To minimize the amount of fission products, Plowshare planners are relying on the availability of "clean" bombs. These are bombs which derive only a small proportion of their energy from fission. The major fraction comes from fusion, a process which does not result in the release of radioactive products; but it is impossible to predict when absolutely "clean" nuclear bombs will be available. Certainly they will never be available if nuclear testing is stopped. Public statements have indicated that the United States has tested bombs which are at least 96 per cent clean. This means for a megaton bomb, however, the release of some 40 kilotons of radioactive products, over twice the amount of fission products released by a Nagasaki bomb. The radioactivity associated with a 96 per cent "clean" bomb is still considerable, but of course not nearly as great as if it were completely "dirty."

The steam which operates the Larderello (Tuscany) geothermal power plant contains natural radioactive substances to the extent of 4 micromicrocuries per cubic centimeter.[12] It will be impossible to avoid extremely small amounts of radiation in Plowshare applications but, if they can be cleansed to concentrations typical of those found in nature, and well below the dosages which can be tolerated in continuous industrial activities, the danger of radiation should cause no greater reluctance to apply Plowshare than to utilize, for example, geothermal steam.

Thirty to forty kilotons of fission per megaton yield seem to be characteristic of the type of bomb which is presently available for

[12] UNESCO, *New Sources of Energy and Economic Development*, (New York: Author, 1957), p. 77.

Plowshare applications, although this situation may improve. This means that the initial radioactivity in the vicinity of an excavation shot will be very high indeed; hence, except for certain fully contained shots, one would consider only those applications in which natural cleansing phenomena would act in the immediate area of the burst. For the Alaska project, ocean currents would quickly dissipate the fission products. However, in the Canal project an area of a few hundred yards on either side would be intensely radioactive, requiring very large clean-up efforts or an exceedingly long waiting period before the excavation could be properly finished. Unforeseen, but not disastrous, venting of radiation (as occurred in the first Plowshare experiment) may further complicate the clean-up problems.

Compounding the difficulty are the large numbers of neutrons released from the nuclear device which activate surrounding media, causing additional radioactivity. However, by surrounding the Plowshare device with a neutron-absorbing substance, it may be possible to lessen neutron-induced activities greatly. Aside from making the bomb itself "cleaner," there is no simple means of eliminating fission products.

Thus the radioactive clean-up work following an excavation job is likely to involve significant expense. One or two million dollars is the amount estimated merely to predict the fallout pattern for a job of the Isthmian magnitude. Obviously before Plowshare applications can be adequately assessed much more data is needed; it can be adequately obtained only by performing a few preliminary tests.

Radioactivity involves yet another cost which is impossible to predict or assess, but which must be taken into account. This is the political cost of fallout, a factor which may well prohibit surface Plowshare activities. The enormous injury suffered by the United States from a poorly handled information program on the fallout from nuclear tests need not be emphasized here. Similar or worse situations could result from a U.S.-sponsored Plowshare program. The Isthmian project would be conducted in an area of great political instability. The role of fallout in the politics of that area is impossible to foresee accurately, but the probability is high that it would worsen the U.S. position. Fallout is a wonderful weapon for the adroit propagandist; inevitably those who have to defend it never appear in the right. No matter what precautions are taken in minimizing atmospheric fallout and in large-scale clean-up activities, some foodstuffs—fish, milk, etc.—will undoubtedly be found to contain measurable, if unharmful, amounts of radioactivity.

International Cooperation

The major deterrents to progress in the Plowshare program had been the unnegotiated suspension of nuclear explosions and the suspicion that Plowshare would be used to mask the development of new nuclear weapons. The negotiation of a *blanket* suspension treaty would of course have ruled out Plowshare applications unless conducted secretly, which would not be compatible with a peaceful and basic research program. Even were exceptions permitted under a negotiated treaty, information control would still be a thorny problem. For example, an international commission could supervise the Plowshare applications of a "black box" containing a nuclear device of some unknown design, but it might be feared the box could hide a weapon undergoing development for a military purpose. Opening the black box and making it accessible to international inspectors might raise domestic suspicion that the United States and the United Kingdom were revealing advanced weapons designs to the U.S.S.R., or vice versa. This situation obviously calls for agreement by the members of the nuclear "club" on standard designs of Plowshare devices.

There are probably some potential Plowshare applications outside "club" domains; hence, means must be found for servicing the needs of other countries. It is essential that the policy of providing these devices be developed concurrently with the technology of producing them, or earlier, lest we find ourselves in the uncomfortable position of dangling before other nations an attractive morsel which they cannot possess.

Another factor makes unilateral revelation or a joint design effort difficult. This is the possible significance of Plowshare devices to an Nth country's weapons program. Weapons must be light-weight and small, but these specifications need not be met by Plowshare devices. It would be interesting to try to design an exclusively peaceful Plowshare explosive which would not aggravate the Nth country problem and which might safely be published.

One initial design characteristic is perhaps obvious. Uranium-235 is likely to remain the more scarce material for Nth countries, and so this mythical "safe" Plowshare device might incorporate that as its primary material. Also, since the device need not be carried in an aircraft or a missile, it may perhaps be possible to design a nuclear explosive which inherently must be extremely heavy and large in size. We cannot rule out that such a device might be developed and, if successful, it would represent a dramatic merger of technology with peace.

Nations wishing to use Plowshare devices for international endeavors might have to submit designs to an international commission for approval on grounds of safety and non-military character. If it were possible to agree on a design for an international Plowshare device or, at a minimum, on a design to be developed by and restricted to all the members of the nuclear club, there would then be a basis for stimulating international action. The teams actually performing detonations, whether or not composed solely of the nationals of the contributing nations, should be under some measure of IAEA supervision, if the Agency does not have full access to the "box." The IAEA, and perhaps other appropriate agencies, should be invited to participate in observing and supervising the external effects.

During the talks on test suspension, the question had been raised, whether the IAEA be the inspecting agency. Opponents argue that the IAEA is purely a peaceful agency, not equipped or intended to handle military problems; they are probably right as regards the present situation. But, if the IAEA is to undergo a slow metamorphosis into an organization which eventually can take a strong position in international nuclear weapons control, perhaps Plowshare would hasten that development.

Emphatically, Plowshare does not provide a means of violating test suspension agreements under cover of peaceful explosions. The contrary is true; Plowshare could contribute to the development of more effective agreements. Proponents of a negotiated test cessation agreement felt that its long-range value lay in the possibility of moving toward a more comprehensive control arrangement. If Plowshare could be separated from the question of test cessation and used as another mechanism, either as suggested above or in some other manner, for achieving long-range understanding, we should by all means strive to do so. Also, research on peaceful nuclear detonations, if it is allowed to continue, will not only confer scientific and economic benefits, but will also provide experience in test detection to those international organizations which may ultimately be charged with responsibility for prohibiting misuse of nuclear explosions. Moreover, the occasional detonation of a peaceful nuclear explosion would serve as a sharp reminder to those who may be lulled into a false sense of security by the absence of openly conducted atomic bomb tests that powerful destructive forces still exist, though they can be directed benignly.

Plowshare's progress may continue to depend on the Soviet Union's cooperation. During the drawn-out test suspension negotiations there was but slight hope of Soviet acquiescence to a Plowshare program. At the 1959 Geneva talks on the cessation of tests, the Russians proposed that Plowshare activities should be conducted on a 50-50 basis; i.e., every time the United States detonated a bomb the U.S.S.R. would perform a single Plowshare experiment, or vice versa. This suggestion was open to two interpretations. The pessimistic view was that the Soviet proposal amounted to a veto of Plowshare; if the Russians maintained that they never wished to detonate a Plowshare bomb, this would prevent the United States from using the device. The other interpretation was that the Soviets did not wish to deprive themselves of operating in this promising area and hence would interpose no objections on a one-for-one basis. Indeed, the Russians could contribute significantly to an international Plowshare effort, for they have had much more experience than any other nation in conducting very large earth-moving explosions as a part of large-scale, long-range plans for the "changing of nature." If they wished to, the Soviets could profit greatly, economically and in propaganda, by reverting to their 1949 principle that in their land atomic bombs were used only for "moving mountains." And possibly they would have liked to do so; but, having initiated a campaign to stop weapons tests, they believed open acquiescence to Plowshare was detrimental to this tactical position in the negotiations. Thus far, the greatest measure of Soviet cooperation in the Plowshare program has been the breaking of their vow not to be first to resume nuclear testing. This permitted the United States to conduct a number of significant Plowshare experiments since December 1961. But the possibility remains that in future armament control discussions the Plowshare artifice might well be used as a blocking device.

Chapter 9

The Quiet Revolution

In 1913 when atomic energy was at most a wild dream of the romanticists among the scientists, the first radioactive "tracer" experiment was performed. But the tool, the radioactive isotope, remained rare. Now with atomic energy a reality though still toddling, still uneconomic, the lowly radioactive isotope is quietly and rapidly providing technological, medical, and economic benefits for mankind. The proliferation of atomic reactors and nuclear accelerators guarantees an abundance, in quantity and in type, of this revolutionary tool. From 1946 through 1959, the United States supplied domestic and foreign users with about one million curies of radioisotopes valued at about $20 million.[1] Since isotopes are produced in quantities in various countries, total world trade might amount to $60 million. The reduction in industrial and agricultural costs resulting from the use of radioisotopes runs into billions of dollars.

The spontaneous generation of various types of radioactive emanations distinguishes the radioisotope from its inert cousins. These emanations are utilized by detecting them under various conditions or by allowing them to interact with matter. By tracking them, or determining their fate as they pass through matter, we can measure the ages of the Dead Sea scrolls, the thickness of gold enamel on ancient Buddhist bronzes, the wear on automobile tires, and many other things. By allowing radiations to interact with

---

[1] Radioisotopes in small amounts are the sole form of atomic material which may be exported to iron curtain countries. (See U.S. AEC, Press Release C-242, December 2, 1960.) And the Soviet Union exports some to the United States.

living matter, destructive food pests can be eliminated, foods preserved, and certain diseases curbed. But even this most important
of all atomic energy tools is not a magic wand.

Abundant and impressive evidence exists on the value of radioisotopes to the industry and agriculture of technically advanced nations. Estimated savings in the realm of hundreds of millions, or
even billions, of dollars for a single nation constitute an eloquent
testimonial. On the whole it seems that this use of atomic energy
has not been oversold. Quite the contrary, there remains much
room for imagination and further application. In areas of the
world which are less advanced technically the primary application
of radioisotopes will be in agriculture and food preservation. Many
industrial techniques should also be re-examined with a view to
possible applications. For example, one U.S. company has developed an instrument for the detection of rotting rail ties. It appears
that the same instrument can be modified to detect rotting tele-
phone poles and termite decay. To help prevent wood decay in
houses, railway beds and elsewhere the radioisotope technique
might be of greater benefit in areas other than the United States.

In medicine, where radiation diagnosis and treatment by radiation is almost standard procedure though obviously not a panacea,
the value of isotopes must be measured not in dollars but in lives.
Fortunately medical researchers, who have always been drawn toward problems not necessarily of domestic origin, are now applying nuclear techniques in many of their investigations.

The cost of a nuclear radioisotope laboratory is probably lowest
on the scale of atomic projects. A fully equipped laboratory can
be had for less than $10,000. In the United States, where the clini-
cal and diagnostic use of radioisotopes is widespread and has developed into a highly sophisticated art, it may be expected to grow
in proportion to expenditures for medical research, which will
triple by 1970. But new applications constantly developing will
increase the use of radioisotopes still further. When one considers
that in many other countries where the medical arts are highly
developed—Norway, Japan, and West Germany—the per capita
utilization of isotopes ranges from one-tenth to one-half of that in
the United States, it is evident that expanded uses elsewhere could

and probably will be more dramatic than in this country.[2] The world market for radioisotopes is already becoming quite competitive and will become more so as reactor facilities proliferate.

In industry and medicine radiation has a multitude of applications; in agriculture the first signficant manifestations will be found in regions where improvement of food production is a prime concern. In veterinary medicine radiation can be used for research, diagnosis, and therapy. In entomology the effectiveness of insecticides can be measured, migratory behavior can be traced, and insect populations controlled either by destroying them or by inhibiting their increase. Plant nutrition, biosynthesis, and growth regulation can be studied. Mutation can be induced to provide hardier plants, new species, and rust-resistant varieties. These are but a few of the applications of radiation in the agricultural sciences.

The equipment required is not as elaborate as in a nuclear power program, and the necessary skills can be easily and quickly taught. The equipment could be of two basic types. It might be a well-shielded unit providing radiation from an internal radioisotope source (or from "cooling," but still highly radioactive, fuel rods from a nuclear reactor), or it might be an accelerator-type machine which could be switched on and off. Both types can be designed to provide safer operation than a nuclear reactor. The maintenance of the accelerator, however, might present a more complex technical problem than the simple isotope source.

The radiation dosages will differ according to the particular application. For example, very high dosages of radiation can provide completely sterile food products. But a more promising application would prolong the shelf life of perishable foods by low dosages.[3] Radiation techniques could be combined with conventional methods such as refrigeration, heat treatment, or antibiotic additives to improve the over-all results. Even lower dosages are

[2] "Radioisotopes in Medicine," report prepared for the Office of Isotopes Development, U.S. Atomic Energy Commission, Stanford Research Institute, Menlo Park, California, December 1959.

[3] "Food Irradiators Look to Low-Dose Treatments," *Nucleonics,* October 1959, pp. 112-113. (See also U.S. AEC Press Release S-16-61, August 30, 1961, "The USA Research Program on Low Dose Radiation Processing of Food.")

sufficient to suppress potato sprouting, to sterilize insects and to kill certain parasites in meat. Though the economies of nuclear power are still far from impressive, certainly in radiation the atom has vindicated itself economically. In areas where damage to crop and animals caused by pests reaches astronomical proportions, the opportunity for the atom is proportionately great.

Food Preservation Through Irradiation

Radiations produce adverse physiological effects in the human body, but they are also able to destroy or render ineffective many forms of life which are inimical to man. In this domain, perhaps, lies the most beneficent potential of atomic energy. Economic analysis might correlate an area's well-being with its electrical power, but most inhabitants of the less developed areas see their problem in the simpler terms of food. The atomic power which might raise the level of industrial production will not be available for some time, and even then it will be economical only in certain situations. Assuring safe and adequate food is as formidable a problem, but much more can already be done about it. Curiously, the United States in its food irradiation research is almost completely blind to the needs of the areas which could derive the greatest benefit from it.

It is particularly disheartening when an Atomic Energy Commissioner, addressing an International Conference on the Peaceful Uses of Atomic Energy, describes progress in food preservation in military terms and uses as his yardstick ". . . the extent to which this new technique can be used to meet the military demands."[4] He was unable to give any substantial answer to the question from an Indian delegate: "Have radiation-sterilized foods been released for civilian consumption in the United States, and with what results?"[5]

The well-fed consumer will not be purchasing irradiated food products for a long time. For one thing, other methods of preservation such as deep refrigeration are common and quite satisfactory. A second reason is that in a number of foods irradiation pro-

---

[4] W. F. Libby, *The Atomic Triad* P/2390, 2nd U.N. International Conference on Peaceful Uses of Atomic Energy (Geneva: U.N., June 1958), v. 19, p. 89.
[5] Same, p. 95.

duces slight changes in flavor, odor, or color which would not be acceptable to consumers who can afford to be particular in selecting their food.[6] A third factor, not insignificant, is the prevalent antiradiation neurosis. Irradiated food need not be radioactive, but it will probably be difficult to obtain general public acceptance of irradiated foods if they are so labeled. Fallout fears will linger long after fallout ceases, and the consumer will not appreciate that his food is slightly radioactive from unavoidable natural causes. The gourmet would be saddened if he were told that the leaner his cut of steak, the more radioactive potassium-40 it must inevitably contain.[7] But it will be comforting to those who cannot keep to their diets that they probably have less radioactive potassium per unit of body weight than the slim folk they envy!

It is clear that self-generated fears of using irradiated products should not become the subject of international political harangues, as have other aspects of radiation. Much of this psychosis arises from the confusion of radiation danger with fallout hazards. It is interesting that, now that the U.S.S.R. Ministry of Health has sanctioned the sale of irradiated potatoes, the Russians feel the need to disassociate these products from any connection with fallout. In fact, the widespread fear of radioactivity is hampering radioisotope applications in many sectors of the Soviet economy.[8]

With regard to the objection that many foods undergo a taste change when irradiated to very high levels, it is true that highly discriminating consumers in the United States and Western Europe will reject any product or food whose familiar taste has been altered even slightly. However, foods which can be pasteurized, or whose shelf life can be extended by low radiation dosages, for the most part do not undergo detectable taste change. In any event, acceptance of irradiated food would be quite different in areas where people are not so discriminating. Irradiation would give

[6] The broad vistas of gastronomic experience of the British are exemplified by their description of irradiated meat: a "wet dog taste." *The New York Times,* January 8, 1961, p. 13.

[7] R. Kulwich, L. Feinstein, E. C. Anderson, "Correlation of potassium-40 concentration and fat-free lean content of hams," *Science,* February 14, 1958, pp. 338-339; Derek H. Pringle and Roman Kulwich, "K[40] Gammas Give Estimate of Lean Meat Content," *Nucleonics,* February 1961, pp. 74-78.

[8] P. Savitsky, *Ekonomicheskaya Gazeta* (Moscow), February 17, 1961.

them more food, its taste slightly changed but digestible and satisfying.

A GI in a remote base would probably prefer an irradiated steak, even with a slight off-flavor, to a fare of canned rations. The military man being a captive consumer psychologically and physically is the primary target of U.S. research on food irradiation. Until recently, practically the entire effort was under the Department of Defense, as the particular responsibility of the Army Quartermaster Corps. In the fall of 1959 at the Army General Depot at Stockton, California, a highly versatile research facility was in advanced stages of construction. The installation was to include a linear accelerator for investigating the effects of bombardment of food by fast electrons and a High Intensity Food Irradiator (HI-FI) utilizing exceedingly powerful irradiation-isotope sources to provide gamma rays for food irradiation. A priority list of comestibles representing a well-rounded military diet was established, a list of foods which most of the hungry peoples of the world would not have recognized—much less consumed. But in the fall of 1959 the Office of Army Research and Development decided that, because of certain apparent adverse effects that occurred when animals were fed irradiated food, the entire program should be abandoned. This, at least, was the impression received by the public, although economic and operational requirements were the primary factors in the decision. These reports intensified the popular impression that irradiated food is toxic. The situation was not helped by the reluctance of the Department of Defense to release information about a subject on which research was supposedly open, as part of President Eisenhower's Atoms for Peace program.[9]

It has not been demonstrated that irradiated food is toxic in any significant degree.[10] Radiation, like conventional heat processing of foods, produces nutritional deficiencies through destruction of vitamins (particularly vitamin K, the anti-hemorrhage factor). The experiments on which the decision was based to practically abandon the irradiated food program showed only that vitamin

[9] Edward Gamarekian, "Army Puts Lid on A-Process in Food Preserving," *The Washington Post Times-Herald*, September 3, 1959.

[10] Herman F. Kraybill, "Are Irradiated Foods Harmful?" *Nucleonics*, January 1960, pp. 112-117.

destruction would occur. Had the same experiments been performed with vitamins carefully added, they would have been far
more significant.

The change of heart on food processing by means of radiation
came in a period of unusual uncertainty and sensitivity about the
implementation of the amendment to the Federal Food, Drug and
Cosmetic Act of September 6, 1958 (Public Law 85-929). In the
furor, public and private, over cranberry pesticides, veterinary
drugs, and other matters, it might be expected that a jaundiced
eye would have been cast at the effects of radiation on foods. However, the beneficial aspects of radiation should not have been dis-
regarded because of poorly demonstrated, preliminary examination of possible harm. In fact certain radioisotope techniques will
be most useful in investigating the nonatomic aspects of additives
under Public Law 85-929. In real life no individual's diet would
consist solely of irradiated food; other foods would furnish proper
vitamin content; or if necessary, vitamins could be artificially
added at very low cost. It is unfortunate that badly interpreted
publicity was given to this inadequate experimental feeding program and that the abandonment of the U.S. irradiation food program should have been attributed to it. Fortunately this feeding
test program is now being approached more objectively and the
first item, irradiated bacon, was approved for public use in 1963.

The army's primary reasons for discontinuance, i.e., economic
factors and the lack of "urgent operational requirement,"[11] were
undoubtedly justified, as were the original investigations. However,
the shock of virtually abandoning the food irradiation program
so important to many other government agencies and to Atoms for
Peace brought the realization that it was being too narrowly ad-
ministered. Editorials with titles like "Army Drops the Ball,"[12]
although somewhat harsh, were effective in attracting public attention. Under this kind of pressure, amplified by Congressional

[11] Letter from A. R. Luedecke, General Manager, U.S. AEC, to H. H. Hughes,
Chairman, Interdepartmental Commission on Radiation Preservation, dated
March 12, 1960. *National Food Irradiation Research Program*, pt. 2, Hearings
before the Subcommittee on Research and Development of the Joint Committee
on Atomic Energy, 86th Cong., 2d sess., March 31, 1960 (Washington: GPO,
1960), p. 768.
[12] *Science*, February 13, 1960, p. 383.

criticism, the army announced a new food program concentrated on pork, beef and chicken.[13] In this reduced program the previous theme was still dominant. The army's Director of Research and Development wrote: "In my view, the Army will continue to make the major future contribution to the fund of available basic knowledge which will ultimately make possible the final determination concerning the role of radiation-preserved foods in the national and international economies."[14]

No *national or international* civilian food irradiation center now exists and no major one is definitely projected. Congressional hearings revealed acute awareness of the importance of food irradiation in the international Atoms for Peace program, but this consideration affected few in a position to make the necessary decisions. Awareness, in some instances, arrived somewhat late. An Atomic Energy Commissioner testified on March 31, 1960: "It is true that the distinction between the two programs was not adequately realized until last fall."[15] But at that time the hiatus was still present in the thinking of the section of the Department of State charged with implementing the Atoms for Peace program; regarding the revised food irradiation program it simply stated: "The Department of State has reviewed the report and has no comment to make."[16]

Thus, a somewhat less than enthusiastic response by the AEC, and a blank reception by others, resulted in a revised five-year food irradiation program with a $5 million budget. Even that minuscule budget received a major setback in 1962. A single nuclear power project is budgeted for ten, twenty or thirty times that amount, yet no power plant on the horizon could have as great impact, political, emotional, and practical, on the emerging nations as a significant breakthrough in food preservation. Yet all we have now is a quartermaster radiation facility at Natick, Massachusetts, and a ridiculously small AEC program directed at civilian U.S. needs.

[13] Dept. of Defense Press Release n. 331-60, March 29, 1960.
[14] Letter from R. S. Morse, Director of Research and Development, Department of Army, to H. H. Hughes, dated March 16, 1960. (*National Food Irradiation Research Program,* cited, pp. 768-769.)
[15] Testimony of John Floberg, U.S. AEC. (Same, p. 730.)
[16] Letter from C. A. Sullivan to H. H. Hughes, dated February 24, 1960. (Same, p. 765.)

Many have recognized that food provides the best opportunity for effectively and economically implementing the Atoms for Peace program. Yet this has been overlooked. What is required at the earliest possible moment is a nonmilitary program inviting immediate international interest and participation in investigating the preservation of rice, breadfruit, bananas, and other major staples of diet which may not be familiar to the U.S. military or civilian consumer. Regardless of the outcome of research on particular items, sponsorship by the United States of a nonmilitary venture aimed at improving the well-being of other populations, could not be interpreted as anything but a deed of peace.

Enthusiastic support would not be difficult to find, for many world-wide groups with limited budgets have sought to demonstrate the benign application of radiation for food processing. At Wantage, England, for some time "the world's most elaborate irradiation facility" has been in operation.[17] The Federal Research Institute for Food Preservation, a quarter-century-old institution at Karlsruhe in West Germany, has been increasing its irradiation budget. "Conservatome," perhaps food irradiation's oldest commercial venture, has combined with other French firms in operating a pilot plant near Lyon.[18] Also at Saclay, the OECD operates a most useful European center for food irradiation information.[19] The European Nuclear Energy Agency is the foremost international organization encouraging food irradiation experimentation. A decision is long overdue for the United States to give firm long-range direction to its food irradiation program and to join this list of purposeful nonmilitary endeavors. An internationally intensified program will not only uncover new ideas; it will also make possible the better analysis of old ideas.

Chapter 7 on propulsion advanced the tentative suggestion that a unique combination of two applications of atomic energy might

[17] John Tunstall, "Britons Open Pilot Plant to Try Radiation Processes," *Nucleonics*, February 1960, pp. 100-104. See also B. Coleby, *et al.*, "Radiation Processing of Foods in Britain," *Nucleonics*, November 1958, pp. 188-197; "Package Irradiation Plant," *Nuclear Engineering*, November 1959, p. 410.

[18] *Nucleonics Week*, October 13, 1960, p. 4.

[19] *AIF Memo* (a monthly publication of the Atomic Industrial Forum, New York), September 1960, p. 20. Also Pierre de Latil, "Conservation de Denrées Alimentaires par les Rayonnements Nucléaires," *Le Figaro* (Paris), February 9, 1961.

be used to make a pelagic food, whale meat, more available. The oceans of the world, particularly their unknown depths which still constitute one of the greatest scientific mysteries, hold the promise that through scientific research the world could vastly enlarge its mineral and food resources. The average American consumes only eleven pounds of seafood per year, but that amount still represents important dietary values. Other areas of the world which depend much more on sea products for their protein find it expedient to use what little arable land is available for raising vegetables rather than for grazing domestic animals. Even the United States will begin to feel deficiencies of seafood products, as increasing population in a number of areas from which such products are imported will force them to use all their catch for domestic consumption.

In most densely populated countries the inhabitants of coastal areas are comparatively well fed, because of the availability of sea products. Catches in most instances could be increased, but incentive is lacking because of difficulty in preserving fish for transport to inland areas. Much research is needed on methods of preservation without refrigeration equipment. It is clear, even on the basis of very preliminary research, that irradiation can help.[20] If irradiation proves practical, one can contemplate safe, portable irradiation units eventually made available at port areas. Further, it might be possible to install irradiation sources on large, modern fishing vessels which operate far out at sea, to preserve the catch until they reach port. The use of irradiation would save considerable space and weight by eliminating bulky refrigeration equipment.

Pest Control, Mutations, Sewage Disposal

Other applications of radiation for sterilization, not directly related to food, are still virtually unexplored. For example, can sewage be economically sterilized to produce safe fertilizers? Which parasites can be eliminated in the chain of their development before they reach man? Is it feasible to use mobile units for periodical sanitization of dwellings and even clothing?

An Australian carpet company was plagued by the necessity of

[20] Ralph E. Winter, "Useful Radiation," *Wall Street Journal*, February 15, 1963, p. 1.

opening bales of imported goat hair to determine whether anthrax bacilli were present, and then destroying or sterilizing infected lots. To get rid of this costly burden, the company subjected all bales to gamma rays which killed any bacilli present. The fact that the carpet company considers this an economic venture, despite costs of installation amounting to several hundred thousand dollars, gives some indication of the vast savings to be made by widely applied use of radiation in similar situations.

Perhaps the most dramatic application of radiation for sterilization thus far has been the attack on the screwworm fly. This classic in radiation annals has wiped out the pest on the island of Curaçao and almost completely eliminated it in other areas.[21] In the southeastern United States an expenditure of about $10 million has virtually ended an infestation that cost livestock growers $20 million a year in losses of animals.

The remarkable experience with the screwworm fly must have application elsewhere. For example, under the Baghdad Pact the British have assisted Turkish investigators to trace the meanderings of the aelia bug, a small flying insect with a voracious appetite for cereal crops. Having captured quantities of the bugs at their hibernation grounds, the scientists paint them with a radioactive substance and then release them. With the aid of Geiger counters their flight destinations can be determined. Knowing the extent of their wanderings, the entomologists can decide whether geography helps or hinders the elimination of the bug by radiation or other techniques.

These techniques can be adapted to the elimination of many other pests. The olive tree fly on the island of Crete would seem a candidate, and perhaps the mealy bug which attacks the base of the stem and the roots of the coffee plant in Uganda. It has already been demonstrated that the flour beetle, the melon fly, the oriental fruit fly, and the Australian sheep blow-fly are susceptible to control by radiation.[22] However, geographical and ecological

[21] Merrill E. Jefferson, "Applied Radiation Case History No. 3: Irradiated Males," *Nucleonics*, February 1960, pp. 73-76.

[22] "Radiation Decreases Beetle Reproduction," *Nucleonics*, November 1958, p. 184. "Sterilization Used to Exterminate Fly," *The New York Times*, April 26, 1961, p. 54. "Talks on Radiation," *Atomic Energy* (Sidney, Australia), July 1960, pp. 18-20.

factors must be taken into account if control of these insects under particular circumstances is to be effected.

The production of different types of plant mutations by means of radiation is another promising activity. It is possible that more hardy and productive strains of certain plants can be produced by irradiating the seeds. Already Michigan farmers are raising a new, bush-type navy bean, produced by mutating the vine-type bean. The new plant is resistant to fungus, spoils less, and produces thirty bushels of beans per acre, compared to previous production of twenty-three bushels. A radiation-induced rice mutant, resistant to certain diseases and having a short straw, has been isolated in Surinam. A rust-resistant oat has been developed and many other things have been accomplished, but the surface has barely been scratched in mutant research.

There is a possibility that some pest organisms can be mutated by radiation and, as a result, new strains of the original organisms might be created and used as vaccines to attack the unmutated strain. Any number of possibilities can be named; one suggested by an International Cooperation Administration mission to Greece, is the irradiation of the liver fluke organism to reduce infection in sheep.

Growing apace with population increase is the problem of sewage disposal. In many areas sewage treatment reintroduces harmful organisms into the biological cycle. The possibilities of treating sewage by radiation are being explored.[23] Although the first results indicate that it would cost substantially more to meet Western standards of sanitation this way than by chlorine sterilization, there are reasons to doubt the preliminary cost figures. For one thing they contemplate using for sewage irradiation an atomic re-

[23] Harry N. Lowe, Jr., *et al.*, "Destruction of Microorganisms in Water, Sewage, and Sewage Sludge by Ionizing Radiations," *Journal American Water Works Association*, November 1956, pp. 1363-1372; "Sewage Irradiation—Is it Economical;" *Nucleonics*, July 1958, p. 106; D. A. Pecsok, *et al., Beneficial Applications of Radiation in Sanitary Engineering*, P/1773, 2nd U.N. International Conference on the Peaceful Uses of Atomic Energy (Geneva: U.N. June 1958), v. 19, pp. 333-337; Nuclear Science and Engineering Corporation, "Some Effects of Radiation on Los Angeles Sewage," NSEC No. 50-11-6002, final report submitted to Hyperion Engineers (Pittsburgh, Penn.: Author, January 31, 1957), pp. 1-17; David L. Narver, Jr., "Is Sterilization of Sewage by Irradiation Economical?" *Civil Engineering*, September 1957, pp. 54-55.

actor which has the same operating costs as the first large power-producing reactor built in the United States. These costs were some five to ten times those of nuclear systems which can be built today. Furthermore, sewage treatment offers another opportunity to use low temperature reactors, without the capital costs of a power adjunct and without the costly features associated with high-temperature, power-producing reactors. A sewage treatment reactor also could have a dual purpose, such as furnishing heat for an industrial process. In situations where the costs of irradiating sewage are prohibitive, the well-being of an area could be significantly raised by eliminating certain of the many species of the higher order of biological pests. They would be more susceptible to irradiation kill than the micro-organisms which are the usual target of sewage treatment in the United States. Perhaps one must aim at something less than perfection. To eliminate even one or two ills would be a major victory.

Obviously, the use of a nuclear reactor would be feasible only in treatment of effluence from large urban areas. However, other equipment might be operated economically in moderate-sized communities, provided that at least some semblance of centralized sewage or water treatment was in effect. But in most areas such centralized control does not exist; for them the only future possibility which one could envision might be the periodic irradiation of soil by portable units.

Other Applications

The application of atomic energy need not be so direct. Numerous benefits can accrue through a better knowledge of growth processes. The effectiveness of the application of hormones and other growth regulators needs fuller evaluation, and the effect of various minerals in feed needs to be determined. An understanding of all these nutritional processes can be considerably aided by radioisotopes.

The use of ionizing radiations for sterilizing disposable medical items, bandages, syringes, catheters, etc., is already a commercial proposition. Sterilized bone and plastic arterial substitutes have been prepared; undoubtedly the concept can be extended to other replacement, or "bank"-type, items.

The art of using radiation to change the physical properties of materials is still largely undeveloped, but the commercial feasibility has already been demonstrated in a few products, for example, electrical insulating material. The irradiation of plastic-like materials appears imminent. Some possibilities are intriguing. For example, it appears that when wood is soaked in certain materials and then irradiated it becomes fireproof, water-resistant, and stronger. Similar polymer-irradiation techniques promise to impart to wool the strength of artificial fibers like nylon, while preserving the softness of the natural material. Already on the market (at a production rate of one million pounds per year) is an especially strong polyethylene film which requires irradiation in the manufacturing process. Used to wrap vegetables, fresh meats and bakery products, it has been demonstrated to be completely safe.[24]

It is conceivable that the unique raw material resources of some areas will prove to have vastly different and economically useful properties when properly subjected to radiation treatment. For example, the irradiation of natural latex at the plantation in order to improve certain characteristics of the product has been under serious study.[25]

These foregoing applications of radiation and radioisotopes by no means exhaust the list of possibilities. Some of them are certain to prove impractical for economic or technical reasons. Yet, it is reasonable to expect, in view of past experience, that many will mature and prove beneficial.

The coupling of radiation with agricultural studies on an international level would seem to be of prime interest to the International Atomic Energy Agency. Except for a conference or two, the IAEA has not been aggressive in this field. The Warsaw Conference, sponsored by the IAEA in 1959, disclosed intense international interest in the utilization of strong radiation sources in the

[24] Vladimir L. Karpov, *et al.*, Moscow and Archangelsk, U.S.S.R., "Radiation Makes Better Woods and Copolymers," *Nucleonics*, March 1960, pp. 88-90; A. Datyner, "Radiation and Wool," *Atomic Energy* (Sidney, Australia), July 1960, p. 10; "Irradiation is Producing Food Wrapping at 10^6 lb/yr," *Nucleonics*, May 1960, pp. 122-124.

[25] Irradiating Natural Rubber on the Plantation," *Nucleonics Week*, September 29, 1960, p. 4.

processing of food, chemicals, etc.[26] Small in comparison with the Geneva Conferences of 1955 and 1958, the Warsaw Conference nevertheless may have had a catalytic effect in its own not too narrow context, with results more significant than the Geneva Conferences accomplished in the fields of fission and fusion.

The U.S. Atomic Energy Commission has for some time provided substantial subsidies to American industry for research in various applications of radioisotopes and radiation. The program has paid off handsomely in new ideas, but it is surprising that industry itself should not fully support the one application of atomic energy which already has proved its economic value so strikingly. As yet industry has tapped but a minor segment of the potential of the radioisotope, and current application to the needs of the less developed areas can be considered nil. If we can subsidize a program for American industry, we can also subsidize a program aimed primarily at the needs and problems of the "have not" areas. The amounts involved are quite small in comparison to the sums required in atomic power research, but the probable results are more meaningful.

[26] S. Jefferson, "The Industrial Future for Large Radiation Sources—A Report from the Warsaw Conference," *Nuclear Power,* November 1959, pp. 104-105; S. Edward Eaton, "Bright Spots on the Radiation Horizon," *Nucleonics,* March 1960, pp. 134-136.

Part III

DISINTEGRATING POLICIES

Chapter 10

The "Haves"

The basic ideas for the technologies we have been discussing could come from any quarter, from a top atomic scientist in Russia or the United States, or from a laboratory assistant at the University of Dakar. But, with the important exception of isotope techniques, the resources required—financial, technical and industrial—are presently available only in a dozen countries, perhaps. These are the "have" nations. Most of them have well-developed atomic programs; a few others have just started but, because of their resources and their intention to develop them, they must be considered part of the "have" group.

It would be foolish, in a study with any pretense of long-range validity, to describe in detail the nuclear programs of these nations as they exist today. Only a few, uneconomic, nuclear power plants are presently in operation in the world. The history of the past eight years has shown nothing but continuous change of plans, including the cancellation of projects already well advanced and on which millions of dollars have been expended. The great number of available descriptions of today's or yesterday's atomic programs are valuable to government administrators who must plan day by day; students will analyze them a decade hence. But they are of little importance in considering the impact of the peaceful atom on world affairs.

The "haves" of course are the United States, U.S.S.R., Great Britain, China, and six or seven European nations. But before they are discussed it would be well to recognize, without giving it undue emphasis, the position that Japan will undoubtedly assume as a leading nuclear power in the Far East.

Japan has made many important contributions to basic nuclear science and has developed a competent group of workers in the field. Several reactors and research institutions already completed or projected will further increase the country's competence. In addition, Japanese technological delegations have repeatedly visited nuclear installations throughout the world—perhaps more frequently than delegations of any other country. With a voracious appetite for nuclear information, Japanese technicians undoubtedly have a firmer grasp of the nuclear power situation than those of any other nation which has not yet installed a large power station. Upon completion (perhaps in 1964) of a large 150-megawatt station at Tokai-Mura, 70 miles northeast of Tokyo, Japan will be the first nation in the Near or Far East to have a large nuclear power plant. This will be a British-type plant operating on natural uranium. After gaining experience in its operation, Japan will probably develop improved models for export. Japan may also provide fabricated fuel elements if sufficient reserves of uranium are discovered domestically or purchased abroad.

The nonpower aspects of atomic energy, also, are being vigorously studied in Japan, particularly radioisotope and radiation applications. And the types of problems which are being investigated, such as the increase of rice yield through the production of new mutants under radiation, are of prime interest to other countries. The dominant role which Japan will be able to assume in irradiation is illustrated by a recent listing of gamma-ray irradiation facilities in the United States and Japan; in each country there are approximately seventy.[1]

India, China, and Australia are the other nuclear powers in the broad reaches of Asia and the south Pacific. Working on problems which may be unique to its own situation, and with only weak cultural ties with other nations of the Far East, Australia may not seriously challenge Japanese influence on the "have not" countries.[2] Of these nations, China will be the first to develop the bomb,

[1] "Gamma Facilities of the United States" *Nucleonics,* February 1961, pp. 96-97; Akibumi Danno, "Gamma-Irradiation Facilities in Japan," same pp. 98-99.
[2] Australia, Atomic Energy Commission, *Atomic Energy* (quarterly bulletin) (Sydney: GPO, June 1958 through July 1962); "Australia in A.D. 2000," *The Times* (London), September 2, 1960, p. 11.

but India and Japan may be more advanced in nuclear power. Japan's participation in the Development Assistance Committee of the Organization for Economic Cooperation and Development gives it a further advantage. It is impossible to say which country will eventually have the most influence on nuclear policy in the area; but it is certain that the three countries, cautiously viewing each other's progress, will determine the atomic balance, peaceful and military, in the Far East.

The United States' northern neighbor, with its history of fine research and international collaboration, must be counted in the ranks of "have" nations. Emphasis in Canada has been on the development of heavy water reactor systems to make economic use, without enrichment, of the vast deposits of uranium in that country. Indeed, technology for that type of system, still among the most promising, is furthest advanced in Canada. A cooperative arrangement with the United States in this field involves exchange of personnel and information and mutual use of research and development installations.[3]

As an exporter, Canada at present is most concerned with finding a market for natural uranium. If the fuel supply policy of the United States should make this country's enriched uranium less acceptable in world markets, Canada with her low-cost power resources might be tempted to construct a diffusion plant, for example at Kitimat in British Columbia.[4]

International Collaboration

Whatever the course of their future nuclear policies, all nations owe a great debt to the region in which nuclear science first developed. The nurturing of the rich European heritage of scientific interchange and cooperation over many centuries has immeasurably enriched every world culture. Even before the Renaissance European philosophers enjoyed a sort of international intellectual jousting through exchange of problems and ideas. The mid-seven-

---

[3] U.S. AEC, "U.S. and Canada Plan Expanded Program in Development of Heavy Water Reactors," Press Release C-151, August 8, 1960. (Mimeographed)
[4] "Enrichment:—A National Policy" (Editorial), *Nuclear Engineering*, July 1958, p. 273.

teenth century saw the organization of a more deliberate, more formalized type of collaboration in the formation of the academies of sciences in London, Florence and Paris, and somewhat later in Berlin, Seville and St. Petersburg.

These academies were not exclusively national; from the beginning, they sought to establish close relationships with academies and prominent scientists abroad. Hardly a seventeenth or eighteenth century savant can be named who did not contribute, in some instances substantially, to the publications of a foreign society. Sparked by the national societies, multinational cooperation began in the latter part of the nineteenth century, relating mainly to weights and measures and to some extent to geodetical and astronomical observations. Really close working relations, particularly in development and engineering, were not the pattern until the exigencies of World War II called for a joint British, Canadian and U.S. project on the atomic bomb. This military research program contributed much to the benign harnessing of the atom and understanding the nature of nuclear forces.

Not to be forgotten are the enormous, and often definitive, earlier European contributions to the atomic energy program by men who eventually became part of the Allied effort, by others who contributed to the abortive German atomic effort, and by many U.S. scientists who had studied in great European centers like Göttingen, Cambridge and Copenhagen.

Five centuries of exchanges confined to pure science appear not to have enabled mankind to make substantial progress toward the reduction of its political ills. But now the scientist is confronted with problems which *demand* that he no longer remain indifferent to the social consequences, both beneficent and destructive, of the new sources of powers he has revealed. The politician can no longer ignore them. The coalescence of nations and individuals in the common understanding and joint resolution of broad technological and social problems should be the unique opportunity, the unique contribution of the atom.

Restrictions in the Atomic Energy Act of 1946 practically canceled collaboration in research between the United States and its wartime allies. In the following years a pall settled over all exchange of information on atomic energy—no matter how "pure," or devoid of military implications. The renascence of research in a limited but extremely important area of nuclear theory and high-energy came in Europe, as might have been expected, but it was sparked by the urging of a U.S. scientist at a Lausanne conference in December 1949. Today, the European Organization for Nuclear Research (CERN) is one of many which have emerged, some less strong than others, into a new pattern of scientific collaboration— a pattern which involves not merely exchange of information and personnel but also intimate, joint working relations on projects ranging from the theoretical and the nebulous which promise practical fulfillment only in the distant future, to the short-range engineering of economic nuclear power systems. Actually, the equipment needed nowadays for fundamental research involves technological and financial outlays so vast that few countries acting alone can afford them. In all these joint endeavors, economic, political, and social forces, as well as scientific knowledge, are now coming into play.

In a 1950 resolution, UNESCO agreed "to assist and encourage the formation and organization of regional research centers and laboratories in order to increase and make more fruitful the international collaboration of scientists in the search for new knowledge in fields where the effort of any one country in the region is insufficient for the task." To implement this resolution, CERN came into being with headquarters at Meyrin on the French-Swiss border just outside Geneva. The major tasks at Meyrin have been the construction and utilization of two machines for accelerating atomic particles to enormous energies. One, a synchrocyclotron started in April 1958, is similar in design to four machines that had come into operation previously, one near Moscow, one at Liverpool, and two in the United States. More significantly, toward the end of 1959, what is presently (1963) one of the world's most powerful accelerators began operating at CERN. (A more powerful one is at Brookhaven National Laboratory on Long Island.) Working on the CERN machines are cooperative teams, mainly from universities in Italy, France, West Germany and Berlin, Sweden, Switzerland and the United States; others of CERN's thirteen members contribute staff from time to time. The United States is not a member of CERN; however, U.S. scientists on Ford Foundation fellowships have been frequent visitors and have served as guest staff members; two of CERN's scientific directors have been U.S. citizens. In 1960 the first exchange of personnel with a Soviet laboratory was arranged.[5] Three Russian scientists promptly arrived, but for some time three Western scientists as eager to accept the reciprocal invitation could not be found, for CERN is really a superior research institution.[6]

CERN, the first significant nuclear effort of a United Nations specialized agency, has set a precedent for smoothly functioning, international collaboration in research. Undoubtedly, one of the secrets of its success is that the work has no immediate commercial application. In CERN political forces, which independent of scientific considerations are responsible for the major political and economic turbulences and changes in Europe, are not active, or are at least subdued. When politics was combined with an equally volatile substance, atomic power, the result was the European Atomic Energy Community.

Envisioning a unified Europe, the French Foreign Minister, Robert Schuman, proposed on May 9, 1950, the coal and steel community which was subsequently formed by Belgium, France, Germany, Italy, Luxembourg and the Netherlands, i.e., the "Six." This was the first of several bold steps—some successful, some not—directed toward political federation. To consider Euratom separately from this sequence of steps, outside the framework of the European Community's broader energy problems, and apart from its significance as one of the instruments for complete political and economic integration, deprives it of the very essence of its being.

In the wake of the defeat of the plan for the European Defense Community, a conference of the six nations at Messina, Sicily, in the spring of 1955 recommended that a commission of experts prepare a general report on cooperation in atomic power. This recommendation had been anticipated somewhat, and paralleled, by the Organisation for European Economic Co-Operation. It was to be expected, however, that the Six, although members of the OEEC,

---

[5] "Dubna—CERN exchange" (Trends and Discoveries), *The New Scientist* (London), August 4, 1960, p. 360.

[6] Walter Sullivan, "12 Nations Make Joint Atom Study," *The New York Times*, September 22, 1960, p. 3.

would crystallize their plans first, for they already possessed a core of common interests and institutions.

Response to the Messina report was immediate. The Action Committee for the United States of Europe, comprising representatives of major political parties and other organizations, unanimously resolved in January 1956 to urge their respective countries to develop nuclear resources through a supranational commission, Euratom. Promises of full support were soon forthcoming from the United States. President Eisenhower assured the Community that "the United States regards continued progress toward European integration as a vital contribution towards security, welfare and freedom during the years ahead."[7] This pledge was quite different from the sentiments then expressed by Britain which, having traditionally opposed the unification of the Continent, correctly interpreted Euratom as an important step in that direction.

In France, debate on the treaty to create a European Atomic Energy Community (Euratom) split the National Assembly in the most important foreign policy debate since the rejection of the European Defense Community in 1954. France was at the time unquestionably the most advanced of the six nations in nuclear techniques. Some argued that to accept Euratom entailed abandonment of the priority of national interests and national sovereignty. There was concern whether France should produce atomic bombs.

Moscow contributed to the debate by denouncing Euratom as a military bloc in notes sent to the Six and many other nations. Then Colonel Nasser made a more decisive contribution. On July 26, 1956, Egypt seized the Suez Canal, thereby stopping the yearly flow of nearly 70 million tons of oil to Western Europe. Pipelines running through Syria and Saudi Arabia had supplied 40 million tons of oil in 1955 to Levant ports. This supply was also endangered by the Suez action. More than half of Britain's annual oil imports came through the Canal; when it was seized she had less than a six weeks' supply. Even smaller stocks were available elsewhere in Western Europe. By the end of October the situation had degenerated into the short-lived, but very critical, Middle East war.

In this highly-charged atmosphere, Britain initiated urgent stud-

---

[7] U.S. Department of State communiqué of February 9, 1956.

ies looking toward increased use of a fuel which was much more easily transportable and whose availability was less subject to fluctuations in the world strategic situation. Early in 1957 Britain announced a tripling of the original goals set in 1955 for atomic power plants.[8] Among the Six there was an intensification of the sense of urgency for action on Euratom that overcame doubts and delays. On March 25, 1957, in Rome, the Euratom Treaty was signed along with the treaty for the European Economic Community.

Functioning as an organic arm of the European Community, Euratom is governed in part by several bodies common to all of the institutions of the European Economic Community. One is the Assembly, comprising 142 delegates from member states, which operates by majority vote. Its main function is to exercise general supervision over the organizations of the EEC and serve as a forum. The other common body is the Court of Justice of the EEC, comprising seven judges who settle disputes arising within Euratom, the Common Market and the Coal and Steel Community. The Treaty also provides Euratom with certain governing bodies peculiar to it. One is the Council of Ministers which coordinates the atomic energy policy of the member states and makes decisions on important specific issues. The other, the Euratom Commission, is the day-by-day operating body with responsibilities similar to those of any national atomic energy commission.

The structure of Euratom and the tenor of its Treaty appear to make that organization a veritable government for atomic energy in Europe. The Treaty encompasses and specifies broad powers in the fields of information control, patent licensing, investments, tariffs, security control, and supply and ownership of fissionable materials. However, there are loopholes, designed to accommodate France, relating mainly to the production and control of fissionable materials intended for purposes of defense. Such materials are essentially excluded from any sort of Euratom control. (Incidentally, the Treaty does grant the Commission the powers to ensure that *all* materials *imported* into the Community are not used for

---

[8] *The Times* (London), March 6, 1957. "A Program of Nuclear Power," a report presented to the Parliament of Great Britain, February 1955 (London: HMSO, 1955).

defense purposes. This interesting provision would be an important precedent for the step-by-step fissionable materials control proposal made in Chapter 5 of this book.) The Community itself can conclude agreements and treaties with other nations; the most significant and controversial treaty has been that with the United States.

The United States and Euratom

The United States had favored Euratom from the first. The action which was eventually to be responsible for a definitive U.S.-Euratom working arrangement was the appointment in late 1956 of three experts to report "on the amount of atomic energy which can be produced in the near future in the six countries, and the means to be employed for this purpose."[9] Their visit to the United States at the invitation of the Secretary of State and the Chairman of the Atomic Energy Commission, did much to arouse interest among American officials and industrialists in closer cooperation with Euratom.

The report of the three experts (inevitably dubbed the "Three Wise Men") envisioned the installation of 15 million kilowatts of nuclear power in the six countries by 1967. This goal, two and a half times that of the expanded British program, was not unreasonable, the ratio of both the population and the electrical output of the European Community to that of Britain being approximately three to one. Leaning heavily on American data and advice, Euratom expected, and was promised, enthusiastic support from the United States in pursuing these goals. After intensive discussions within working groups, accord was reached on a broad cooperative power program to be implemented jointly by the United States and the Six.

By far the touchiest point in the preliminary negotiations for the Joint Program was inspection. The manner in which it was resolved has haunted the Program ever since. In all bilateral agreements, excepting those with Britain and Canada which were al-

---

[9] *A Target for Euratom*, report submitted by Mr. Louis Armand, Mr. Franz Etzel, and Mr. Francesco Giordani at the request of the governments of Belgium, France, the German Federal Republic, Italy, Luxembourg and the Netherlands, May 1957, p. 13.

ready atomic powers, the United States had insisted on on-the-spot inspection and accounting of nuclear materials. Euratom demanded the exemptions which had been granted Britain and Canada, insisting that the United States should accept the multinational accounting and inspection system provided in the Euratom Treaty. Accord was reached in a compromise wherein it was agreed that (1) the Euratom inspection regulations would meet the standard set by the United States and (2) the inspection would be carried out by Euratom personnel, although U.S. representatives might be invited to participate.

The controversy affected a fundamental issue going beyond relations between the United States and Europe, namely, the effect which autonomy of inspection would have on the principle of international inspection incorporated in the agreement for the newly created International Atomic Energy Agency. It is barely possible that if the United States had insisted that Euratom, the first group receiving aid, should submit to IAEA controls, this might have catapulted the IAEA into a stronger role than it now plays. Euratom was understandably reluctant to pioneer in this respect when the major nuclear nations—the United States, Britain, Canada and Russia—showed no inclination to put any part of their programs under IAEA scrutiny. Moreover, the power programs were felt to be urgent; negotiating and providing an appropriate type of IAEA participation would have delayed them. The eventual agreement between Euratom and the United States did not call for IAEA participation, but the issue left a sensitive scar which Euratom opponents have not hesitated to rub.

The Joint Program provided for the installation by Euratom of six to eight reactors of U.S. design totaling about one million megawatts, at a cost of about $350 million. The deadline was 1963. The United States Export-Import Bank was to make a long-term credit of $135 million available at the favorable rate of 4.5 per cent. A joint research and development program was also provided, the United States and Euratom each committing $50 million during a five-year period. Most important of all, since all the proposed plants would require enriched uranium, the United States agreed to furnish Euratom up to 30 thousand kilograms of U-235 on credit at 4 per cent interest; it also promised to guarantee the integrity of the fuel rods for the reactors and to insure that the cost of the fuel rods to Euratom would not exceed a certain limit. The terms were highly favorable but no more so, in general, than those offered U.S. industry. Furthermore, the U.S. government would not have to guarantee the fuel elements unless the manufacturer's guarantee was not as good or better than those promised, and it seemed unlikely that fuel offers would be accepted unless the manufacturer's guarantee was adequate.

A U.S.-Euratom reactor board was convened in mid-1959 to consider submissions under the Joint Program. But by that time the rapid shift from a world shortage to a glut of fuel supplies, and improved efficiency in generating power from conventional fuels, had erased the memories of Suez. A temporary decline in the rate of economic expansion in 1958 and 1959 caused energy consumption to fall slightly below the 1957 rate. Coal prices dropped and the North African oil boom became Europe's new tonic. Exploitation of natural gas deposits (as, for example, at Lacq in southwest France, apparently one of the world's largest) began to give Europe a most encouraging fuel outlook.[10] Just as in the days of booming expectations for atomic energy, over-optimism in the outlook for oil supplies could not be suppressed.[11] But because the glut was so truly great, this over-optimism could be afforded; as regards atomic energy, it could not.

At the same time, capital costs of conventional generating equipment fell drastically and efficiency improved. A British journalist described the game:

First the nuclear engineers take a step forward and cut costs. As soon as they are not looking, the "conventional" power-station advances boldly. The end result is to postpone still further the date when nuclear power will be truly competitive.[12]

[10] "Miracle of Béarn," *The Economist* (London), June 4, 1960, p. 994. Incidentally, in the course of extracting the conventional fuel at Lacq, a by-product atomic energy material, heavy water, could be obtained. (*L'Economie*, Paris, n. 710, December 24, 1959, p. 13.)

[11] Ray Vicker, "Algeria's Oil," *The Wall Street Journal*, December 16, 1960, p. 1..

[12] John Davy, "The Latest Word in Generators," *The Observer* (London), December 18, 1960, p. 2.

The result was that in 1960 conventional electrical costs were, in many instances, about a mill below the 1957 figures. Utilities in Europe were no longer eager to plunge headfirst into a nuclear power program; the U.S.-Euratom Joint Reactor Board postponed its deadline several times in the vain hope of receiving specific proposals from them. It became increasingly clear that the Joint Program would not total anywhere near one million kilowatts.

SENN and Its Aims

Only an Italian consortium, Societa Elettronucleare Nazionale (SENN), made a positive response to the Joint Program's plea in time to meet the 1963 construction deadline. Since SENN was conceived and nurtured to a relatively healthy state by influences outside Euratom, its proposal cannot be regarded strictly as a triumph of the Joint Program. However, it gave evidence of Italian support of Euratom and produced for SENN certain of the joint U.S.-Euratom benefits.

The genesis of SENN was in a mélange of national and international, political and commercial interests which will bring about, perhaps by 1964, the operation of the Punta Fiume Power Station south of Rome. To meet the anticipated energy requirements in central and southern Italy, an average annual increase in generation facilities of 7 per cent had been projected for the period 1958 to 1965. Most of this expansion was to have been met by the installation of oil-burning power stations. But because the cost of conventional power in this area is already high (about 50 per cent more than in northern Italy) and there was a strong desire to accumulate experience in the construction and operation of nuclear power plants, SENN (a joint stock company of Italian utilities and industries) was established for this purpose in March 1957. A study completed in June 1956 led the International Bank for Reconstruction and Development (IBRD) to decide that southern Italy met all the requisites for the construction of a 150 megawatts nuclear power plant. At about the same time that SENN was established, the Italian government and the IBRD agreed to sponsor a special study of all aspects of the proposed plant.

By October 1957 the project had begun to assume an international aspect. Invitations to bid were sent to seventeen firms which had indicated an interest in the project: eight U.S. firms, five British, two French, one Canadian, and one British-U.S. Only nine firms (four U.S., three British, one British-U.S., and one French) submitted tenders by the closing date, April 1958. With some exceptions, the tenders were for the construction of gas-cooled systems operating on natural uranium fuel (systems in which the British and French were proficient) and several types of U.S. systems operating on enriched fuels. The United Kingdom Atomic Energy Authority and the U.S. Atomic Energy Commission agreed to review the technical aspects of the bids which fell under their competence. Thus, the SENN project evolved into a simultaneously cooperative and competitive relationship, involving the governments and industries of at least five nations. World attention became focused in the summer of 1958 upon the deliberations of an international panel of experts which met in Rome to review the tenders submitted and to make various special technical evaluations. The panel, composed of one Canadian, two U.S., two British, one French and one Italian expert, was not charged with the actual selection of the best proposal—this was SENN's prerogative.

The bids were quite similar so far as prices were concerned, but selection was not made on this basis alone.[13] It involved technical and engineering comparisons also. As a result of its deliberations the panel presented SENN with a report not actually recommending the acceptance of any tender, but indicating outstanding merits of two bids—one British and the other U.S.[14] After further deliberations SENN selected the U.S. plant for construction. The eight organizations whose bids were not selected were badly disappointed (each had spent $200,000 or more in making the bid). But the hardest hit was probably the British which had seen in SENN an opportunity to strengthen its attempted nuclear beach-head in Europe. The blow was somewhat softened, however, by the announcement that a private British consortium had signed a contract with another Italian group for a reactor at Latina, south of Rome. In any

[13] Carlo Matteini, "Why SENN Chose GE Reactor," *Nucleonics*, May 1959, pp. 95-99.
[14] "Summary Report of the International Panel." The International Bank for Reconstruction and Development, Washington, D.C., March 1959.

event, differing means of selection (one essentially private and the other with an international tone) resulted at approximately the same time in the export from the United States and the United Kingdom of their first major power reactors, both to the area south of Rome.

The SENN project is having its aftermath and its lessons. Technical difficulties threaten to increase the reactor's operating cost. (This, it should be noted, undoubtedly would have happened if any of the other bids had been accepted.) The reactor is operative in 1963, but the manufacturers or governments, or both, have borne significant costs in meeting unforeseen problems. The lesson is that many hidden factors will come to the surface in the course of developing and operating *any* nuclear system now being marketed by any nation. The "have" governments and their business firms can afford, and must expect to sustain, such losses as a part of their costs and their responsibility in the long-range development of nuclear power. Other nations, less able technologically and financially to sustain those losses, if they purchase a large power reactor system guaranteed on the basis of today's knowledge, run the hazard of having on their hands in the future a massive, white, nuclear elephant—economically speaking, at least.

Results of the Joint Program

Viewed in the narrow perspective of the large plants which will be in operation by 1963 or 1964, the Joint Program has been described as a failure. It may have been a "failure," in the sense that U.S. exports did not develop more positively. It perhaps could be characterized also as a failure of European industry and public utilities to take advantage of very favorable terms which might not be available later. By not entering the Joint Program, European enterprises were gambling that the resources of conventional fuels, which currently give Europe so much confidence, will not be cut off by a confluence of unfavorable circumstances. The prevailing philosophy is to take the gamble (if it is recognized as a gamble), and to develop nuclear power only on a long-range basis.

Some denunciations of the Joint Program sounded like epitaphs. "They [Euratom and European utilities] do not want to see reactors built unless they get a Christmas tree with donations hanging all over it from the American public," a member of the Joint Committee on Atomic Energy of the U.S. Congress charged. A writer in a scientific magazine observed: "Euratom is a pretty cold corpse right now and . . . it will undoubtedly die within a short time. Euratom will not do the things that might be productive [concentrate on research]."[15] Two common errors are revealed in such criticisms: (a) considering the attainment of kilowatt goals the sole symbol of success; and (b) identifying the U.S.-Euratom Joint Program with Euratom in its entirety.

Let us first dismiss the fallacy of kilowatt goals. In the Joint Program something in the range of 20 to 60 per cent of the 1963 goals will be met (the upper range would involve an extension to 1965). SENN is now one of the three large-scale plants under the Joint Program extended to that date. France has several dual purpose (power and plutonium) plants in operation; and others, totaling over 500,000 electrical kilowatts, will be in operation by 1965. The other plants under the Joint Program are the SENA plant to be operated by a Franco-Belgian syndicate in the Ardennes Forest and the KRB plant to be located on the Danube, fifty miles west of Munich. Still the over-all totals for 1967 will be but a fraction of the 15 million kilowatts envisioned in the report of the Three Wise Men.

As this pattern is the same everywhere, Euratom cannot be singled out as more of a "failure" in this respect than other programs. In the U.S.S.R. the original program called for the installation of 2 to 2.5 million electrical kilowatts of atomic power by 1960, but it is evident that as late as 1963 only a few hundred thousand kilowatts of nonmilitary atomic power will be in operation. In 1955 Britain announced 1965 goals of something like 2,000 megawatts of power, and in 1957 increased the figure to 5,000-7,000 megawatts, but bit by bit the time for reaching that total has been put back to 1968 or later.[16] But in interpreting the British program

[15] Both quoted in *Nucleonics*, June 1960, p. 20.
[16] Great Britain, *White Paper (HMSO Cmnd. 1083)*, presented to Parliament by the Minister of Power, June 20, 1960 (London: HMSO, 1960); "Third Thoughts on Atomic Power," *The Economist* (London), June 25, 1960, pp. 1355-1356.

it must be recalled that their reactors and those of the French have been producing plutonium. The reactors which are due to come into operation in the near future are for the purpose of power production, but they will also produce plutonium that will be available for defense requirements.

Grandiose kilowatt goals of the early, ignorant years of atomic power now seem meaningless. They did not reflect the strength and vigor of any nation's or any group's atomic power program. They did have one virtue. The attempt to reach the goals caused nuclear engineers to reach technically and economically valid atomic power estimates much sooner than they otherwise would have. This bonus of reality should reduce the unhappiness over unattained kilowatt objectives.

U.S. industry naturally has been disappointed by the loss of business represented by the collapse of the Joint Program's goals. The development, preparation, and presentation of proposals involved considerable expenditure. Although it is impossible to enter the acceleration in knowledge as a credit in corporation accounts, the development of a fair-sized European market, the detailed examination of proposals by SENN and by European utilities, the competition between international and national firms, and other activities have nevertheless produced a much better understanding, company by company, of what each can promise in the way of an atomic power plant, and how each can operate more effectively (or rather more wisely!) in the European market.

U.S. industry will probably export far less nuclear equipment than it expected to, but it will still have important business through participation in future European atomic power programs through licenses and joint enterprises. Projections indicate that the European Community's energy demand in 1980 will be equivalent to 100 million metric tons of coal, double the 1960 figure. According to a recent estimate, atomic plants will contribute to this demand a total of 40 million kilowatts. This estimate, which is based on a better knowledge of both conventional and nuclear energy positions, is probably more reliable than The Wise Men's projection. But cautious veterans of the disastrous nuclear planning program will agree with the Chairman of the U.K. Atomic Energy Authority that "Forward estimates of availability of materials and resources, as well as of the course of prices, are notoriously unreliable."[17]

The actual rate of installation of nuclear power in the European Economic Community will depend on the resolution of its general energy problem.[18] Currently, coal is principally the responsibility of the European Coal and Steel Community, oil is under the Common Market, and nuclear energy is under the jurisdiction of Euratom. Ultimately these three communities must have a common directorate if these resources, including the atom, are to contribute in harmony to the Community. Since in all three cases national governments continue to have major responsibility, they will have to agree on the terms of a common energy policy before the merged Communities can make it effective.

Nuclear independence, another goal of the Wise Men, undoubtedly will have been achieved. They made this goal quite clear:

Strong cooperative ties with other countries — by which we obtain, now and later, the help of those who have explored nuclear possibilities more fully than we have, and in return offer our help in future to them and to other interested nations — must be the foundation of Europe's atomic progress. Far from undermining our independence, it is the only way we can gain our place as equals in the field. The road to dependence would be the opposite one, to confirm our backwardness by resorting to the illusion of self-sufficiency. Cooperation with others will not limit our opportunities, but create new ones, so that our industries can eventually acquire their own, distinct nuclear personality.[19]

The intent was clearly to push toward *industrial* independence, and this is evidently coming to pass; but, since the majority of reactor designs of interest to the European Community are based upon the use of enriched fuels, the dependence upon the United States for supplies of U-235 will persist for a longer period.

[17] Sir Roger Makins, "Nuclear Power Policy in the United Kingdom," an address by the Chairman of the U.K. Atomic Energy Authority to a symposium at Trombay, India, on January 18, 1961, *Atom* (London), n. 52, February 1961, p. 12.

[18] Jan Hasbrouck, "Why EEC's Energy Policy is Bogged Down," *The New York Herald Tribune* (Paris edition), May 2, 1961, p. 8.

[19] Cited, *A Target for Euratom*, p. 28.

The vitality imparted by the Joint Program after the Treaty of Rome, did much to sustain and strengthen Euratom. Did Euratom's founders—whose aims were broadly political—anticipate this effect, regardless of the attainment of physical goals? If so, the Joint Program must be considered a success. With an identity of its own as one of the three agencies of the European Community, Euratom has become a major political factor in fusing the three agencies into a single, powerful European executive. This process, now well under way, is regarded by its engineers as the next important step toward a United States of Europe.

The Larger Group in ENEA

The Six are not an isolated group, but there are many divergencies in outlook and goals between them and the rest of Europe. But the broader group, which includes the Six, also has a framework for cooperation in atomic policy in the Organization for Economic Cooperation and Development (OECD) and its atomic arm, the European Nuclear Energy Agency (ENEA). ENEA was established February 1, 1958, as the end result of a resolution adopted by the OECD's predecessor, the OEEC, in June 1955, about the time that Euratom took root.[20]

The OECD is a larger, looser organization than the Community of the Six and lacks the political objectives of the Six.[21] Although the organization encompasses nations of a great diversity of political economic and social aims, both it and its predecessor have proved able to get agreement on substantial measures of economic cooperation. The split in Europe between the Six and the rest, and particularly "The Seven" who formed a rival trade bloc, the European Free Trade Association (EFTA), put strains on the OEEC that contributed to its reorganization into OECD.[22] There was reason to fear, therefore, that Euratom and ENEA would conflict. In fact,

[20] Organisation for European Economic Co-Operation, *Possibilities of Action in the Field of Nuclear Energy* (Paris: Author, January 1956), p. 7.
[21] Member nations of OECD are: Austria, Belgium, Canada, Denmark, France, Germany, Greece, Iceland, Ireland, Italy, Luxembourg, Netherlands, Norway, Portugal, Spain, Sweden, Switzerland, Turkey, United Kingdom, United States.
[22] Member nations of EFTA are: Austria, Denmark, Norway, Portugal, Sweden, Switzerland, United Kingdom.

however, substantial progress has been made in reconciling divergent views and significant cooperative measures have been taken.

ENEA is a real boon to many of the OECD members—Greece, Iceland, Ireland, and others—who would be unable to budget the substantial funds needed for nuclear research and development. In addition, these countries can participate through ENEA in the consideration and formulation of international standards for legislation. ENEA's most successful enterprise of this sort has been the drafting of an international convention on third-party liability (see Chapter 5). Another important achievement has been the agreement of July 1959 that all materials, equipment, and services involved in joint undertakings of the ENEA group will not be used for military purposes. Although loosely formulated in order to allow for divergencies of opinion and action among the member states, it nevertheless serves as an important precedent in the consideration of broader international problems.

In addition to making a large number of studies, ENEA has major operational responsibilities. In contrast to Euratom, ENEA does not govern or finance the joint undertakings, nor does every member of ENEA participate in each project. A separate convention with differing membership governs each project. The first ENEA joint project to become a reality was the heavy water experimental reactor which went into operation at Halden, Norway, about seventy miles south of Oslo, on June 29, 1959. The reactor's practical function is to supply fifteen tons of steam per hour to the Saugbrugsforeningen, a pulp and paper factory, but it is regarded essentially as an experimental plant which will provide data for advanced reactors.[23] Originally the Halden reactor was designed as a sole project of the Norwegian Joint Establishment for Nuclear Energy Research (JENER), which is operated by Norway and the Netherlands. However, since July 1959 it has been under ENEA, with a joint staff recruited from the participant nations, including technicians and scientists from the Euratom group. Although not participating directly, the United States has provided heavy water

[23] Etienne J. Guerin, "Norway Builds World's First Boiling Heavy Water Reactor," *Research/Development* (Chicago, Ill.), v. 11, n. 12, December 1960, pp. 56-60.

for the reactor under the terms of the bilateral assistance agreement with Norway. The United Kingdom under its bilateral treaty with Norway has provided uranium to fuel the plant. Thus, the Halden project has become multinational. In addition to technical data, it should provide valuable experience in interweaving various types of international cooperative programs.

A second major research program, located at Winfrith Heath in England, involves the development of a high-temperature, gas-cooled reactor. As an international project, Dragon, as it is called, is unique in that it encompasses all phases of the work from research and development through design and construction.[24]

Dragon is one starting point for an illustration of the chain of factors through which technical developments influence international atomic relations. Partly through participation in Dragon and partly through independent efforts such as the construction of an advanced gas-cooled reactor (AGR), Britain is revising drastically its earlier thinking on the advisability of a large network of natural uranium reactors. AGR and Dragon will bear an evolutionary resemblance to early British reactors, but will operate at higher temperature. This means they will need a nonmetallic fuel element, and fuel slightly enriched in U-235 will be required. The economic future of this reactor concept is tied to the future cost and availability of enriched fuel. Countries looking to Britain for assistance in their atomic energy programs will demand her latest technology, her most efficient plant.

At Mol, Belgium, ENEA has established Eurochemic, a plant for the chemical processing of irradiated fuels, to provide an international service in Europe previously available on a national scale only in England and France. Internationally supervised processing centers can make a significant contribution to the international control of fissionable material. For it is at this point that one of the greatest possibilities for diversion exists. Multilateral supervision of processing could actually lead to the relaxation of controls imposed under bilateral arrangements. Thus Mol represents an im-

[24] C. A. Rennie, "The Dragon Project," a paper presented by the Chief Executive, Dragon Project, at the IAEA Conference on Small and Medium Power Reactors in Vienna, September 1960, *Atom* (London), no. 48, October 1960, p. 6.

portant political, as well as a practical, step in the development of nuclear energy. The project has gone rather smoothly, as nuclear projects go, but even in this instance differences of opinion, national and technological, have arisen. With some justification, Italy feels that it is too distant to make efficient use of the Mol facilities and, to say the least, has been lukewarm toward the project. Instead, Italy has been proceeding rapidly with its own plans for a processing plant, which will take care of thorium fuels as well. Britain, too, does not participate in the Mol project. With these exceptions, though, the Euratom countries and Britain take part in the ENEA projects. In these various ways ENEA provides a framework for limited cooperation at least.

Britain's Place

In Euratom's blossoming period some British industrialists, casting envious eyes on the business which the Joint Program was expected to provide for U.S. firms, foresaw advantages in becoming a senior partner in the new organization. In an editorial calling for closer ties with Euratom, a leading British industrial journal stated:

This country may claim a pre-eminence in original thinking and the U.S.A. in repetition projects, but Western Europe is capable of the very best in design — the faculty which in the long run can be of greatest significance.[25]

A contrasting, insular attitude was expressed by Lord Chandos (Oliver Lyttelton, a noted British industrialist and former Secretary of State for Colonial Affairs):

A nation cannot be cut off from something which it has. On the contrary, "to him that hath shall be given", and it is now possible to trade our present knowledge and, as part of the bargain, secure long-term agreements for the interchange of future knowledge.[26]

Whatever the merits of the various arguments, the collapse of the

[25] "The U.K. and Euratom," *Nuclear Engineering*, July 1957, p. 268. (See also further editorial in the same vein in *Nuclear Engineering*, April 1958, pp. 137-139; February 1959, pp. 49-50; June 1959, pp. 239-240.)
[26] "On Not Joining Euratom," *The Times* (London), September 25, 1957.

Joint Program ended its short-range value for business. Britain, moreover, was not yet ready to accept the broad political implications of membership in Euratom. But the creation of EFTA and then Britain's application for admission to the Community changed the terms of the problem.

Another source of change is in thinking about the British energy position. Extensive recent revisions in British coal and nuclear policies indicate much official uncertainty, perhaps even uneasiness, about the future relations of oil, coal and the atom as sources of energy.[27] One editorial describes the situation quite strongly: "It is ... clear that United Kingdom fuel policies have become something of a joke."[28] This uncertainty opens up the possibility of exploring the advantages of the United Kingdom's coordinating its future fuel policies with those of the European Community.

At the Assembly of the Western European Union in Paris on June 2, 1960, the British Minister of State for Foreign Affairs announced that "The British Government, without regard to all that has happened in the last few years, will certainly be ready to consider anew the proposal that Britain should join Euratom and indeed the European Coal and Steel Community as well. ...[29] With the omission of the Common Market this trial balloon made it clear that Britain was not yet ready to accept full membership in the Community and felt that differences between the Six and the Outer Seven were still strong. Moreover, whether or not Britain wanted Euratom, it was questionable whether Euratom wanted Britain, that is, without her capitulation on the Community's long-range political objectives. This seemed, at the time, a condition Britain would not accept. Later the British changed their perspective and in October 1961 announced their intention to enter into negotiations on affiliation with all of the institutions of the European Community.

Some other members of EFTA followed Britain in their ex-

---

[27] Great Britain, National Coal Board, *Revised Plan for Coal; Progress of Reconstruction and Revised Estimates of Demand and Output* (London: Author, October 1959).

[28] "The New Programme," *Nuclear Power*, July 1960, p. 59.

[29] "Britain Ready for Euratom Invitation," *The Times* (London), June 3, 1960.

pressed interest. For all, membership in the EEC raised tremendous problems. The Six are geographically contiguous; the Seven are not. This affects energy distribution, transport and, eventually, the sharing of nuclear hazards. Geographically, the Six could be considered as the "glue" that binds together those nations of the Seven which have no common boundary. Cohesion of the Six with the Seven would make a group already geographically contiguous, politically closer. The "neutral" nations of EFTA (i.e., Austria, Sweden and Switzerland), may find that full membership in all phases of community activities suggests too close a political union. For them some looser association may be formed, but how it would affect their place in Euratom is not clear.

But then in January 1963, in a detailed and candid expression of his aspirations for France, within his concept of what a new Europe should be, De Gaulle halted and reversed what appeared to be a very definite trend toward coalescence of the two major European communities. The issues were more complex than those relating to any single institution, like Euratom, within the European Community. But it is possible that some of the earlier conceptions, which resulted in the present shape and form of Euratom, were erroneous and contributed significantly to the over-all debacle. In particular, whenever military cooperation between two countries or groups of countries is minimal or does not exist, it seems desirable to emphasize whatever distinctions there are between the military and peaceful aspects of the atom. But, when these ties of defense do exist and it is desired to strengthen them, it is almost farcical to maintain the illusion. When a nation's small supply of plutonium is freed for weapons studies because the United States has made available special nuclear materials for peaceful studies, or if highly advanced engineering techniques subject to exchange in the sphere of peaceful energy can be adapted for other purposes, can one then continue to pretend that this is exclusively peaceful sharing? These questions cannot be discussed without considering the complex NATO problems, specific weapons systems, and so forth.

Serious as the rupture in the transition toward an Atlantic alliance seemed to be, the effect hopefully is only transitional and indeed possibly salubrious, for it forced the first serious re-examination in a long time of our Atlantic relationships. It is impossible to predict the nature of the final rapport. It may well involve a more intimate coupling of the peaceful and military aspects of atomic energy. And undoubtedly it will involve, at a minimum, a re-examination of joint responsibilities in research and development. In fact, there is so much mutual agreement on the vital necessity of cooperative efforts in the latter aspect that it should be possible to proceed expeditiously on the problem of an Atlantic alliance in research and development without awaiting solution of some of the more complex issues.

It is worth noting that several times in his rejection of British entry, De Gaulle seemed to make special exception to the possibility of technological cooperation with Britain. For example, he said:

Therefore, I repeat, if the Brussels negotiations were not to succeed at this time, nothing would prevent the conclusion of an agreement of association between the Common Market and Great Britain in such a way as to safeguard trade; neither would anything prevent the maintenance of the close relations between Britain and France and the continuation and development of their direct cooperation in all fields, especially those of science, technology and industry as, indeed, the two countries have just proven by deciding on the joint construction of the supersonic "Concorde" aircraft.[30]

There is no European leader more aware of the benefits of technology. He has spurned at least one scientific collaboration (a NATO university), but a different package deal involving a stronger, more meaningful international effort might well be more appealing. Stormy as French participation in Euratom has been, the difficulties there have been less severe than in the areas of trade, military association, and political union. In the area of cooperation in research and development, and more particularly in Euratom, there are certain opportunities for the European nations to heal this serious break. But, in planning these opportunities, it is essential that they be based upon something in which all will profit and in which the national sensibilities are not offended.

[30] President De Gaulle's press conference of January 14, 1963.

Implications For U.S. Policy

The OECD has three principal tasks: the coordination of the economic policies of member countries; the general development of world trade; aid to developing countries. This third task is the one most closely related to peaceful atomic policy. A more specific orientation toward economic development seems the inevitable direction of the Atoms for Peace program. OECD provides the opportunity for the United States in developing its policies to participate with a group of nations, some of which possess great experience and understanding of the subject in assisting nations which are undergoing a metamorphosis, both political and technical. Moreover, through membership in the new organization the United States can render aid through a pooled arrangement—as it were, anonymously—in a way that would in many instances be more palatable to the recipient.

The OECD also offers an opportunity to re-evaluate U.S. nuclear participation with a group of nations, most of which are becoming quite knowledgeable and proficient in the arts of applying the atom. A repetition of a U.S.-Euratom Joint Program seems unnecessary. Europe is no longer that far behind. The effort needed now is a cooperative research program discussed within the framework of an organization which represents the broader national capabilities of the membership of the European Nuclear Energy Agency.

With the United States showing much interest in the gas-cooled reactor technologies which Britain has pioneered, with Britain turning toward the enriched fuel technologies of the United States, with both the United Kingdom and the United States turning some of their attention toward the heavy water reactor technologies of Canada, and with the advanced contribution of European nations to the nuclear arts, it would be folly not to coordinate research and development programs more closely.

During periods of uncertainty, Euratom found much comfort in planning and developing its research program. It had allocated sizeable research funds of its own, over $200 million for a five-year period—about the same amount the United States spends for the same purpose in one year. Out of this sum, Euratom contributed, on a dollar-for-dollar matching basis, to a $100 million joint U.S.

Euratom research program. ("Matching" is now firmly ensconced in U.S. nuclear policy.) But again the Joint Program is not the whole of Euratom's research program. The research budget for the second five-year plan, 1963-1967, has been increased to an average of about $80 million per year.

Euratom was born at a time when its member nations were expanding their atomic power research. It would not have been possible to replace the growing national research centers with a newly created central laboratory; so Euratom policy was to encourage some of the existing laboratories to accept international financing and staffing. Ispra, in the Italian lake country, is the site of the most internationalized of Euratom's research installations. Initially an Italian laboratory, Ispra, had a painful transformation as an international laboratory due to the political complications, but now it seems ready to serve the Community as a truly internationalized nuclear research laboratory. A small group taken over by Euratom, the Transuranium Institute, is part of the German Karlsruhe Research Center, which has the first all-German-designed research reactor. The Institute will concentrate on the problem of burning plutonium in reactors and the utilization of transuranic elements in general. At Geel, in Belgium, a research reactor assists in the Euratom program on nuclear measurements and the development of standards for the nuclear industry. A fourth center, working on various reactor problems, is at Petten in The Netherlands.

These four centers, together with ENEA's Dragon and Halden programs, will be the main recipients of Euratom research allocations. Unfortunately, a trend is evident *away* from both basic and applied research in the Euratom program. In July 1961 the Council of Ministers of the Six decided to allocate up to $32 million of the five-year research budget (about 15 per cent), in supporting the construction of near-term power reactors, like SENN.[31] Beyond knocking the economic comparability of the reactors into a cocked hat, this decision provided the reaffirmation that Euratom is still very much power-minded, despite its setbacks.

[31] "The Euratom Research Program and the Italian Contribution," address given on November 7, 1961 by Prof. Felice Ippolito. *Europe House Papers, 1961-1962 Lectures, 2.* (London: Europe House, 1961), p. 6.

There is always the question of the distinction between basic and applied research, and the philosophy that "it is a basic rule with us that to divorce applied and fundamental research would be fatal to an atomic energy research establishment" is laudable.[32] Nevertheless, the research effort is by and large an *applied* program. This almost blind drive for nuclear power which characterizes Euratom is its weakness. Indeed, when we still know so little in both the basic and applied areas of atomic energy, and when the demand for research funds is insatiate, it is difficult to understand why substantial sums originally allocated for research were not held in reserve for that purpose, even if the facilities and manpower for basic research programs were at the time insufficient to use that amount.

The $100 million U.S.-Euratom joint research program is coordinated by a Joint Research and Development Board which sits in Brussels. The Board, which does a fine job of eliminating duplication, has already approved a number of contracts for studies to be conducted by European and U.S. private firms and research institutions. Of the 92 research proposals which had been authorized under the Joint Program, essentially all of them were concerned with practical development proposals relating to the design of near-term reactor systems.[33]

Euratom exists and will survive; whether or not it should have been created is a superfluous question. The major question now is: How shall it operate most effectively, for Europe and for the West? Since any grand designs which might have been operative were so effectively interrupted by De Gaulle, and since the situation is so fluid, most specifics proffered are likely to become superfluous in a short time. But above all we must not forget what we often tend to forget—that the United States may have a policy toward the institutions of the European Community, but those institutions are not controlled instruments of U.S. policy.

One might well dwell, however, on a specific aspect of common interest, which need not be affected by the present situation, and

[32] Jules Guéron, "Euratom and Nuclear Research," *Euratom Bulletin* (a quarterly publication of the European Atomic Energy Community), 1962, No. 3, p. 4.
[33] U.S. AEC Press Release E-240, July 9, 1962.

this is the pursuit of common research and development goals. To achieve close coordination the present work of the Joint Research and Development Board, good as it is, is not sufficient. Coordination should be continued and extended to research projects beyond those financed under the Joint Program. But a closer type of collaboration is needed requiring the joint operation of research and development programs by all qualified members of the OECD. It would involve not only exchange of data but also exchange of personnel, materials and equipment. As a full member of OECD the United States should participate actively in the research arrangements which have been, and may be, established by the ENEA.

Patents and other factors which preserve competitive positions of firms—whether they be British, German, U.S., or of any other origin—will be tricky problems. Competition should be preserved in order to develop the economic viability of atomic power. Thus, it may be necessary to limit the more intimate aspects of the joint efforts to basic research. But, within this limitation, the cooperative effort should be unstinted.

"The basic objectives of the OEEC have been achieved. The industrialized nations of Europe have not merely recovered but have achieved unprecedented economic vigor."[34] How true. In 1960, the gross national product of the United States increased by 2.7 per cent while that of the European Community rose about 7 per cent.[35] The United States spends well over 2 per cent of its gross national product in research and development. Only Britain and the Soviet Union come close to matching this investment in survival and future well-being. The rest of the industrialized nations of Europe invest about one per cent or less in research and development. Taken together, the nations of Europe have a larger population than the United States or Russia. They exceed Russia in consumption of industrial energy and consume about one-half of the amount that the United States uses. But, with respect to the technology of production the nations of Europe are living in a bor-

[34] U.S. Dept. of State, *The Organization for Economic Cooperation and Development,* an address by Dean Rusk, Secretary of State, before the Government-Industry Conference, Washington, D.C., February 13, 1961 (Washington: GPO, 1961), p. 3.
[35] "Community GNP Climbs Seven Per Cent," *Bulletin from the European Community,* n. 44, February 1961, p. 3.

rowed environment. They are investing comparatively little in the development of technologies which will be vital in future economic growth.

Not long ago, the United States was the recipient of European ideas. It developed a highly inventive economy, and is still inventive. But pressures to develop new products have exposed deficiencies in basic research, which we are remedying. On the other hand, Europe since World War II has been able to draw extensively on basic ideas developed elsewhere in order to achieve a fantastic economic growth. One interesting indication of this change in emphasis from the basic to the applied is the fact that whereas Europe long dominated the world in winning Nobel prizes, the United States in the postwar world eclipses Europe in the number of Nobel prizes awarded in the field of science.[36] This emphasis on development has caused a slow erosion of attitudes toward the usefulness of basic research, which will continue unless new vitality is given to research programs, not only in atomic energy, but in all other fields of scientific endeavor.

America's debt to Europe can be regarded as repaid. Now Europe will begin to feel the same pressures toward the development of basic ideas that the United States and the U.S.S.R. are experiencing. In Europe there will be a renaissance of basic science in which the United States must participate. This new mode of thinking is likely to occur during the period when the nations of Europe and the United States have decided to tackle a problem whose solution is already evident, but which, for reasons that are none too clear, seems premature. The problem is the coexistence of two major economic communities, the OECD and the Common Market —communities with very similar goals and overlapping membership. In the course of time, it will seem increasingly less advantageous to a nation to support a membership in both organizations. Even now, in the field of atomic energy, there are such anomalies as the payment of funds to Euratom which, in turn, transfers them to ENEA to operate some of the Agency's most important projects.

---

[36] George W. Gray, "Which Scientists Win Nobel Prizes?," *Harper's Magazine*, May 1961, pp. 78-82.

Such a cumbersome procedure seems only to increase the administrative staffs of both agencies.

These generalizations of course have broad scientific implications beyond the field of atomic energy. The various European organizations, which owe their origin to the glamour of the new atomic science and to the false near-term promises it held out, have implanted in the European mind a seed of growing realization of the need in other fields for increased research and development. If the Western world, by joint effort can nurture that seed as the seeds of scientific enquiry were nurtured centuries ago in Europe, without question it can retain its position as the primary economic, technological, and moral force. And the catalyst, the atom, despite the disappointments of its slow development as a factor in Europe's economy, will justly receive a large share of the credit.

Chapter 11

The Fence, Inside and Out

In May 1956 non-bloc scientists were permitted for the first time to visit the scientific center at Dubna (then called Bol'shaya Volga), some 70 miles north of Moscow. A visitor glimpsing some ill-clothed workers beyond a barbed wire fence hastily concluded that he was observing a slave labor camp. A Polish scientist corrected him, saying, "You are faced with a problem of topology. Those people are *outside* the fence."[1]

Inside the fence is one of the Soviet Union's highly publicized answers to Western international atomic cooperation. Dubna (under various names) has existed since 1947 when work was started on a gigantic accelerator which for a time was the world's largest. This distinction was lost for a while when several Western machines came into operation. However, in May 1957 when a new type of accelerator, shooting protons at an energy of 10 billion electron volts, achieved full-beam energy at Dubna, the Russians temporarily regained their pre-eminent position. (Since then their accelerator has again been eclipsed by machines at CERN and in the United States.) The machines and their associated equipment should have made Dubna one of the foremost accelerator research centers in the world, but to date the results obtained in fundamental physics have not been nearly as impressive as those obtained outside the Soviet Union. One reason was that the strength of the beam from the large machine never fulfilled expectations; another was that a large part of the effort at Dubna had to go into training inexperienced research personnel.

---

[1] Murray Gell-Mann, "An American Physicist in Moscow," *Caltech Alumni Review*, October 1956, p. 28.

After Dubna had enlarged its basic research, it became in early 1956 a center of research activity for the Soviet bloc. Accordingly, its facilities became part of the Joint Institute of Nuclear Research. Members of the Institute contribute to its support in the following proportions: the U.S.S.R., 47.25 per cent; China, 20 per cent; East Germany and Poland, 6.75 per cent each; Czechoslovakia and Rumania, 5.75 per cent each; Hungary, 4 per cent; Bulgaria, 3.6 per cent; Albania, North Korea and Mongolia, .05 per cent each; and Viet-Nam, nil. These figures are interesting indications of the Soviet's assessment of the relative importance, or potential, in the nuclear field of each of the satellite nations. Particularly significant is China's contribution—three times that of any other bloc nation outside the U.S.S.R.

Since the facilities for basic research at Dubna are far beyond the economic reach of any of the other bloc nations, the Joint Institute affords an opportunity for scientists to perform experiments and to develop their skills in a way not possible in their own countries. But a closer analysis indicates that the Soviet Union's generosity in extending the use of its facilities is in reality a magnificently contrived and controlled measure to limit the immediate expansion of independent atomic energy activities in the bloc nations, where funds and trained manpower are extremely scarce. In most cases the member nations' contributions toward the support of the Joint Institute represent the greater fraction of their atomic research budgets and the men whom they send to work at Dubna are their scarce, top talent. If the satellite scientists are enthusiastic about their experiences at Dubna, public expression of this sentiment is difficult, if not impossible, to find. The indications are that they are restricted pretty much to the particular section of the research center which concerns their own work. And, there are difficulties which arise in their relations both with Soviet scientists and with scientists from other bloc nations.

The support of over 50 per cent of Dubna's costs by non-Soviet funds is a direct subsidy for the Russians. They also profit from the assistance of non-Soviet scientists which frees many of their own men for work of more immediate urgency to the state. Thus, for Russia the arrangements at Dubna work out very well indeed. Research at Dubna has little pertinence to the development of a capability to produce atomic power or atomic bombs, but it is important for the training of personnel. In the meantime the net result is probably to delay nuclear expansion in nations behind the iron curtain, except for the U.S.S.R. This amounts to a partial solution of the Nth country problem.

The organization of the Joint Institute of Nuclear Research was probably stimulated by the formation of three other agencies, ENEA, Euratom, and CERN. No doubt many of the satellite nations had begun to look enviously at these cooperative groupings in the West; a similar arrangement was needed to assuage their feelings. Actually, there is a measure of Soviet cooperation in CERN; at a number of its conferences Russian scientists have reported some rather interesting and significant results and there has been a small exchange of visiting, working scientists.

After the particularly disappointing General Conference of the IAEA in the fall of 1960, bloc members, meeting in Moscow, formed a new nuclear assistance group which appears to have more practical, or applied, intent than does Dubna. The Permanent Commission on Peaceful Uses of Atomic Energy, which functions under the existing Council of Mutual Economic Assistance (CEMA), presumably will have something to do with bilateral assistance treaties in effect among the bloc nations.[2] The Permanent Commission is their answer to IAEA.

Soviet Bilateral Aid

Under the Soviet bilateral programs most bloc nations are receiving 2,000-kilowatt nuclear research reactors and small research cyclotrons. Scientific information, technical data, and training assistance also are supplied. The satellite nations have to pay for the equipment they receive. The Soviet bilateral agreements, unlike U.S. bilaterals, do not provide for a free grant of half the cost of the research reactor projects.[3] The Soviets have highly publicized other

[2] Vasily S. Yemelyanov, "Aggressive Atomists and Their Advocates," *Pravda* (Moscow), November 1, 1960, p. 3.

[3] Applications for this 50 per cent support provision up to a cost of $350,000, expired by mid-1960. About twenty-six such grants were committed during the five years they were available under the U.S. Atoms for Peace program. Note, again, the "matching" provision which characterizes U.S. nuclear policy. It does not seem to have a Soviet counterpart.

features of their bilaterals which differ from those of the United States. Purportedly, they do not specify Soviet control over the equipment and materials supplied, or periodic reporting of the results of research and experimentation. But the U.S.S.R. is as control-conscious as the United States—probably more so. The Russians can forego formal arrangements because they know that their political controls and their information on activities in the bloc nations are sufficient to provide exact knowledge of everything that is being done with their equipment. There are no fuel reprocessing plants in any of the other bloc nations, excepting most probably China, and no indications that any such facilities are contemplated. Thus, reactor fuel used for research must be returned to the Soviet Union for processing: analysis of the fuel will indicate fairly precisely the operating conditions, and whether or not there have been attempts at diversion.

There is one significant means of discrimination in the Soviet bilateral assistance program. All the bloc nations are receiving research reactors which utilize uranium enriched up to 10 per cent, except China and Yugoslavia which receive reactors utilizing uranium enriched only to 2 per cent. It is not much of a task to bring 10 per cent uranium up to weapons grade, but to do the same for 2 per cent uranium would require a fair amount of additional separative work and a fairly large installation. The diversion of reactor fuel-loading for military purposes is undoubtedly considered far less probable in the satellite nations than in Yugoslavia or China; this may account for the difference in the types of reactors supplied. This is an interesting technical indication of Russia's judgment of the relative political reliability of China and Yugoslavia, on the one hand, and of countries like Poland and Czechoslovakia on the other. To these countries and to East Germany, Russia is now giving a greater measure of atomic assistance in the form of instruction and large-scale atomic plants.

No exact comparison can be made of Soviet and American nuclear generosity since the specific terms of the Soviet peaceful bilateral treaties on such matters as price are not available. Limited information indicates that recipients of Soviet aid have not received what may be described as bargains. Significant delays in the time schedules of atomic aid are matters of record.[4] The price of the fissionable material may be low, as the Soviets have stated, but a number of recipients have complained that the prices of equipment are high. Apparently there is no fixed price schedule for large-scale nuclear exports from the U.S.S.R. The Poles, for example, were asked to pay 14 million rubles for their first research reactor, but when they protested they finally had to pay only 6.5 million rubles (about $1 million at the pre-1960 rate).[5] Furthermore, there are good indications that the reliability of the Soviet equipment is low; East Germany, Yugoslavia, and China have experienced delays and other difficulties with Soviet reactors. It is quite conceivable that defective equipment was supplied deliberately in order to keep atomic development elsewhere in the bloc at a snail's pace.

Impatient China is in a special category of nuclear aid. Publicly, China has only a ten-megawatt research reactor, which if operated continuously for production might yield enough material for a bomb every two or three years but would require a number of loadings of enriched uranium. This is not enough for a "Great Leap Forward," and undoubtedly unpublicized nuclear installations are in operation and under construction in the Chinese People's Republic. The Soviets would naturally refrain from publicizing a major nuclear assistance program, if such exists for China, in order not to arouse fear in the nations of Asia, particularly India. And by helping India substantially the Soviets would antagonize China. Russia, too, has bilateral assistance problems.

Thus far, the Soviets have proffered little nuclear assistance outside the bloc. Yugoslavia has accepted research reactors from both the United States and the U.S.S.R., as has Indonesia. Soviet overtures looking toward power assistance have been made to India, then withdrawn, then made again—the difficulty probably being China. Egypt, Iraq, and Ghana have also had help.

The modesty of these efforts may be related to the fact that

[4] George Ginsburgs, "The Soviet Union and International Cooperation in the Peaceful Use of Atomic Energy: Bilateral Agreements," *American Journal of International Law,* July 1960, pp. 605-614.

[5] D. J. Hughes, "Physics in Poland and Russia," *Physics Today,* December 1957, p. 10.

Russia has made greater cuts, proportionately, in her nuclear power program since 1955 than any other nation. But when the technical and economic circumstances warrant it, a Soviet nuclear aid policy may grow in importance as a political tool. If, someday, the Soviet atomic assistance program starts to roll, it might develop along one or more of the following lines:

a) Like other Soviet aid measures, nuclear assistance might be directed toward former colonial areas in order to reduce remnants of Western influence.

b) The Russians might offer to increase, through IAEA and by independent invitation, the number of foreign students being trained in atomic work in the U.S.S.R.

c) The U.S.S.R. might invite more foreign scientists from outside the bloc to perform experimental work at selected Soviet installations and might also offer assistance for small-scale experiments in their native countries.

d) The Russians might decide to supply small power reactors to make their aid more meaningful. Such reactors are uneconomic today, principally because the initial capital investment of dollars or rubles per installed kilowatt is extremely high. Even if future research fails to reduce the cost, the U.S.S.R. might supply such units at cut-rate prices, thus making them economically attractive for some areas.

e) The Russians may decide to launch a long-range "plutonium for peace—not weapons" offensive, when the technique of using plutonium as a reactor fuel becomes fully developed.

Plutonium and Rockets

This last possibility listed above is one of the most important. A plutonium offensive is one of the few remaining atomic power overtures with possible dramatic impact. Initial Soviet plans exceeded those of the United States and Britain in the nuclear power to be installed by 1960. But like others, the Russians discovered that atomic power would not prove economical at an early date and cut down their program. No new atomic challenge has appeared. One has an instinctive belief, however, that the Russians are still to be heard from in the realm of technical innovation.

There is a strong possibility that their effort will be directed toward "Plutonium for Peace." At present plutonium is useless except for weapons, as was pointed out in Chapter 3, but the development of highly efficient, plutonium-burning reactors would constitute an important step in minimizing the Nth country problem and in improving the economic outlook for nuclear power.

It is not possible to say that research on plutonium utilization in the U.S.S.R. is more advanced than in the United States or the United Kingdom.[6] However, Soviet studies seem to place greater emphasis on the possibility of burning all qualities of plutonium (including that containing plutonium-240), and on the utilization of plutonium in breeder reactors. The Soviet investigators seem rather optimistic about the research they have done, for in 1958 one of their scientists concluded his very important paper with the following:

> The basic conclusion from the above-described investigations of fast-neutron experimental reactors consists in confirmation of the possibility of obtaining, in these reactors, very high breeding ratios of nuclear fuel.

> This circumstance ensures the possibility of fully utilizing the reserves of nuclear raw materials for the needs of the rapidly developing nuclear power programmes and makes the building of fast-neutron power reactors a very promising field.[7]

The first nation to demonstrate the practical, economic burning of plutonium will thereby establish one of the most significant landmarks in the development and control of atomic energy. Although the United States and the United Kingdom now seem to have approximately the same capacity as the U.S.S.R. for achieving that distinction, there is every indication that the U.S.S.R. recognizes just as fully the political importance of plutonium and intends to take advantage of that knowledge when it is able to.

Another major entry in the nuclear sweepstakes will be the rocket propulsive system. It would be possible to quote statements and technical data which hint that the Soviet Union is actively engaged in developing a nuclear rocket. But this should not be

---

[6] R. R. Matthews, "Soviet Fast Reactor—BR 5" (report of a British team after inspecting the Russian plutonium reactor work), *Nuclear Engineering*, October 1959, pp. 359-360.

[7] A. I. Leipunsky, "Studies in the Physics of Fast Neutron Reactors," (P/2038, *Peaceful Uses of Atomic Energy*, 2nd U.N. International Conference. (Geneva: U.N. 1958), v. 12, p. 15.

necessary, for to assume the contrary would be the height of folly. The Russians have repeatedly and vividly demonstrated their awareness of the military, political, and psychological advantages of a space program; the nuclear rocket is the next significant step forward. By achieving this step the United States could catch up in payload capacity—and if only for this reason, the U.S.S.R. is not standing idly by. A nuclear rocket, possibly using some advanced concepts like ionic propulsion, is the ultimate vehicle in pioneering outer space; should Russia be the first to demonstrate it, the rocket may well constitute the final proof, for other nations, of the technical superiority of the socialist system. Politically speaking, the peaceful atom may be nearing the end of its brief "age" in world history; the Space Age will be less transient.

This is another specific technological goal for the West. Whether it is proceeding toward that goal at the proper pace has been a matter of dispute for some time.[8] In this instance, however, we must not rely on the old adage: "only time will tell."

Ideological Factors and the Peaceful Atom

None of the possible technical and political ploys which may emerge relate fundamentally to the role which the peaceful atom might play in the resolution of the broad problem of world peace. The Soviets, like the West, have no unique policy in this respect —no even moderately exciting suggestion has ever been voiced from their corner, or from the other corners. The Soviets, however, rely on what they regard as sound, basic code for all phases of their conduct, namely, Marxist-Leninist dogma. Consequently, no analysis of what the Soviet may or may not do is valid or complete without recognition of factors relating to their ideology. Two, already encountered in nuclear negotiations, will suffice for present purposes.

Maxim Litvinoff, in 1922, was probably not the first to express Soviet opinion of "neutral" judges by saying that "only an angel could be unbiased in judging Soviet affairs."[9] This basic tenet,

---

[8] John W. Finney, "Delay is Charged on Atomic Rocket," *The New York Times,* April 16, 1961, p. 52; "The Nuclear Space Age" (Editorial), *Nucleonics,* April 1961, p. 156. (This is also an excellent summary issue of the status of nuclear propulsion projects.)

[9] Netherlands, Dept. of Foreign Affairs, *Conference at The Hague I. Non-*

always present, is rediscovered from time to time with surprise by Western analysts. Walter Lippmann, after his interview with Khrushchev in April 1961, hails it as a new dogma "that there are no neutral men."[10] This firmly ensconced bit of attitude strongly implies that the Soviets will never accept any international control commission, without maintaining a right of veto.

Thus, traditional Soviet policy explains the "surprise" move which in 1961 dealt a major blow to the Geneva test-suspension conference. The demand for a three-power authority, each with veto power, effectively overrode and made immaterial all the technical considerations of that conference. Were a joint international nuclear research effort, involving the Soviet bloc, ever to come under serious discussion, a most predictable barrier will be the Russian demand for veto power in matters of administration, the allocation of financial and material resources, and so forth. But this should not preclude cooperative efforts involving the exchange of information, samples, and personnel among nationally conducted projects. The International Geophysical Year, conducted in this manner by joint *scientific* councils, has been regarded as most successful.

The second factor, more often encountered, is the crutch of secrecy. It is amazing how often in international negotiations this excuse is actually treated by other delegates with an aura of understanding and respect. Retention of this asymmetrical situation obviates any Soviet incentive to agree to any inspection mechanism, for they already have all of the "inspection" that they need.

The Soviet insistence on secrecy is sometimes deeply rooted but often is simply a negotiating tactic for a particular situation. One would be entirely too bold in offering any suggestion to modulate this aspect of the Soviet personality, but there may be minor ways to assist gradual reduction of this most fundamental barrier to mutual understanding.

Russian Commission II. Russian Commission, June 26 - July 20, 1922. Minutes and Documents (The Hague: GPO, 1922), p. 126. (See also *The Times* [London], February 18, 1961.)

[10] Walter Lippmann, "Khrushchev Sees Less Threat," *The New York Herald-Tribune* (Paris edition), April 17, 1961, p. 2.

For example, the specialist's desk sags under the weight of technical journals, bulletins, reports, all in his narrow field of interest. Presumably, the average scientist also wishes to refresh and add to his knowledge of other technical subjects, and in this respect he is aided by several excellent journals of a general nature. But to aid him in the appreciation of the fantastic amount of research of direct interest to him, much more needs to be done. Research on the peaceful atom offers one of the most difficult information challenges.

Every nation interested in technological developments has information-gathering and coordination activities. The results of these extraordinarily large efforts have been restricted to a privileged few, for the activities are usually classified under the heading of "intelligence." Fortunately, a realization has gradually developed in some quarters that a good part of this national asset could and should be put to greater use. This part is that great mass of information which is openly published.

It should not come as a surprise, then, that the nation which has shown an ability to make maximum use of its intelligence resources was the first to recognize this fact—even in the era of Stalin, before Atoms for Peace forced open some of the portals. In 1952 the Soviets established their All-Union Institution of Scientific and Technical Information (VINITI), which abstracts Soviet and non-Soviet periodicals, furnishes "express" information of new developments, translates foreign works, etc., in the mammoth issues it publishes.

No Western information center on the scale of VINITI exists. However, progress has been made in providing Western scientists with Soviet information, particularly, but the activities are only weakly coordinated. The U.S. National Science Foundation, the AEC, and the Department of Commerce have sponsored most of these translation activities, and a great deal of this work is now carried on by commercial corporations.[11] It is particularly gratifying that, beginning in 1959, abstracts of Russian technical literature made by the Central Intelligence Agency became available to the public for the first time.

[11] For atomic energy, sources are summarized in *Nucleonics,* May 1961, pp. 111-112, "Keeping Up With Foreign Nuclear Literature."

Many other nations and international bodies conduct their independent scientific information activities, and a great deal of overlapping and duplication results. This would seem to be a fertile field for international collaboration, both in the pursuit of computer indexing and machine translation techniques and in the actual centralization of translating and abstracting activities, in a body which would then disseminate the information throughout the world with as much dispatch as possible.

Such a center has been created within the U.S.S.R. and perhaps it would be most expedient to create a world-wide reference organization about that core. Since the interest is broader than just the field of atomic energy, this could be done by placing appropriate sections of the All-Union Institute under the nominal direction of the several international bodies concerned, such as IAEA and UNESCO. Of course, if making such a liberal suggestion to Moscow is too bold, the IAEA would do well to study the problems of a world-wide information center which would minimize duplication and facilitate dissemination procedures—at least within the field of nuclear energy.

The science of finding out is developing as rapidly as other technologies, and all major nations make maximum use of the latest capabilities. Openness is like entropy—continually increasing, never subject to recall. Attainment of an open world is a natural and inevitable process. While it is not possible to achieve this goal in a single step, it may well be possible to accelerate the process, and it certainly is impossible to impede completely. The Atoms for Peace proposal has indeed already demonstratively accelerated this process, and there is no reason to suppose that the usefulness of the peaceful atom is, in this respect, at an end.

Despite basic differences of philosophy, the United States and the U.S.S.R. have a mutual interest in not letting the technological revolution get out of hand; safety problems, the Nth country, the high costs of advanced pure nuclear research, and other matters still offer common ground for discussion and cooperation. All of these avenues of approach, although alone ineffective to ward off the danger of the world-wide nuclear annihilation, must be kept clear and explored.

Chapter 12

Nations in Transition

Our bipolar world is transient. Whatever the future may bring, the world will probably not be dominated by either of the two competing ideologies, for both have been tardy in recognizing and understanding demographic change. They do not know how to cope with the consequences of one new human being born every second. Studies applying the "inexact" sciences, the political and social, have been abundant, but for the most part unilluminating. The relationship of the "exact" or technological sciences to population growth is essentially unexplored. Certainly, in their contributions to the well-being of the mass of humanity, atomic energy and the Atoms for Peace program have been particularly disappointing. The program has probably only accentuated for most people in the emerging nations the immense gap which exists between the "haves" and the "have nots."

Pause, for a moment, to reflect upon a little game that is popular among analysts of the problems of the emerging nations. They, the analysts, shy from the term "underdeveloped country," and, indeed, some of the nations themselves resent that description. Thus was created the game of finding other adjectives such as: less developed, emerging, arising, and developing. The game serves no useful purpose, for the nations under discussion are indeed underdeveloped; they do themselves a disservice by considering their technologies and economies more advanced than they actually are.

The advanced nations do the others a disservice by heralding any new technological invention as a miracle tool. This is what atomic energy was called in 1954 and for a few years afterwards.

Now, as a result of enormous international technical efforts, many facets of the promise of atomic energy are seen much more clearly. But, curiously, if there exists in any of the "have" nations a division, a group, or even a single man, whose full-time, long-range responsibility is to evaluate and recommend means of using atomic energy in underdeveloped areas, that activity is the best kept secret of this atomic era. The creation of staffs for evaluation and recommendation is inevitable. Problems proliferate, although specialists do not. With proper authority and assistance the specialist will find quickly that, when compared with all the agricultural, medical and technical arts which are necessary for a nation in transition, the atom will play a minor role. But wherever the atom enters the scene, its role will be magnified because it is, after all, the fabled atom.

Less marvellous mysteries of the machine age confront the developing nations. As a delegate to a world conference on technical needs of underdeveloped areas has said, "In my country you can see hundreds of automobiles abandoned beside the roads. They need repair, but nobody does anything about them. Everybody thinks the automobiles stopped because they died. We are not quite ready for nuclear reactors."[1]

The economist will be dismayed to find that his classic concepts are not valid here. We are entering an era of vast material and technical assistance which will eclipse and differ radically from the military and economic assistance programs in which we have been engaged. Technical assistance will by no means be a profitable operation; it has other reasons, other motives. The long-range results will in large measure depend upon the spirit in which the programs are conducted. They should not mirror the blunt philosophy: "We value trade least for economic reasons and most for political purposes."[2] In most instances the plan of two distinguished gentlemen (who surely must deserve the reward for providing the best collective name for those nations in transition, the "unprovided countries") offer a suitable rationale:

[1] Lawrence Fellows, "Israeli Scientific Meeting Aids New Nations on Modern Needs," *The New York Times*, August 27, 1960, p. 2.

[2] N. S. Khrushchev as quoted in "The Sino-Soviet Economic Offensive in the Less Developed Countries," Department of State Publication 6632 (Washington: GPO, May 1958), p. 6.

Many voyages have been undertaken with view of profit or of plunder, or to gratify resentment; to procure some advantage to ourselves, or to do some mischief to others: but a voyage is now proposed, to visit a distant people on the other side of the globe; not to cheat them, not to rob them, not to seize their lands, or enslave their persons; but merely to do them good, and make them, as far as in our power lies, to live as comfortably as ourselves.

It seems a laudable wish, that all the nations of the earth were connected by a knowledge of each other; and a mutual exchange of benefits: but a commercial nation particularly should wish for a general civilization of mankind, since trade is always carried on to much greater extent with people who have the arts and conveniences of life, than it can be with naked savages. We may therefore hope, in this undertaking, to be of some service to our country as well as to those poor people, who, however distant from us, are in truth related to us, and whose interests do, in some degree, concern every one who can say, *Homo sum etc.*[3]

Since each country, area, and sub-area has its unique development problems, it would be impossible to discuss any broadly typical case. Some applications of atomic energy, particularly those which relate to power production, will be appropriate to special industrial situations—mainly in nations in the later stages of transition. Other applications, relating to the improvement of health, crop control, and so forth, may be applicable almost universally. For certain nations like Brazil, China, India, and Israel, it is possible to consider, if not solve, a great many problems in the context of atomic energy. One of these nations, India, is selected as the pivot of discussion; if in certain passages the discussion is harsh or kind, it carries no implication that India deserves to be considered unique.

Power and Its Problems

India is well along the path toward nuclear proficiency, although official statements that "There is no question of India being abreast of the leading atomic powers in knowledge of atomic weapons or the resources to make them" are politically inspired

---

[3] "Plan, by Messieurs Franklin and Dalrymple, for benefitting distant, unprovided Countries," *The Works of Benjamin Franklin,* v. IV (Philadelphia, Pa.: William Duane, 1809), pp. 200-203.

and somewhat exaggerated.[4] But India has every right to boast about her nuclear science. Long before the advent of the atomic bomb, Indian physicists had made very significant contributions to the understanding of the atom, so that it is easy to see why the Indian atomic energy effort was initiated as early as 1948. India's vast deposits of thorium—deposits which, except for Brazil's, constitute virtually a world monopoly of this potential fuel—would alone furnish an incentive for a nuclear energy program.

The first Indian reactor, "Apsara," began to operate August 4, 1956, for radioisotope production and research experience. Another, four times as powerful as China's first ten-megawatt research reactor, came into operation about two years later. Provided by Canada under the Colombo Plan, this reactor, utilizing heavy water and natural uranium, is an important research tool in developing the types of *power* reactors India would like to build.[5] The third research reactor, "Zerlina," designed and built by India alone, will be used to study the design of larger plants. Zerlina went critical on January 14, 1961, a date when India's nuclear power plans were in an equally critical state.

As India begins large-scale, nuclear power effort, she has requested technological aid, and will request more, from all parties able to grant it. The demands present the United States with issues far thornier than those in, say, the joint U.S.-Euratom program. If the problems relating to the economics and technologies of the Indian plants are troublesome, they are simple when compared to the headaches caused by India's attitude toward controls.

At the September 1956 U.N. Conference for drafting the statutes of IAEA, Dr. Homi J. Bhabha, head of the Indian atomic energy project, voiced concern over provisions for inspection and control. "The present safeguards," he said, "will have their maximum effect in the case of the technically underdeveloped countries who most require external help in order to develop peaceful atomic power programs and who are *ipso facto* least in a position to make atomic weapons. Since most of the countries of Asia, Africa, and

[4] *The Times* (London), December 17, 1959, p. 8.
[5] W. B. Lewis and H. J. Bhabha, *The Canada-India Reactor: An Exercise in International Co-Operation*, P/2424, 2d U.N. International Conference on Peaceful Uses of Atomic Energy (Geneva: U.N. 1958), v. 1, pp. 355-358.

Latin America are in this position, the present safeguards will give the Agency maximum powers of interference in such areas."[6] Nevertheless India accepted the statutes and became the eighteenth nation to enter IAEA (the United States was the twenty-second). Acceptance of the statutes, however, does not necessarily mean acceptance of actual aid under their provisions. It is still Indian policy, considered at the highest levels, not to start an atomic energy program based upon fuels which must be accompanied by IAEA inspection. Shying from these "strings," India concluded two small research bilaterals with Britain and Canada, but until 1961 did not make any significant overtures outside the Commonwealth.

At that time Indian planners were in the midst of drafting their third five-year plan, which started in 1961. That plan incorporates an ambitious goal for the installation of several thousands of kilowatts of nuclear power by 1966. Despite India's considerable domestic scientific talents and her aspirations eventually to mount an atomic energy program based on her vast thorium resources, the achievement of that goal *must* require extensive outside aid. In most countries, and particularly in India, a major economic plan is primarily a political document. Its implementation, particularly in an underdeveloped area, is so difficult that goals are almost always overstated with the hope and expectation that something less, but at least something of significance, will be achieved. Almost invariably the foreign assistance allowed for in such plans is greater than the planners realistically expect. Undoubtedly, nuclear energy goals in India's third five-year plan possess this characteristic of boldness, but one must assume determination to meet a good part of them.

The vast thorium resources of India, perhaps the largest in the world, provide the basis for India's belief that she can eventually become self-sufficient in atomic power via the thorium-uranium-233 breeding route. The plan calls for the attainment of this objective in three stages. First, India will fabricate her small uranium resources into fuel for use in appropriate natural uranium reactors. The plutonium thus produced will be used in a second generation of power systems which will provide approximately a half

---

[6] *The New York Times*, September 28, 1956. See the statement of Dr. Bhabha, quoted on page 65, above.

gram of U-233 for each gram of plutonium burned. At this second stage, more fissionable material will be burned than is created. India's hopes lie in a third stage in which a power reactor system will burn uranium-233 in such a manner that more of this substance is produced than is consumed, because of the thorium implanted in it. India believes that if she can progress through these three stages, she will attain within fifteen or twenty years the atomic self-sufficiency that she desires.

While India has the raw materials for her program, she requires outside help in the first and intermediate stages. Initially, she will accept a reactor system, or systems, which have been fully engineered elsewhere, but as her program progresses an opportunity might arise for joint development of more advanced concepts. Possibly, the countries which aid initially would also participate in later stages of the cooperative research and development teams —or just as possibly, they would be excluded.

India's insistence upon the use of its own natural uranium greatly restricted the choice of sources of aid. The United States has not constructed any natural uranium power reactors, but reactors of that type moderated with heavy water are in the current AEC ten-year program. Other advanced power systems of this type may follow, constituting a significant U.S. contribution to aiding nations that may maintain a certain amount of freedom from the major powers in the production of nuclear fuels. Canada is engaged in an effort similar to India's, with even more optimistic expectations as regards fuel costs. Already Canada has participated with India in the construction of an advanced research reactor on Trombay Island in Bombay Harbor. This cooperative project has had a turbulent history, with escalation of initial cost estimates. A detailed study of its history would probably provide valuable hints for realistically estimating and implementing nuclear aid projects in relatively nonindustrialized countries. A second joint venture, presumably incorporating the Trombay experience, has been a study of the costs of duplicating a Canadian plant in India.[7] To turn elsewhere in the Commonwealth, India would have to accept what the British already consider an out-

[7] *Nucleonics Week,* August 10, 1961, p. 2.

moded design; British efforts are now being directed toward enriched uranium. Thus, in the initial stages of her power program India would have sacrificed much to retain what she considers sovereign nuclear rights if she had insisted on natural uranium systems.

Upon finding that the large capital costs (and perhaps other characteristics) of the natural uranium reactors were not attractive, Indian policy took what appeared to be a curious turn. In mid-1962 India indicated that she would be willing to accept the United States reactor, operating on enriched fuel. But it was stipulated that, while India would be willing to accept the usual bilateral inspection arrangement with the United States, she would not at all consider accepting inspection by the International Atomic Energy Agency.

At first glance this might seem to be a simple matter of pride. After all, the United States has inspection arrangements with a number of nations and with Euratom to which the IAEA is not a party. It seemed perhaps that India wished to obtain this same status—for what that was worth. On the other hand, there is probably a more practical explanation for India's attitude. Her plans for reactors in the future depend on the local availability of enriched materials—plutonium or uranium-233. The reactor which India would receive from the United States is the only one which would be controlled. Meanwhile, India would reap the benefit of knowledge and experience with this reactor to be able to construct her future uncontrolled reactors. Acceptance of a United States bilateral arrangement with a single reactor, by established precedence, does not imply any future obligation of the nation to accept United States inspection of any of her other nuclear activities. Acceptance of an IAEA arrangement, on the other hand, almost has the connotation of a moral commitment to other projects. This probably explains why India is willing to accept an initial amount of real or quasi inspection by a single nation, whether it be Canada, the United Kingdom, the United States, or the U.S.S.R., so that she may be able to carry out future undertakings in what she considers to be an unobligated manner.

The Soviet Union in March 1960 offered large-scale atomic assistance to India on terms similar to those of its other aid projects.[8] The offer included a conventional 250,000-kilowatt thermal power station, to be paid for over a period of twelve years following the completion of the project. The interest rate was fixed at 2½ per cent. These terms are indeed attractive. The only stipulation the Russians made, one quite reasonable from their point of view, was that India should not invite world-wide bids for the reactor. Evidently Russia does not consider her loans equivalent to those of the International Bank for Reconstruction and Development that financed SENN in Italy. The plant would be an independent India-U.S.S.R. venture. China, which had received assistance from Russia in her atomic program, must look askance upon any aid given India. In fact, Soviet atomic assistance to India might have served China as a lever in bargaining for more atomic aid. The Soviets undoubtedly would not relish such an escalating process. Probably this is the main factor which cooled Russian enthusiasm for aiding India. During 1961, mention of the Russo-Indian project became infrequent; whether or not it will ever be implemented depends upon unpredictable political, not nuclear, developments. The agreement that India and the U.S.S.R. concluded in October 1961 referred only to research and not to power as earlier announcements indicated.

Enough has already been said in this book to make it clear that economic considerations do not now justify the installation of large nuclear power plants in underdeveloped countries. The limited market for power alone—the low load factor (see Chapter 6)—makes it hard to cover capital costs through revenue. Probably, at least ten times the investment in the plant producing the power should be spent on equipment and machines to distribute and utilize it if the venture is to make economic sense.[9] Other factors, such as financing and the availability of alternate energy sources can be debated eloquently, both pro and con, as they have been in India.[10] But the margins of advantage over conventional power

[8] "Russians to Build India Atom Plant," *The New York Times*, March 8, 1960, p. 6.

[9] G. Hoyt Whipple and William Kerr, *A Generalized Atomic Energy Program*, P/1043, 2d U.N. International Conference on Peaceful Uses of Atomic Energy (Geneva: U.N. 1958), v. 1, pp. 165-171.

[10] For a pro example see H. J. Bhabha, *A Study of the Contribution of Atomic Energy to a Power Program in India*, P/1624, Same, v. 1, pp. 89-101. For con

196 / Disintegrating Policies

that can be demonstrated are too narrow, the cost comparisons are questionable, and the arguments too forced for this debate to have provided a convincing answer. If there is one rule of thumb in this budding age of the atom, it is that any unforeseen development will always increase costs and that unforeseen developments always occur. Ergo, atomic plants are always more expensive than one would wish them to be.

Disagreements about economics will not stop India from going ahead with its nuclear energy program. In doing so it will face many technical difficulties. We need only remember that many problems of uranium-fueled systems remain unsolved. Plutonium-fueled systems are practically unknown. Uranium-233 systems are in a pre-natal stage; none yet exists. India must pass through a vast unknown territory before she can use the native nuclear fuel resources as she would like. The question to be resolved is how to use her limited financial, technical, and trained manpower resources in the best manner; it is not at all clear that a large power reactor program undertaken at the present time represents the best allocation of these resources.

The contemplated Indian fuel cycles present many metallurgical and chemical problems.[11] But much nuclear knowledge can be gained through the operation of small systems which do not generate power and are far less costly than those which do. For any nation, an insistence on immediate large-scale power coupled with a reluctance toward any control, even over very small amounts of fissionable materials, is likely to be disastrous. A nation that strictly adheres to the philosophy of no control whatsoever may impair its future nuclear potential. Like India, they will no doubt acquiesce to at least bilateral control. But the question persists as to whether those nations in a position to give should insist on IAEA or regional control.

---

examples see I.M.D. Little, "Atomic Bombay?" *The Economic Weekly* (Bombay), November 29, 1958, pp. 1483-6; "Economics of Nuclear Power," *Commerce* (Bombay), August 22, 1959, p. 304.

[11] Ulysses M. Staebler, Division of Reactor Development, U.S. AEC, "Thorium As a Nuclear Fuel," paper presented before the 6th Nuclear Congress, Rome, Italy, June 13, 1961 (released by the U.S. AEC in Press Release IN-225, June 22, 1961).

The Uses of Radiation

The advanced nations would probably be more enthusiastic about supporting research projects requiring relatively low-cost facilities, and the loan of critical materials, than financing and aiding large projects whose long-run purpose is really to exclude them from joint participation. Such projects would make sense only if the research undertakings were to be conducted in the spirit of gaining knowledge for all participants, both donor and recipient. The resources of the "club" nations, too, are limited; there is no reason why developing nations like Brazil and India, for example, which have the economic incentive to develop certain natural resources, should not contribute to the task of gaining fundamental knowledge.

Other nonpower routes to nuclear capability which are important to developing nations must not be ignored. And even without a domestic nuclear power program, a nation could become important in the world power picture by exporting significant quantities of the raw nuclear materials and also by manufacturing secondary nuclear materials. For example, a U.S. company has aided India to construct in the Punjab a dual-purpose plant for heavy water and sorely-needed chemical fertilizer, thus providing two seemingly diverse products, at least one of which has a major effect on agricultural output.[12] Eventually, India's chemical fertilizer requirements will equal or exceed those of the U.S.[13] By expanding the manufacture of fertilizers and heavy water India could become a leading world producer, and perhaps exporter, of the latter.

Additional gains from this type of activity will be the development both of individuals skilled in the arts of using radioisotopes and of facilities for producing them in large quantities. Most have-not nations will be, or should be, thinking of radioisotopes as their first and most useful entry into the nuclear race. In India, a nonpower reactor as a major producer of isotopes would constitute a

[12] Sherman E. Johnson for the National Planning Association, "Use of Farm Resources to Help India," Document M-4053 (Washington: NPA, March 10, 1960).

[13] D. C. Gami, *et al., Production of Heavy Water in India*, P/1649, 2d U.N. International Conference on Peaceful Uses of Atomic Energy (Geneva: U.N. 1958), v. 4, pp. 534-539.

symbol of nuclear strength which would tend to make other nations in Southeast Asia turn toward that country for atomic aid. There is no reason why this tendency should not be encouraged. India might be more cognizant than more industrialized countries of the needs and possible applications of radioisotopes in underdeveloped or partially developed areas. And would not a major food irradiation center in India mean more to South Asia and to the peaceful atomic policy of the United States, than an army quartermaster plant in Natick, Massachusetts?

The applications of radiation and nuclear power in such areas as South Asia are likely to be quite different from those in industrialized countries. In India, for example, religious restraints have a major effect on the economic situation. Religious taboos are responsible for the increase of cattle until the ratio of cows to people exceeds one to two. This, of course, aggravates the food problem, for the significant quantities of grain consumed by cattle could greatly alleviate the undernourishment of portions of the Indian population. The cattle are not entirely useless, but their contribution to the economy tends to worsen the agricultural situation. Dried cattle dung is a major source of noncommercial fuel in India. Statistics on the utilization of cattle dung are hard to come by, but the following rough approximation presents interesting data: A pound of the common Indian fuel has roughly about 3/1000ths of the fuel value of one pound of bituminous coal. India's cattle, numbering something like 200 million, supply about 200 million pounds of fuel per year. This calculation assumes that 40 per cent of cattle dung is used as fuel, 40 per cent as fertilizer and the other 20 per cent is lost.[14] If the 40 per cent consumed as fuel were used as fertilizer, the value of the resulting increase in agricultural production would far exceed the fuel value now obtained.

Superficial consideration of the problem might indicate that if an alternate energy source, such as atomic energy, were supplied, more farm wastes would be used for fertilizer. This would increase agricultural yields, enabling the producer to pay for his electricity. The fallacy in this reasoning is that atomic energy is likely to be

[14] Palmer Cosslett Putnam, *Energy in the Future* (New York: D. Van Nostrand Company, Inc., 1953), pp. 326, 351-352, 444.

applied in commercial enterprises in heavily industrialized areas where the availability of alternative fuels has already reduced to a minimum the burning of cattle dung. Clearly, if the manure is to be utilized to a greater extent for fertilizer, alternative power sources must be supplied almost village by village. The growing use of the small solar energy cooker affords one possibility. It is conceivable that if the cooker could be supplied cheaply enough, cattle dung could be diverted to agricultural use.[15] But, all in all, it is only vaguely possible that atomic energy for a very long period can increase the energy supply of those areas in India which rely primarily on animal wastes for fuel.

A better solution can be found in attacking the cattle problem directly. An agricultural production team has shown that reducing the numbers of useless cattle and buffaloes will increase the quantity of feed available to productive animals, thereby increasing significantly their output of milk and manure.[16] Since there is a ban on cattle slaughter, the team has recommended castration of a good proportion of young bulls and the sterilization of surplus cows and heifers. Because these surgical procedures involve the shedding of blood, it has been difficult to overcome social-religious opposition. Nuclear science might help. Small portable units depending upon radioactive isotopes for their operation have been developed for field X-ray use. Would it not be possible to design similar units, operated by skilled but easily trained teams, to perform nonsurgical sterilization of cattle? Political or religious subtleties may rule out even this technique, nevertheless the suggestion re-enforces the point that in each "have not" nation certain unique problems, involving a melange of technical, political, and social implications, might be solved by procedures which would have no application whatsoever in the "have" nations.

Atomic energy could also lead to better utilization of the 40 per cent of cattle dung which is used as a fertilizer. Organic fertilizer of any type introduces large quantities of parasitic pests which are

[15] H. Stamm, "Cheap but Practical Solar Kitchen," Paper E/CONF. 35/S/24, U.N. Conference on New Sources of Energy (Rome: U.N., August 1961).

[16] "Report on India's Food Crisis and Steps to Meet It," The Agricultural Production Team sponsored by the Ford Foundation, published by the Government of India, Ministry of Food and Agriculture and Ministry of Community Development and Cooperation, April 1959.

detrimental to human health and to crops. It is quite probable that irradiation will destroy, or render sterile, a good proportion of the noxious parasites present in organic fertilizers. Hence, the possibility ought to be examined of providing inexpensive and technically simple central irradiation stations where farmers could quickly process manure before applying it. More elaborate schemes for sterilizing fertilized soil have been proposed. For example, a team at the University of California claims that a portable reactor moving at six to seven miles per hour over an area could sterilize the soil at a cost of $70 per acre.[17] But need this be a reactor? Perhaps a large-curie, cobalt-60 source, because of its greater simplicity and mobile possibilities would be appropriate for some situations. Other interesting applications of soil irradiation include the treatment of the breeding grounds of locusts in order to destroy their eggs before plagues can occur. Certainly the losses due to locust plagues in many parts of the world are astronomical.

The portable reactor is certainly a thing of the future; it should not be considered practical in the short run. But radiation sources which are simple to use are becoming increasingly available. A program looking toward large-scale agricultural applications of radiation should be initiated by one agency or another without delay.

All methods of applying radiation must be examined from the standpoint of economics, recognizing, also, that the technical perfection sought in the United States may not be a realistic goal elsewhere. The extremely large uncertainties in estimates of irradiation costs alone call for concerted effort to obtain better data. But, assuming that a figure like the $70 per acre estimated for the portable irradiation reactor is correct, would this expense be justified? In certain areas it might be. Over half of India's eight hundred million acres is arable. If all this land were utilized, it would amount to a little over one acre per capita, which normally would be sufficient to supply the population with its customary vegetarian diet. But the yield per acre is remarkably low. For example, an Indian farmer obtains only 670 pounds of wheat per acre an-

[17] S. G. Wildman and A. Norman, University of California Medical School, "Soil Irradiation by Portable Nuclear Reactors as a Means for Increasing World Crop Production." 1958 (Unpublished).

nually, compared to Japanese or Egyptian yields of over 2000 pounds. In India, the poor yield results from a number of factors including inefficient agricultural techniques, inadequate fertilization, the poor quality of seed, and unreliable irrigation. The cost of providing an acre of land with permanent irrigation facilities varies from about $50 per acre in the north of India to $125 per acre in the south.[18] These costs seem roughly comparable to the cost per acre of applying irradiation techniques. Hence, if it could be shown that irradiation techniques would increase the yield by a factor of two, then clearly they would be profitable.

Mobility of equipment which is important in soil irradiation is probably the most important mechanical and economic factor in many of the applications of atomic energy in less developed countries. In Chapter 7, the advantages of an ocean-borne, food irradiator were discussed. A unit adapted to railroad travel was once seriously suggested as a means for bringing treatment to crops of infested fruit.[19] Under design, and probably to be constructed, is a floating, nuclear power plant which could bring emergency power to various areas, for military use or to aid victims of disasters.[20] In situations where seasonal crop processing or sporadic industrial demands would not support a permanent nuclear power plant, it might be possible to program the movements of a mobile plant so as to make it economically feasible.

Water

For India, whose wants are not at all unique among the less developed nations of the world, the basic needs are as simple to describe as they are difficult to provide. And the simplest of them all is water—water for food, for hygiene, for industry. Some areas have too much water, most have too little of the kind they can use. For

[18] A typical case is that of Mr. Gunpappa, who farms in a small village near Mysore. His irrigation costs amounted to $800 for seven acres. He was able to repay this amount in two years. (Tibor Mende, "Inside Hangala Pura, One of India's 500,000 Villages," *World Health,* published by WHO, v. XIV, no. 1, January-February 1961, pp. 4-9.)

[19] "Atom Unit Meets on Pest Control," *The New York Times,* December 8, 1960, p. 53.

[20] "Army Engineers Award Contract for Floating Nuclear Power Plant," U.S. Dept. of Defense Press Release N. 781-61, August 3, 1961.

every pound of oil refined, 20 pounds of water are needed; 200 pounds of water are required to produce a pound of viscose yarn. To grow enough wheat for a pound of bread requires four *tons* of water, about 40 gallons per slice![21]

Three-fourths of the earth's surface is covered by water, but the greater amount of this life-giving substance is not provided by nature in a readily usable form, nor is it distributed according to need. The discovery of cheap processes for demineralizing sea water is a major research goal, but it is far from obvious that atomic energy can play a definitive role in this dramatic undertaking. If it could, however, the application of this potentially destructive force to supplying a basic human need would have an associative value transcending bare technical facts and figures. "If we could ever, competitively at a cheap rate get fresh water from salt water, that . . . in the long-range interests of humanity would really dwarf any other scientific accomplishment."[22]

The nations which most need water are doing practically nothing in research directed toward obtaining a larger and more reliable supply. To devote a fraction of their atomic energy budgets to desalinization research would most certainly prove a good investment. Among the technologically-developing nations, Israel is probably the exception in this respect. By 1965 practically all of the Israeli fresh water sources will be exploited at the maximum rate of supply, so that thereafter water shortage will present an absolute barrier to further agricultural development. As time presses, Israel is engineering processes like vacuum freezing and solar distillation which have fewer unknowns. But she is also looking at one or two atomic energy processes which hold promise. For a country which needs power, an obvious path of investigation would be the use of low-temperature "reject heat" from a nuclear power plant to distill sea water. Such a plant, in its entirety, might well be a "water plant"—for Israel uses well over a quarter of her power capacity to pump irrigation water.

[21] Sir Harold Hartley, "Energy as a Factor in the Progress of Under-developed Countries," Paper E/CONF. 35/GEN/4, U.N. Conferences on New Sources of Energy (Rome: U.N. August 1961).

[22] President Kennedy's Press Conference as reported in *The New York Times*, April 13, 1961, p. 18.

There are other atomic energy techniques which remain practically unexplored. The water-brine separation techniques developed in Israeli vacuum freezing plants might aid in making other refrigeration separation processes feasible.[23] In many of the classic desalinization processes, nuclear radiation might help (or inhibit) the basic separation phenomena by using ionization to effect nucleation, ion transport, and other steps. Certainly, radioisotope tracers can aid the investigation of non-nuclear processes. The large quantities of radioactive isotopes in the wastes from nuclear reactors can be used to provide water conversion devices which, although expensive, might still be practical in special situations.[24] Furthermore, the detonation of a nuclear explosive, using Plowshare techniques (see Chapter 8), promises the production of huge quantities of fresh water.[25]

The most significant water production research is now being done in the United States but, for all its importance, with a budget about as large as that for the Washington Zoo. Public Law 85-883 is being implemented in the construction of several fresh water demonstration plants. (The atomic distillation plant which had been specified is now defunct.) None of the projects, atomic or nonatomic, were designed for international participation, although it was hoped that they would have application abroad.

There are still excellent opportunities to initiate meaningful international projects for water supply and for other purposes of importance to the emerging nations. But first, an appropriate agency must be given a broad spectrum of administrative responsibilities, enabling it to coordinate the technical capabilities of specialized government agencies. It is questionable whether the Office of Saline Water in the Department of Interior or the Atomic Energy Commission could appropriately coordinate an international water program. Their interests are too narrow; budgetary

[23] Arnold Kramish, "Nuclear Refrigeration," Paper 3-62, *Proceedings of the 10th International Congress of Refrigeration* (London: Pergamon Press, 1960), v. 2, pp. 225-228.
[24] *Research Needs for Salt Water Conversion*, Report no. 61 of the House Committee on Science and Astronautics, 87th Cong., 1st sess. (Washington: GPO, 1961), p. 138. (This is an excellent information handbook on this subject.)
[25] Same, pp. 136-138.

stop

stop

stop

stop

and other conflicts are apt to interfere. Often administrative restraints and definitions result in amusing but harmful limitations of the scope of a government project. Take this statement for example: "We have the right to use the solar system, the solar energies that are in the field, and I think we probably have authority in one or two other fields that could be used, but to use the tide as a source of power, I do not think our authority reaches that far."[26] Perhaps, the speaker forgot that a minor body in the solar system influences the tides.

A Responsible Agency

Regarding the technical demands of the emerging nations, President Kennedy has said: "Existing foreign aid programs and concepts are largely unsatisfactory and unsuited for our needs and for the needs of the underdeveloped world as it enters the Sixties."[27] In the realm of the peaceful atom, the agency which should have been strong, the International Cooperation Administration, had deliberately been kept weak by the parent Department and the AEC. Even so, one of the most successful, small-budget operations of the Atoms for Peace program has been ICA's sponsorship of the visits of *consulting* experts from the University of Michigan to perhaps a score of grateful small nations. ICA's successor, the Agency for International Development, has no strength in the atomic field either.

Processes of transition within nations foreshadow changes in international organizations. The Treaty setting up the European Economic Community gave colonial dependencies a special place. Now EEC must seek new partnership agreements with the former colonies. Besides the Common Market, "the possibility should be envisaged of extending the future association to the other two

[26] "Review of the Saline Water Conversion Program," Statement of Dr. A. L. Miller, Director, Office of Saline Water, in *Policies, Programs, and Activities of the Department of Interior,* Serial no. 1, Hearings before the House Committee on Interior and Insular Affairs, 87th Cong., 1st sess., Jan. 16, 1961 (Washington: GPO, 1961), p. 291.

[27] President Kennedy's special message to Congress, March 22, 1961, as reported by the *The New York Times,* March 23, 1961, p. 14.

Communities—Euratom and the ECSC [European Coal and Steel Community]."[28]

Another regional organization for nuclear cooperation covers a huge underdeveloped territory, that to the south of the United States. At the meeting of presidents of the American republics in Panama in July 1956, President Eisenhower proposed that a means be established for more effective cooperation among the American republics in the field of atomic energy. The Organization of American States (OAS) approved the establishment of the Inter-American Nuclear Energy Commission (IANEC) in April 1959, and later in that year efforts were made to achieve a *modus operandi* and to spell out the general goals of the new Commission. Although semi-autonomous, IANEC has strong ties with OAS; its relation to that body is similar to that of the UN to its specialized agencies. But the new Commission's work plan is even less specific than that of the International Atomic Energy Agency; hence, for the present it must be considered a goodwill group which will act as a very general consultative body and a channel for communications. IANEC's primary function at first will probably be the creation of training and educational programs which are prerequisite for most of the Latin American nations before they can initiate nuclear programs. Meanwhile, the Commission probably will have plenty of time to define its relationships with other international groups, such as the International Atomic Energy Agency. The problems that face the IAEA today will not be a serious concern of the IANEC for some time to come.

European groups will be seeking ties with individual South American nations, as Euratom has already done with Brazil.[29] This interweaving, world-wide pattern will expand and, stimulated by serious circumstance, some debates doubtless will be held on just what the IAEA's role should be in catering to the needs of the emerging nations. Certain to arise are questions of coordination so

[28] "New Partnership with African Countries," *Bulletin from the European Community*, no. 48, July 1961, p. 5.

[29] "Brazil Sets Atom Pact," *The New York Times*, June 4, 1961, p. 56; Pact signed at Brasilia, June 9, 1961 (see *Bulletin from the European Community*, no. 47, June 1961, p. 11).

as to avoid duplication of effort and the allocation of funds to accomplish the tasks originally envisaged as the responsibility of an International Atomic Energy Agency.

It is usual to speak of the responsibilities of the international agencies of the "have" nations; rarely are the responsibilities of the "have not" nations, no longer a minority political force, brought into discussion. But certainly it would be pertinent to remind the new nations of the responsibilities which they, also, bear in a world whose political and economic boundaries would not be recognized by atomic fallout.

The Indonesian delegate to the 4th General Conference of the IAEA stated that his nation would gratefully accept any assistance which would help it to achieve its ends.[30] This is a natural philosophy for any nation low on the scale of economic development. But it is a fact that most of the nuclear aid which some nations have been prone to request, and accept, reflects self-indulgence rather than determination to solve pressing problems. And in requesting needless aid, with all of its political overtones, a nation willingly or unwillingly does its bit to worsen the international situation.

"Neutral" nations are apt to be great proponents of disarmament. They have tended to assume, as have the rest of us, that only the major powers could do something about disarmament. The complicated questions of arms control pass them by, and meanwhile insecurity in the underdeveloped world, rivalries among the new nations, and the stimulus they give to friction between the two great power blocs contribute to the risk of war. Is it too far-fetched to suggest that perhaps in the realm of atomic energy itself the new countries have a chance to make a contribution to arms control?

Perhaps intimacy with the disarmament problem for the past fifteen years has blurred the senses of those who have wrestled with the new mechanics of possible arms control arrangements. Fresh approaches and new ideas are needed. A "have not" nation might well be the wellspring of a good practical idea. Even a small, simple action serving as a catalyst might produce important

[30] Indonesia will have one each of the most advanced research reactors that the United States and the U.S.S.R. can offer, plus laboratories, equipment, etc.

results. Suppose Indonesia, rather than simply accepting reactors from both East and West, were to adopt a position of positive neutrality by demanding, instead of rejecting, IAEA inspection? If the request specified that both U.S. and Soviet personnel inspect all reactors, Indonesia would preserve neutrality while providing arms control precedents and experience in operating international inspection teams. What would happen if Indonesia were to insist that her *enriched* nuclear fuels be supplied on a 50-50 basis by the United States and the U.S.S.R. through the IAEA?

There are other simple opportunities for positive contributions to the creation of a stable world, but they cannot be forced upon nations; in most instances they cannot even be suggested. In the serious pursuit of world peace, a developing nation can find opportunities to repay its obligations to donor powers and to acquire maturity.

Chapter 13

The Microcosm of Vienna

The first mechanism to preserve peace by international regulation is believed to have been the Amphictyonic Council of ancient Greece. Bound by the worship of a common deity, representatives of the amphictyony held council and festival at a shrine symbolizing their mutual desire to avoid extreme measures of hostility. Despite its noble theme, often repeated in history with surprisingly little variation, the Amphictyonic Council finally degenerated into the political tool of Philip of Macedonia. But about a century before the demise of this first grand concept for peaceful coexistence, a Greek philosopher unknowingly created a shrine for a future amphictyony of all the nations of the world. Democritus brought into being the concept of the atom.

Today's Delphic temple is the International Atomic Energy Agency's office, occupying what used to be the Grand Hotel in central Vienna. The Agency, just a few years old and still tottery, originally may have had a noble purpose—at least many nations hoped it did—but now it shows no signs of ever being able to fulfill even the most modest of the initial expectations.

When on July 27, 1957, the United States became the last of the "Club" members, the twenty-second nation, to ratify its Statute, the International Atomic Energy Agency came into being. The Agency was the direct result of President Eisenhower's dramatic proposals of December 8, 1953, but its objectives, after three years of negotiation, were somewhat more modestly phrased than the President's. He wanted a mechanism which would:

First—encourage world-wide investigation into the most effective peacetime uses of fissionable material, and with the certainty that they had all the material needed for the conduct of all experiments that were appropriate;

Second—begin to diminish the potential destructive power of the world's atomic stockpiles;

Third—allow all peoples of all nations to see that, in this enlightened age, the great powers of the earth, both of the East and of the West, are interested in human aspirations first, rather than in building up the armaments of war;

Fourth—open up a new channel for peaceful discussion and initiate at least a new approach to the many difficult problems that must be solved in both private and public conversations, if the world is to shake off the inertia imposed by fear, and is to make positive progress toward peace.[1]

Those who recall the dramatic atmosphere surrounding this proposal—the President's hurried flight to New York, interrupting a meeting with Winston Churchill in Bermuda; the television view of an intensely earnest President and the expectant faces of his audience; the unrestrained applause of all, including the Russian delegation—have cause to wonder at the modesty of the section of the IAEA Statute which only dimly reflects the President's ambitious goals:

Article II: The Agency shall seek to accelerate and enlarge the contribution of atomic energy to peace, health, and prosperity throughout the world. It shall ensure, so far as it is able, that assistance provided by it or at its request or under its supervision or control is not used in such a way as to further any military purpose.

Since "military purpose" is nowhere defined in the Statute, the mission of the IAEA is general enough to accomplish anything, were the signatory nations willing—or practically nothing, as, indeed, they have been inclined.

The explanation of the Agency's weakness can be found in the three and one-half years which elapsed between the historic speech defining its ideal mission and its founding. The major problem during this period was how to obtain Soviet agreement to discuss the Agency. But even before representations were made on this subject, a U.S. interdepartmental working group had decided to

[1] Dwight D. Eisenhower, "The Atom for Progress and Peace," Dept. of State Publication 5403 (Washington: GPO, 1954).

relegate the second point of the President's proposal (calling for diminution of the world stockpiles of fissionable materials) to an expectation rather than a subject for negotiation.

It is debatable whether the Soviet Union would have supported the Agency if the latter had as its primary responsibility the safeguarding of a stock of fissionable materials, either small or large. It is difficult, also, to understand precisely why the Soviet Union, after the subsequent bilateral exchange of notes, the General Assembly discussions, and the multistate meetings and conferences, eventually decided to participate in the creation of the Agency. And it is not possible to guess what the Agency might be like today had the United States been more persistent in its pursuit of the President's goals.

The concept of the IAEA having custody of a pool of fissionable materials was gradually lost and replaced by the "clearing house" idea, meaning that bilateral agreements would somehow be channeled through the IAEA, but not be controlled by the Agency. Ambassador Henry Cabot Lodge proffered an economic reason for this important change in the Agency's purpose in the United Nations on November 5, 1954: "Since the resources of the agency obviously will be limited, it seems more useful to us to use the resources available to the agency for additional programs rather than for expensive custodial arrangements."[2] At the same time, Ambassador Lodge signified U.S. intent to proceed independently "for the conclusion of bilateral agreements" with other countries.

The determination of the United States to create IAEA with or without the Soviet Union, and to proceed on a parallel front with bilateral agreements, almost surely persuaded the Soviet Union that she could further her interests more effectively inside the international organization than out. And the example of the United States in pursuing an independent, bilateral course allowed the Soviet Union to do likewise without fear of Agency control.

In the end, the Soviet Union accepted the idea that the IAEA should act as a custodian of stocks of fissionable materials as well as a clearing house; but the Agency has not undertaken either function.

Despite the modest aims expressed in the final version of its

[2] *The New York Times,* November 6, 1954, p. 6.

charter, the Agency has made little substantive progress toward their implementation. Who is at fault? Professor Gunnar Randers, a key figure in the establishment of IAEA, has penned this frank confession:

Scientists do not generally know what an enormous effort lies behind the creation of a full-fledged international agency. They also do not know what an irresistible momentum lies in international organizations. It may be difficult to create one, but it is practically impossible to terminate one in peacetime. It is therefore only a question of the degree of usefulness of these indestructable giants which can be influenced. And here is a point of criticism of ourselves, the scientists and technologists of the world —we have not as a group realized the potential power of the instrument created, and have failed to follow up with action our decade of speaking and writing about the duty of scientists.

With few exceptions, we have not even tried to influence the selection of representatives of our countries for important positions in the agency organs. No organized attempt by scientists has been made to make the agency promote the ideas or the programs about which we have talked and written. Scientists who have gone there have usually done so without any knowledge of the real purpose of the Agency. Most scientists do not know whether the Agency needs top-notch scientific specialists or scientific organizers and administrators. The last question would probably be answered 50-50, one way or the other, even by the present Board of Governors.

To sum up: the scientists have not had the vision necessary to make use of a new powerful tool.

It will be clear from what I have said that one cannot turn to the scientists for a well-considered answer to the question: What use should be made of the IAEA?"[3]

A bold indictment, undoubtedly valid in large measure, but let not the scientists alone bear the burden of blame. Those non-scientists who conceived the idea of the IAEA, and so tenaciously sought its establishment, had no clear ideas about its functions after establishment. The totally unexpected emotional impact of President Eisenhower's speech and the momentum it generated confused for a time those U.S. planners whose task it was to define practical attitudes toward the Agency.

[3] Gunnar Randers, "The Scientist's View," *Bulletin of the Atomic Scientists* (Chicago), April 1960, p. 164.

The Work of IAEA

Professor Randers has cogently raised the question: "What use should be made of the IAEA?" Some uses are being made of the Agency for which it is not particularly well adapted. They, nevertheless, deserve description.

The October 1957 General Conference recommended that the IAEA "should give high priority to its activities which will give the maximum benefit from the peaceful application of atomic energy in improving the conditions and raising the standard of living of the peoples in the underdeveloped areas." But regardless of the ultimate strength of the IAEA and the range of services which it may be prepared to offer, many countries will not be able to take advantage of their membership privileges because of the lack of trained technicians. It is fitting, therefore, that the IAEA program having the greatest impetus should be designed to fill this training void. This is one of the few programs which can presently proceed, in view of the limited resources thus far available to the Agency. Training programs already established involve periods of study of six months to six years. Two types of fellowships are available. Type I are financed by contributions toward a general fund which can be used in the educational, scientific institutions of the member states, not necessarily those which made the contribution. The United States supplies a substantial amount of these funds. Type II fellowships are offered directly by member states for specialized training in their own institutions. The Soviet Union, which has offered a considerable number of these regards them as most important. This view, which is shared by the rest of the Soviet bloc, is consistent with their attitude taken in the IAEA that if a country is interested in Soviet aid—technical or cultural—it must be willing to accept Soviet equipment and instruction.[4]

If IAEA operations yield any benefits in its early period, they will accrue to the underdeveloped countries largely through the training program. Can the donor nations, and in particular the U.S.S.R. and the United States, also expect to benefit from this program; or must they consider it, like all other activities of the IAEA,

[4] "The IAEA General Conference," *Nuclear Engineering*, November 1958, p. 478.

merely an act of generosity? The Soviet Union, to judge from its early participation, considers training the most important of the Agency's activities. In the allotment of places on the staff of the Agency the Soviet Union pressed for the post of Deputy Director for Education and Information, and the first two incumbents were able Russian professors. It is gratifying that the Soviet Union urges the appointment of men of such capabilities to Agency positions. This should be interpreted, however, not as an indication of enthusiastic support of the Agency, but of the importance which the Soviet Union attaches to contacts with the intellectual elite in the uncommitted nations.

Underdeveloped countries will welcome the opportunities for nuclear training offered in the next several years, no matter what the source. This applies especially to courses which will be of immediate practical use. But in some nations an oversupply of atomic technicians may soon develop. Even the most elementary applications of radioisotopes require acquaintance with basic industrial technology or with somewhat advanced agricultural technology. The effort expended in training individuals of scientific or technical bent for such applications might in some instances be better directed toward occupations other than nuclear work.

A truly international, nuclear science school, without even the minimal political connotation of national sponsorship, does not yet exist. It would seem a useful activity for the IAEA to study the possibility of setting up such an institution and its advantages and disadvantages.

Since many of IAEA's initial programs will relate to the use of radioisotopes, it has established a committee on this subject, made up of experts from ten countries. The committee has completed a health and safety manual and has made it available for international distribution. In addition, IAEA is prepared to assist less developed countries in the use of radioisotopes, and has expressed a willingness to provide consultant and emergency services.

The first research contract awarded by the IAEA was concerned with health and safety. The investigation, which involves the distribution of fission products in the biosphere, is being conducted by a research institute in Vienna. This is the first of a number of studies which will be necessary in developing standards with respect to waste disposal. The IAEA has awarded some $200 million for other research projects on the principle that "preference on awarding research contracts goes to those centers where capable research workers are hampered by lack of funds."[5] France and Italy, each of which has a substantial atomic energy budget, have received, between them, over 20 per cent of all the Agency's awards.

Perhaps the IAEA's most significant activity thus far is the development of a $1.75 million, three-year irradiation research program in Yugoslavia, concentraing on problems of agriculture. (Yugoslavia herself provided 70 per cent of the funds; the IAEA, the rest.) It will seek ways in which atomic energy can help to improve the use of fertilization, irrigation, crop selection, and livestock management. Yugoslavia, as a testing ground, can be said to be one of the IAEA's more enthusiastic supporters.

In one of its more publicized exploits the IAEA requested and was granted permission to send an international team to the Yugoslavian research center of Vinča, to investigate a nuclear accident which occurred in October 1958.[6] One technician died as a result of the accident and several others received serious injuries. The study of the accident involved actual re-enactment of the circumstances preceding the accident in order to determine what procedures or equipment had been at fault. In this interesting experiment in international cooperation the Yugoslav government gave unlimited cooperation. The French government provided a team of reactor control specialists, Britain supplied heavy water to duplicate the experiment, and the United States supplied experts and equipment to measure radiation dosages. The U.S.S.R. did not participate. Continued studies of nuclear accidents, actual and potential, by the IAEA should make valuable contributions to problems of health and safety.

Prevention of accidents is a more valuable activity than their subsequent investigation. At the request of the Swiss government the IAEA has provided an international team of experts to evalu-

[5] U.S. AEC, *IAEA Research Projects*, TID-11404 (Oak Ridge, Tennessee: Author, April 1961).

[6] "Experiment at Vinča," *IAEA Bulletin*, April 1960, pp. 4-12; "A Unique Experiment: Measurement of Radiation Doses at Vinča," same, July 1960, pp. 3-6; G. W. C. Tait, "Effects of radiation on man: an international experiment," *The New Scientist*, June 2, 1960, pp. 1397-1401.

ate a new research reactor. Their report, transmitted to the Swiss government, was apparently received with satisfaction. Reactor evaluation should be an expanding activity, and the initial work on smaller research reactors can eventually be extended to the more meaningful evaluation of large power reactors.

This work on health and safety is among the most useful of the IAEA's activities. Yet the Agency should be more ambitious. There is urgent need to establish international standards for health and safety in atomic energy activities. Such standards are already in existence, or in preparation, in the states which are advanced in nuclear technology, but radiation does not respect international boundaries. One of the most useful things the Agency could do would be to harmonize existing standards in a generally acceptable, world radiation safety code. Were this work completed with dispatch, it would prevent duplication of effort by many states. If proper cooperation can be obtained with other specialized agencies, such as the World Health Organization and the International Labor Organization, standard health and safety codes and concepts might be formulated.

A panel of ten experts, including several from East Europe, has been discussing a draft international convention on fixing standard liabilities for third parties in event of nuclear accident. But the limits which the panel has set for itself illustrate how inadequate the IAEA mechanism still is for resolving the unique problems of the atomic age. The panel's guiding principle is "that the state in which a nuclear installation causing damage was located should alone be competent to establish detailed rules concerning liability, apportion liability between private parties and the state, and designate a court to process claims." Thus, it appears that fixing the responsibility for an accident in one state which contaminates another raises difficult questions of international law to which the panel would prefer not to address itself.

Other activities of the IAEA are of the useful but innocuous type that any agency, strong or weak, would be expected to undertake without making much ado about them. Like some of the health and safety activities described above, they are *minimum* responsibilities. Various surveys have been undertaken, some of which required on-the-site investigations by IAEA teams, and others merely paper work in Vienna. The first mission was a four-week tour of Latin America to study regional needs for training centers (The near-term or ultimate effect of that visit on Brazil's atomic program would be difficult to discover.) A second mission, to Egypt, had a somewhat more definite purpose. The two-man team was composed of a Russian to advise on the extraction of uranium from phosphate ores, and an American to investigate the possibilities of heavy water production. This, perhaps, is history's first example of the cooperation of East and West in specific technical problems relating to atomic energy.

The IAEA has sent experts at frequent intervals to Burma, Greece, Ceylon, Thailand, and other countries to study their needs for training, for radioisotope applications, and for other activities. The value of these missions, in most instances, will be found in the nebulous but important benefits afforded by personal contact, rather than in the accomplishment of their nominal purposes. In a few instances the reformulation of local thought, removing misconceptions on atomic energy, also may have been of value.

IAEA studies deal with problems of waste disposal in the seas, power-need surveys, preparation of catalogues of nuclear reactors of the world, an international directory of radioisotopes, etc. A quarterly bulletin describes these activities in very general terms. The Agency could perform a very useful service by publishing, perhaps in a specially created journal, the more interesting of the technical reports on the international exchange programs channeled through it. For example, reports resulting from the U.S.-U.S.S.R. exchange agreement are to be channeled through the IAEA, but how many can travel to the Agency's library in Vienna to read them? Reports of visits are very hard to come by; indeed, their existence is usually unknown. In good proportion these reports duplicate one another and contain information available in technical publications. However, a judicious selection, editing, and publication of exchange reports would be most instructive to the world scientific community and would impart greater useful value to the information they generate.

All in all, most of the activities of the IAEA might well be performed by an atomic trade association. Whether or not this is what the IAEA will degenerate into largely depends on what its sire, the United States, decides to do about its bewildered child.

The Agency's Difficulties

The IAEA is so beset with serious internal and external troubles that officials at the highest levels of the United Nations Secretariat are said to have expressed the opinion that the Agency should never have been created. Various UN specialized agencies, FAO, UNESCO, ILO, and others, which before the IAEA came into existence were concerned to some extent with special atomic energy problems, have been reluctant to see the new organization become predominant in their particular domains of nuclear interest. Perhaps some of the difficulties arose from IAEA's unique position as a quasi-autonomous organization. The specialized agencies of the United Nations, like WHO and UNESCO, report to the Economic and Social Council of the UN; the Agency is responsible directly to the General Assembly. This more intimate relationship with a politically responsible part of the United Nations would be more appropriate were the Agency performing the world security tasks originally envisioned. With its diminished scope, the status of a specialized agency seems more appropriate.

Internal working difficulties hamper the solution of the Agency's immediate problems. Its staff, in general, is characterized either by moderate competence or by dedication (or both), but those who possess the latter have difficulty retaining it. There are exceptions to this rule, of course, but the problem of obtaining staff members from technologically advanced nations is hampered by a scale of salaries in many instances lower than civil service pay and certainly lower than competent individuals can obtain in the nuclear industries of the advanced economies. There is a grave lack of funds for minimum programs approved by the Board of Governors. The bulk of voluntary funds is pledged by the United States. States with an equal voice in approving the Agency's programs refuse to support them financially. The majority of national representatives to the IAEA seem less than sanguine about its prospects. There is no perceptible indication that *any* of the member nations have a clear notion of the goals, immediate or ultimate, at which IAEA should aim.

Essentially, the Agency owes its continuing existence to collective guilt, and to the conscience of nations who fear to destroy the single existing aproach to international arms control.

Presumably, one of the reasons for the Agency's existence is the hope of eventual atomic rapport between the United States and the Soviet Union. Hence, the Soviet attitude toward the IAEA is of some significance. The Russians have insisted that "whatever the Western delegates may say on the subject, it is clear that the Agency is not an insulated scientific organization divorced from politics and existing in some kind of vacuum."[7] How true; this is as it should be. But East and West differ widely in their respective behavior in implementing this principle. There is no more fascinating reading in vituperative diplomacy than the verbatim records of the Agency's General Conferences.

Soviet participation has been characterized by frequent outbursts, emphasizing familiar differences of opinion. At the Second General Conference in September 1958, the Soviet Delegate charged that the United States and a group of other states were trying to dictate IAEA activities, and that the United States was attempting to profit from Atoms for Peace. The well-worn "ban-the-bomb" theme was repeated with a description of the current U.S. tests in Nevada as "background music." Concurrently test units of the Soviet Northern Fleet were tuning up for their concert honoring the final days of the Conference. When in June 1959 the Director-General of the IAEA submitted a proposal relating to the very essence of the Agency's being—effective nuclear control and inspection—the Soviet delegation, adopting a predictable attitude, observed: "There is no doubt that the aim of this proposal is to place the national atomic industries developing in the countries receiving assistance from the agency under the control of Western monopolies. This proposal was inspired by the U.S. delegation."[8]

These and numerous other remarks are to be expected, for they are merely extensions of familiar Soviet policy and tactics to the forum of the IAEA. The attacks, descending sometimes to the personal level, seem meaningless so far as long-range policies are con-

---

[7] *Izvestia* (Moscow), October 18, 1957, p. 4.
[8] TASS (in English Hellschreiber to Europe), June 17, 1959.

cerned.[9] The most mysterious Soviet maneuver in recent years, one which many thought indicated a change in Soviet attitudes toward the Agency, was the appointment in 1960 of Vyacheslav Molotov as permanent representative. But at the Fourth General Conference of the Board of Governors in the fall of 1960 Molotov clearly played a puppet role. His appointment to Vienna was probably a private joke of Khrushchev, who may have regarded the IAEA as a more nearly perfect diplomatic vacuum than Outer Mongolia. Thus the Soviets, in their own inimitable way, are doing what they accuse others of doing in the Agency; i.e., marking time.[10]

Meanwhile, the IAEA is a forum in which to echo and amplify the prevailing themes of the day. For example, during the 1961 annual conference, much personal abuse was heaped upon Dr. Arne Sigvard Eklund by Professor Yemelyanov, but the former was confirmed as the new Director-General of the IAEA, and the latter staged a dramatic walkout. After all, if at the same time the Secretary-General of the United Nations was being accused of being an un-neutral, it would have been inconsistent to admit that neutrality of a fellow citizen of Mr. Hammarskjold.

The big question during the 1961 debate was, "Does this mean Russian withdrawal from the IAEA?" For the moment it did not; Soviet political tacticians know full well that it is easier to use an organization from within than from without.

What the Agency Could Do

The only outward evidence of U.S. policy toward the IAEA has been the generous overtures which are characteristic of other U.S. aid policies. The United States contributes the greatest share of IAEA's administrative budget (about a third; the next largest contributor is the Soviet Union, about an eighth). There is in addition a "voluntary" budget, to which the United States is in the habit of

[9] M. S. Handler, "U.S.-Soviet Clash Marks Atom Talk," *The New York Times*, February 7, 1961, p. 2. Typical headlines for the Fourth General Conference: "Clash Ends Truce at Atom Parley," *The New York Times*, September 22, 1960; "Soviet Impugns U.S. Aid on Atom," Same, September 23, 1960; "Molotov Scores U.S. Atomic Plan," Same, September 27, 1960.

[10] Vasily Yemelyanov, "Marking Time," *New Times* (Moscow), n. 47, 1960, pp. 11-13.

contributing about half. If there is any real drive behind U.S. policy, either to strengthen or weaken the Agency, it has been well muted. The stated policy of the United States is to "devote itself wholeheartedly to the accomplishment of the Agency's great objectives." If the performance of useful but very limited tasks is to be regarded as "accomplishment," then all that can be hoped for is an organization that is sterile so far as its great possibilities are concerned and that stands only as a symbol of man's vain aspirations for peace. But if the objectives are to be interpreted in the terms of President Eisenhower's speech of December 8, 1953, the world's great powers must give the Agency far stronger support.

The more limited course raises no problem, beyond keeping the Agency alive through moderate financial support and the encouragement of minor tasks. To pursue the broader aim of creating a vigorous IAEA will require imaginative measures going beyond the mere extension of nuclear generosity. Generosity itself is not enough because the means have to be found of applying effective controls in a world where many nations see them as "strings attached." But it is in this field that the IAEA has its greatest practical potential, for a great number of less developed nations require the aid which the IAEA would like to render, and which it should be in a position to provide.

What have the donor nations to gain besides good will? Presumably, the major profit which could accrue to them, as well as to the rest of the world, would be the establishment of channels of communication for the lessening of world tensions and the strengthening of peace. But one should not be deluded into thinking that the IAEA now represents anything of the sort. It is simply an agency from which certain services are, or might be, available.

Article IX of the Agency's Statute provides that donor nations may make available for use by recipient nations such quantities of special fissionable materials as they deem advisable. Accordingly, natural uranium in various forms of concentration has been offered to the Agency by Canada, Portugal, the Union of South Africa, and Czechoslovakia. Ceylon and India have offered thorium. Offers of enriched material have been made by the United Kingdom (20 kilograms) and by the U.S.S.R. (50 kilograms). The United States has offered 5,000 kilograms, plus an amount that matched the contributions made by all other members to July 1, 1960. The total amount of enriched uranium now available, *not as a gift, but for purchase by the Agency,* is therefore 5,140 kilograms.

The Soviet Union's statement in making its contribution, which amounts to less than 1 per cent of that of the United States, is interesting: "This quantity of uranium (50 kilograms) is sufficient for the operation of several reactors of medium capacity. It should be noted that the Agency's program for the immediate future provides for the construction of only a few reactors of medium capacity. Their requirements as regards nuclear fuel can therefore be covered entirely by the Soviet Union's contribution."[11] The statement is realistic in recognizing that in the next several years underdeveloped countries are most unlikely to request from the Agency large amounts of materials for power reactors. Nations whose industries require power reactors will purchase them directly from the United States, Canada, or the United Kingdom, and they will undoubtedly arrange to obtain special materials through bilateral agreements. The U.S.S.R. in the next several years will probably offer to supply enriched uranium to practically any underdeveloped nation which desires to have a *research* reactor. And there is nothing to prevent the Soviet Union from supplying the materials at low prices, as it has promised.

Price may be a major factor inhibiting the Agency's distribution of the very generous U.S. quota of over 5,000 kilograms. The first request for nuclear materials came at the Second General Conference in September 1958 when the Japanese representative, Dr. H. Furuuchi, announced his government's formal request for the purchase through the Agency of approximately three tons of reactor-grade natural uranium for a research reactor. At the same time, in his double-barreled speech, Dr. Furuuchi told the General Conference that Japan was informing the United States that, with respect to the bilateral agreement which the two governments had entered into, his government would "request administration of the safeguards provisions by the International Atomic Energy Agency, at such time as the Agency is in a position to perform this service."

A request of the latter type had to come eventually from some

[11] *Isvestia,* cited.

nation and should have been expected. It is to the credit of Japan that this concrete problem was forced upon the Agency at such an early date. The United States delegation, which seems to have been completely surprised by Japan's action, the next day expressed its gratification. But, regardles of U.S. good intent in acceding to this and subsequent requests of a similar nature, restrictions in the Atomic Energy Act of 1954 will be a source of continual embarrassment in responding.

Of course, the Japanese request applied to *source materials,* not *special materials* (see Chapter 2). An amendment to Section 54 of the Act stipulates that the Atomic Energy Commission "shall be compensated for special nuclear material" distributed through the Agency "at not less than the . . . charges applicable to the domestic distribution of such material, . . ."[12] Therefore, it is difficult to see how a recipient nation could obtain special materials through the Agency more cheaply than under a bilateral arrangement, unless the IAEA would sell at a loss. But since a large fraction of the Agency budget is borne by the United States, this country would be providing an indirect subsidy that would be nonsensical unless some further purpose were served.

A nation might wish to get its special materials through the Agency because it preferred IAEA control provisions to those imposed by the United States. But Agency controls would result in an increased price. For under the provisions of Article XIV (E) of the IAEA Statute, recipient nations (not the Agency) must bear the costs of safeguard services. In contrast, the United States under its present bilateral agreements, including that with Euratom, assumes all the costs of inspecting the special materials supplied. Direct negotiation with the United States therefore results in a better price for special materials than indirect negotiation through the IAEA. But the United States is not a unique supplier of source materials. In this market the U.S. supplier is not legally bound by price consideration and will compete with suppliers in many other nations.

To satisfy the Japanese request the IAEA, some two months later, invited bids from ten nations assumed to be in a position to

---

[12] An exception is made for relatively small amounts of material to be used in medical research.

supply the uranium. The results were disappointing; only three bids came in and they were widely disparate in price. Canada generously offered as an absolute gift to the Agency three tons of uranium which it could sell to Japan at a price which the Canadians stipulated was to bear some reasonable relationship to the current world price. The Director-General of the IAEA cabled Ottawa a grateful acceptance, declaring that the offer "serves as inspiration to the Secretariat and provides a constructive example for the future support of the Agency." The second bid was made by a Belgian firm which agreed to supply uranium at $34 per kilogram f.o.b. Antwerp. The third bid, submitted by an American firm, offered uranium metal at $54.34 per kilogram f.o.b. Baltimore. When the bids were analyzed by the IAEA staff, it required no wisdom of a Solomon to predict the compromise solution. The Agency accepted the Canadian offer and announced that Japan would be billed at the intermediate Belgian price of $34, plus an additional $1.50 representing the Agency's handling charges and the costs of health and safety measures, safeguards, etc., during the useful lifetime of the material supplied. Although the amount of material involved was small, the transaction temporarily established an international price for metallic uranium at a rather high level. The price, however, was significantly lower than that of material obtained from the United States, either directly or through the IAEA.

In fact, a glut of uranium has been upon us for some time; South Africa, for one, is actively seeking to dispose of its vast production in the open world market. Competition through the medium of the IAEA has already manifested itself. In January 1959 Belgium offered to supply the Agency with uranium concentrates (not metal) at $18 per kilogram of contained uranium oxide. At the same time South Africa made an offer of $21 per kilogram, but a few months later brought its price down to the Belgian bid, in order to remain in a competitive position. Since that time not only South Africa, but many producers, including several companies in the United States, have indicated that they are willing to supply uranium at less than $10 a kilogram. But as yet, neither the IAEA nor any other body provides a mechanism which can guarantee the peaceful application of nuclear materials.

IAEA's charge of $1.50 per kilogram of uranium metal is an

important indicator of the price for inspection and other services performed by an international organization. This figure will undoubtedly have to be increased for the control of enriched material or plutonium, both of which require more complex procedures. An indication that the added charges may be significant is found in the statement by the IAEA that "because of the low operating power of the Japanese research reactor for which IAEA is providing assistance, its plutonium production will be small. The safeguards required under the IAEA-Japan Agreement will, therefore, be less comprehensive than would be needed if highly enriched uranium were used or if there were a large plutonium output."[13] The implications of the added administrative charges for the economics of the large-scale utilization of nuclear power are not unimportant. The new responsibilities forced upon the Agency by the Japanese request set in motion serious studies on safeguards and control procedures. The Agency placed initial research contracts in Belgium, France, and the United States, looking toward the development of simple techniques for determining the U-235 and plutonium contents of fuel elements. These techniques should also be useful in monitoring the fuel supplies of large power reactors, if they should ever come under the control of the IAEA.

Japan's initiative undoubtedly catalyzed IAEA's materials control program. It is still weak, but a beginning has been made. At the Fourth General Conference, Japan, Brazil, China, Denmark, Greece, Norway, and Thailand indicated[14] that they were willing to transfer to the IAEA the administration of the safeguards in their bilateral programs. The same conference approved a safeguards procedure (43 in favor, 19 against, 2 abstentions). Somewhat revised, this document was approved early in 1961 by IAEA's Board of Governors. The controls would be applied whenever IAEA acts either as middleman or as original *supplier* of certain minimum amounts of fissionable materials.

The first Director-General of the IAEA has asked these cogent questions about the future of the Agency:

[13] *AIF Memo*, (A monthly publication of the Atomic Industrial Forum, New York), April 1959, p. 18.

[14] M. S. Handler, "Soviet Charges on Atom Rejected," *The New York Times*, September 24, 1960, p. 13.

First policy question
Shall the atomic energy contribution of the technologically advanced and materially endowed nations to other countries in the world be given and applied through truly international channels; or shall we continue to channel such aid through networks of bilateral agreements for selective nation-to-nation exchange without benefit of the balance wheel of international consideration?

Second
Shall the peacetime production and utilization of nuclear materials around the world be carried out under international codes and standards for health and safety; or shall we permit the peaceful exploitation of atomic energy under varying, perhaps conflicting, and certainly confusing, and only partially effective nationally imposed standards for health and safety?

Finally
Shall the nations seek in unison to establish and maintain uniform, practical rules to prevent the diversion to military purposes of nuclear materials or make their own rules and apply them as they deem desirable under predictable conditions of inter-nation competition?[15]

It will be seen that all three questions relate to control, whether control for health and safety measures, control of materials in international trade, or control of the ultimate uses of fissionable materials. The Agency of course has other interests outside the sphere of control, and one must ask whether the latter aspect has been unduly emphasized. But, regardless of its present limited functioning as both a service and a control organization, its existence would not be justified even if the service functions alone were strengthened.

The ultimate justification for the Agency rests upon whether or not it is going in the direction which will someday enable it to assume the role of the essential adjunct in a comprehensive arms control arrangement. In this respect one is entitled to question closely whether contemporary control philosophy and techniques are realistic, and whether they are possibly damaging to reaching agreement on an arms control pact.

[15] Remarks of W. Sterling Cole, Director-General, IAEA, before the Ninth Annual Conference of National Organizations under the auspices of the American Association for the United Nations, Hotel Statler, Washington, D.C., March 9, 1959.

There has been a certain minuscule progress toward resolution of the policy questions enumerated by Mr. Cole. Clearly, the transfer of Canadian fuel to Japan by the IAEA is relative to the first policy question. Some other countries have agreed to the transfer of small quantities of enriched fuel (i.e., special materials) through the IAEA. It has already occurred in transfers of U.S. fuel to Norway and Pakistan.[16] These are small but perhaps significant starts.

IAEA committee work has resulted in certain agreed health and safety standards for all nations; but if there is to be any insurance on an international level that all countries are conducting their peaceful atomic energy activities without danger to themselves and neighboring nations, there must be a certain minimal type of international control. Thus, we encounter the same difficulties as in internal inspection for the production of nuclear materials. However, it is possible that the question of inspection could be more effectively approached by initial concentration on the health and safety aspects because of their minimal nature.

The third question relates to internal production of fissionable materials. Clearly, the "have" nations cannot continue to insist that it is only those who receive who must be subjected to control. A way must be found for gradually including the production facilities of the "haves" as well as the "have nots" in a grand plan of international arms control. Again, a significant step has been taken by the United States by offering to place four of its reactor research facilities under the safeguards of the International Atomic Energy Agency.[17] However, this was a very limited arrangement involving a small number of inspections during a period of two years for three of the reactors, and of one year for the remaining reactor.

Whatever the results from the preliminary actions by the United States to attempt to give some meaning to the IAEA, it is clear

[16] U.S. AEC Press Release D-85, April 10, 1961, "IAEA, Norway and U.S. Sign Trilateral Contract for Transfer of Fuel"; U.S. AEC Press Release E-64, March 6, 1962, "AEC Signs Trilateral Fuel Supply Contract with IAEA and Pakistan."

[17] U.S. AEC Press Release C-187, September 21, 1960, "Additional Information on U.S. Offer to Place Four Reactor Facilities under IAEA Safeguards"; U.S. AEC Press Release S-19-60, September 21, 1960, Summary of remarks by Chairman John A. McCone delivered at the Fourth Conference of the IAEA, September 21, 1960.

that the IAEA will never be able to operate as it should until it possesses fissionable materials as well as channels. Actually, possession of such materials would require it to create international inspection teams and procedures, at least for its own stocks. In no other way could it better learn the caretaking tasks which it must eventually perform.

With regard to the receipt and possession of significant quantities of fissionable materials from the United States, the artifices of American law prevent that—simply because neither the IAEA nor any other organization can afford to buy and sell a commodity at the same price. Laws can and obviously must be amended to give a peaceful atom the same opportunities for flexible action as the military atom. But perhaps, pricing questions aside, there are other means for the IAEA to accumulate its own stockpiles without having to strain its already insufficient budget.

There is indeed a simple mechanism by means of which the IAEA could begin to accumulate and distribute significant stocks of fissionable materials. The scale of budgetary contributions of member nations to the IAEA very roughly indicates the relative atomic position of the principal contributors, with the exception of the U.S.S.R. Were any plan for the wholesale turnover of nuclear materials ever to come into effect, a similar but more accurate scale of contributions, this time of fissionable materials, would have to be agreed upon. The present IAEA scale for *financial* contributions should serve very well as a starting point for a plan which involved the gradual diminution of national stockpiles of potentially destructive materials. The IAEA budget is most modest; a proportionately modest but important and effective step toward the diminution of stockpiles can now be taken.

Suppose that a nation, unilaterally were henceforth to respond to IAEA's call by contributing, instead of cash, fissionable materials of equivalent value; and suppose, further, that the IAEA to meet its expenses should sell such materials to nations not possessing them? The IAEA would then be faced immediately with the problem of safeguarding a stockpile of fissionable materials that was dumped into its lap. It would have to accelerate the development of safeguards which, by the terms of the charter, the purchasing nations are bound to accept. The exchange of fissionable materials (see Chapter V) also might be possible. Thus, the IAEA would be forced to initiate on an urgent basis, with the aid of its members, the studies and to provide the physical facilities necessary to safeguard the materials. The nucleus of an international stockpile devoted to peaceful intent would be created. Such a nucleus does not now exist.

There is an opportunity for a good proportion of member nations to contribute natural as well as enriched materials. Indeed, many of the so-called "have not" nations have stocks of natural uranium but no facilities for processing that uranium into useful oxide or metal material or for extracting the U-235 component. Since a number of those nations can offer raw uranium at most advantageous prices, it should be possible for the IAEA to arrange for the processing of that material and offer a completed product competitive on the world market. Furthermore, if those nations possessing U-235 enrichment facilities would offer those facilities for "toll" enrichment of contributions, it might be possible to make the IAEA a preferred independent supplier of enriched materials.

The element of sacrifice on the part of the "have" nations, involved in building an international stockpile, would impress the great bloc of uncommitted nations far more than contributions in cash. (In the "have" countries money is supposed to flow like water.) For the "have not" nations the stockpile would provide an incentive to support and keep the Agency alive, to assure long-range supplies of nuclear fuel free from identification with any large power. For the large powers the plan provides a cheap way of forcing a solution of the urgent problem of arms control.

The international stockpile plan would involve an increase in the present IAEA budget, now about $8 million per year, which could arouse criticism. But reflect upon the economics of nuclear war and peace. Scattered throughout the world in holes, caves, and other secure containers are the national stockpiles of fissionable materials, fabricated for use as weapons. They represent history's most extravagant accumulation of materials which, so the majority of the world's populations would hope, are nonutilizable. Inert, they represent investments of tens of billions of dollars; if used, they would destroy property worth thousands of billions. In comparison, the investments which governments have made to effect a transition to the peaceful *utilization* of those stockpiles are trivial. Clearly the realm of the economics of peace contains anomalies which we do not yet understand. Institutions, like the IAEA, which operate within that realm must not be bound by the pseudo-realities which a nuclear war would drastically alter.

Chapter 14

The Tasks Ahead

The original vision of Atoms for Peace has dimmed almost to the point of extinction. As an instrument for catalyzing an arms control arrangement, it has failed; to the contrary, it has accentuated the problem of the "Nth country." As something which would bring power and other vital necessities to the unprovided nations, Atoms for Peace has, for the most part, only widened the gulf between the "haves" and the "have-nots."

The "failure" is not absolute. We now know, far earlier than we would have known, the difficulties of attaining economically useful atomic power and thus can, or should be able to, project more soberly when and how this new source of power will be used—at least in the rapidly developing national economies. Atoms for Peace gave the world a better appreciation of over-all nuclear progress and capabilities. But, its most important effect was as a pre-Sputnik stimulator of technical growth, even more so in countries like those of Europe, India and Japan than in the United States.

The dismay wrought by the premature promise of atomic bounty gave substance to the technological gap between the "haves" and the "have-nots." And for both it gave impetus to evaluations and implementations of actions which would raise the general technological levels.

Now the tremendous emotional momentum of Atoms for Peace has been lost. Even superb technical innovations will not regain that momentum. One could hope, but not expect, that a revolutionary nuclear discovery would suddenly burst forth to recapture some of the spirit of Atoms for Peace; but were that to come to pass, we should be ill-prepared for it.

The promise of atomic power, however, will not remain unfulfilled. Before the end of the decade a sprinkling of nuclear power plants will be operating with economic factors oscillating marginally about that line which defines "competitive" atomic power. These will be in normally high-cost areas, and even very small marginal differences would mean important integrated savings for the utilities involved. If atomic power can produce electricity just a tenth of a mill (one ten-thousandth of a dollar) cheaper per kilowatt hour in an area where, say, three hundred thousand kilowatts can be utilized almost full time, the yearly savings would amount to almost a quarter of a million dollars.

Viewed in such terms, atomic power becomes attractive again, but the economic pendulum could easily swing the other way because of unexpected technical difficulties (the rule rather than the exception) and changes in the cost of producing power with conventional fuels. The promise of "marginally competitive" atomic power is a dangerous promise unless, as in the United States and industrialized Europe, unforeseen losses can be, indeed must be, afforded and debited to "experience."

For the United States the complicating factor of disparity between military and peaceful prices for plutonium seems to be resolving itself. The uranium-235 price also seems to be seeking its proper level. The effect will be to produce more realistic nuclear power costs for projection at home and abroad. But, as we become more sure of our economic and technological foundations in making projections about the future of nuclear power, we must also be certain that similar studies of the effects of an ever-improving technology for conventional energy resources are available.

Economic considerations will be overriden by special applications which are increasing in number and variety for military power requirements on land and sea and for the exploration of outer space. Isotopic power sources, particularly for use in sea buoys, isolated weather stations, undersea instrument stations, and so forth, hold much promise of wide-scope application.

Actually, it is the unglamorized isotope whose radiations have thus far been the basis of the only "profitable" atomic energy operations. In every phase of scientific research, in medical treatment, in industrial process control, radioisotopes are now essential and commonplace materials.

In all of the research on the Atom for Peace we have failed to give convincing substance to our concern of bringing the benefits of technology to the less-provided nations. To be sure, a large fraction of the efforts directed toward adapting the atom to the technologies of interest to the advanced nations will eventually be of value to the less advanced. But we have not sought the psychological, and undoubtedly the many specific technical, benefits which would have accrued by engaging in programs directly and primarily concerned with the needs of the less developed areas.

For the six-year period ending June 30, 1960, 99 per cent of all U.S. expenditures "... related to implementing international atomic objectives" were devoted to administration, research reactor grants and school programs. One per cent[1] was spent for research and development in direct support of foreign needs—and that for Euratom which needed the gesture rather than the half million dollars. Many atomic agencies, domestic and foreign, now serve the technological aims of the peaceful atom; but none specifically serves those vast populations seeking direct adaptation of today's technologies to their problems or show signs of being able to contribute ideas and service toward an effective arms control arrangement.

It would be folly to create new international institutions without making the utmost effort to see how at least the three major ones can be molded to serve the atom as an instrument for peace. And they must be molded to conform with the realities of a political scene in which changes are occurring without the atom as a primary factor.

---

[1] Robert McKinney, "Cost Summary," *Review of the International Atomic Policies and Problems of the United States*, report to the U.S. Joint Committee on Atomic Energy (Washington: GPO, October 1960). v. 3, pp. 917-919. This so-called "second McKinney report" contains much valuable reference material in its five volumes.

The Future of ENEA and Euratom

With the Six of Europe, which may yet evolve, De Gaulle notwithstanding, into a larger grouping of nations, the United States has a Euratom treaty. The United States is now a member of a group of twenty nations termed the Organization for Economic Cooperation and Development (OECD), and its membership may broaden in number and in geography, for Israel and Japan at least would like to receive the advantages of an economic cooperative grouping. We cooperate with the European Nuclear Energy Agency of the OECD, which includes the members of the Six. The existence of two separate European nuclear energy groups of seemingly similar purposes will become less and less reasonable; ENEA and Euratom must find nonconflicting identities.

ENEA seemed at first to be a natural extension of the technical and economic interests of an organization which was greatly encouraged by the United States, the OEEC. It seemed important for the United States to support anything which would strengthen the OEEC, but at the same time U.S. policy had become strongly ingrained with the concept of a united Europe. It seemed important to support that new entity, Euratom, and indeed it was. In addition to supporting the policy of the Common Market nations, the experience with Euratom (particularly that experience gained in the Joint Program) has revealed some of the problems of any future stronger relationship which might involve the United States and Europe in other areas.

Initially, while both U.S. industry and the program of Euratom were floundering in the midst of public power policy, while projected nuclear power costs were in their most unattractive phase, and while the threat of British trade to the continental European market was concerned, it seemed propitious for U.S. industry to support Euratom. Indeed, the program has served to energize U.S. industry even if it did not provide the hope for an international market. But the competition which the Joint Euratom Program created for U.S. industry may yet lead to further expressions of regret on the latter's part.

Looking at the hard economic and technical "facts," one actually finds very little justification whatsoever for the existence of Euratom. Those nations of Europe which are serious about atomic power would have made similar progress with the assistance of individual bilateral arrangements with the United States. Euratom is justified largely by the expedient of political argument, by its role in contributing to a united Europe.

A similar hard look at what it does, rather than at what it was supposed to have done, fails to give *raison d'être* for ENEA, and in the latter the intense political spirit of Euratom is lacking. Only that vaguely defined political attribute of "common action" remains.

Yet, which organization is better adapted to serve the long-range needs of the European community? For the purposes of foreign policy, is Euratom too narrow, ENEA too dilute? Electrical power is the one thing which has the most immediate economic effect in a community and, quite naturally, it is upon this aspect that the Euratom effort is concentrated. The Euratom research program is still an *applied* research program of essentially short-range goals. The programs sponsored by the European Nuclear Energy Agency (but admittedly financed to a great extent by Euratom) are also applied, having somewhat longer-range implications. It takes time to create a good long-range program; presumably this will occur within the European community, but it is obviously going to be a set of actions in which Euratom and ENEA have similar interests under their present charters. It becomes clear that, for the well-developed economic core which Euratom will represent, the existence of one of the groups is becoming superfluous. In view of the overriding political drive and superior budget of one of them, it is clear which organization will dominate.

There will be a coalescence of most of the power-oriented functions of Euratom and ENEA. Euratom is destined to become simply the atomic energy agency for the Common Market community. Recently it seemed that its political significance was at its apex during the formative years which are now passed; but, following the collapse of the Common Market negotiations with Britain, it may be that Euratom has yet another definitive role to play on the political scene. Whether or not countries like France and the United Kingdom decide to merge the totality of their atomic programs, including the military, depends now on situations beyond the fact that a civilian atomic industry exists to absorb them. It will be recalled that Euratom originally was to control the production of all fissionable materials, whether for military or peaceful purposes, and that, to accommodate France, the control arrangement was made less comprehensive. Undoubtedly the French still hold to their insistence on the exclusion of their military program from Euratom; and to suggest at this time that Euratom might have some sort of military function might actually be harmful to its present peaceful program. Nevertheless, the U.S., British, and French peaceful and military programs are intimately related, technologically and economically, each to each. In a continental Europe where either a national or an international atomic force of some sort will be abuilding, where there will be a not insignificant atomic arms industry, it will be quite anomalous if an equally great civilian atomic industry can indeed be kept quite separate.

This is a complex question which, because it involves a discussion of weapons systems and deterrence, is outside the scope of a study on the peaceful uses of the atom. But one can only re-emphasize the strong relationships between the benign and military atom and the necessity often to consider their interactions upon each other. Frequently in NATO the joint international teams worry about military atomic strategies. It is suggested that this is a most appropriate time for other serious studies to be initiated, with international participation and appropriately within NATO, of the probable future interaction of a growing peaceful atomic industry in Europe with the problems of the defense of Europe and of the Atlantic community. The members of the Common Market are all members of NATO so that these studies can take into account all of the special problems pertaining to Euratom. On another front, the OECD, of which we are a member, can perhaps tackle the problem of the economic and social impact of the atom.

Some member nations of the OECD will, for some time to come, not be willing or able to seek full membership in that hard core of the OECD, the European Economic Community. Those nations have as their primary atomic energy forum the European Nuclear Energy Agency. This is principally what ENEA will remain—a forum for the discussion of mutual problems of the entire membership of the OECD, including those countries which are also members of Euratom. It is difficult to picture the OECD as an organization having major powers of operation in the atomic energy field. It has already assumed an obligation of this sort, the chemical separation plant in Belgium, but this plant is essentially controlled by members of Euratom (holding well over 50 per cent of the votes).

The small-scale subsidiary responsibilities of ENEA are important and should be continued, for such activities tend to be ignored by large-budget organizations which always seek the projects of grander scope. There are at least three important tasks for ENEA. First there are the atomic-oriented advisory services which would assist those member nations of OECD whose development is on a level with those of the European Economic Community down through every intermediate level to the vaguely defined "underdeveloped country." Further, *as a body,* the OECD, through its Development Assistance Committee (DAC), is to extend its services to less developed areas outside of its membership. Where appropriate, the ENEA should work with the DAC.

A second continuing aim of the OECD should be that of stimulating the thought that the "developed" nations have an unending responsibility to encourage and support research, especially *basic* research, for the common good of the community of nations.

The ever-widening horizons of research have dictated that the research and development budget in the United States expand at an annual rate about three times the rate of the expansion of the Gross National Product. Clearly, this rate of expansion cannot continue; there must be a more judicious selection of research projects. Europe, which with the exception of Great Britain has research and development budgets representing much smaller fractions of the GNP, must contribute more to this burden. For the field of atomic energy the "second McKinney report" was particularly valuable in pointing out some possible modes of cooperation, but much needs to be done in spelling out the exact mechanisms for accomplishing these tasks.

A clear part of this problem is the national level of support which a nation must give international organizations and programs. The United States currently spends about one-third of a billion dollars per year for such programs, and much serious thought is being given to how best to carry out an international program and what the proper level of U.S. support might be. If this is beginning now to be a serious question for the United States, it has for some time been a problem for smaller countries. The budgets for some of them are now saturated with dues, fees, travel expenses, and other costs connected with international organizations. It would be an important function for OECD to examine, at least within the realm of science, this problem for their membership.

A third area for OECD, currently under examination, is the type of assistance it could give member nations in formulating reasonable national science policies for improving the allocation of financial and manpower resources. The ENEA should participate in the nuclear sector of these examinations.

Thus there are two organizations, Euratom and ENEA, which can maintain meaningful roles both in the context of Europe's own problems and of American relationships to Europe. Some of these problems are related directly or indirectly to problems of relationships with the U.S.S.R. But many of the goals are worth pursuing in themselves without reference to problems of nuclear survival.

Transforming the IAEA

The future of the International Atomic Energy Agency presents a more difficult problem. To deliberately weaken it would be an abandonment of an essential goal. To let it continue as it is, is to support a dying and impotent symbol—to give substance to the exultation that "unfortunately the conclusion is unavoidable that life is passing the Agency by."[2]

Recently the Department of State appointed an Advisory Committee to consider this problem. Its report differs from what might have been written in the early days of the Agency by realistically confining the discussions of large-scale nuclear power to the technologically advanced nations and in putting aside that nasty prob-

[2] Statement of U.S.S.R. Delegate Vasily S. Yemelyanov at the General Conference of the IAEA, September 19, 1962, as reported by *Nucleonics Week*, October 11, 1962, p. 5.

lem of what to do about the Soviet Union.[3] The report is correct in not subscribing to the view that the *primary* purpose of the IAEA is to offer technical assistance to the less developed states; but this view might dampen the hopes of some nations that could still benefit from IAEA assistance, whether or not such aid is a major responsibility of the Agency. Apart from this, the report usefully surveys present U.S. policy on the peaceful atom. Its recommendations provide a good framework to summarize some of the points made in this study.

> 1. *The United States reaffirm and constructively support its policy of furthering the utilization of atomic energy for peaceful purposes throughout the world.*

One could not quarrel with or improve on this policy position if we could be sure that all of its implications were understood. The tone of the committee report reflects the "judgment that the development of nuclear power is the key issue in determining the fate of the Agency and that nuclear power is on the threshold of economic attractiveness in a number of technologically advanced parts of the world." The phrase, "technologically advanced," is important. But there is a strong implication here that, unless a country is technologically advanced, the atom, through the IAEA, can offer only relatively unimportant services. This will be disputed in the discussion of recommendation 3c, below.

> 2. *The International Atomic Energy Agency be recognized as the most effective means by which the United States can carry out that policy. To that end, activities now being conducted under existing bilateral agreements should be transferred to Agency auspices wherever practical.*

One must also agree completely with this recommendation. The moot point of whether or not the International Atomic Energy Agency would have been more effective had the bilateral method of rendering assistance never been adopted, can be discussed end-

---

[3] U.S. Department of State, *Report of the Advisory Committee on U.S. Policy toward the International Atomic Energy Agency* (Washington: Author, May 19, 1962). The recommendations quoted (italics are supplied) on this and the following pages are from page 2 of the report.

lessly. At best, the error of not *channeling* all aid from the beginning through the IAEA might be conceded. Certainly, *performance* of all the aid functions, especially those concerned with power, by the IAEA would never have been feasible and undoubtedly will not be. Would that the Committee had given a good definition of "wherever practical"!

> 3. *The United States take the lead in securing international agreement that the Agency be recognized as the instrument most appropriate for carrying out certain important functions in the field of atomic energy. In the opinion of the Committee, these include the following:*

This recommendation is hardly questionable, but one must proceed with caution on the specific subgroups:

> 3a. *The provision of the best attainable assurance against diversion of material and equipment to military purposes;*

The most difficult, and the most important, action toward the IAEA is that of strengthening it in the performance of those activities which will enable it to assume its ultimate role adjunct to an international disarmament organization. Such expedients as attempting to make it an atomic power producer, or to give it broader research responsibilities than in the field of atomic energy, do not serve the progress of atomic energy and bear no relationship to the problem of arms control. By one device or another, the IAEA can be given "broker" responsibilities for fissionable materials and can be assigned associated health monitoring and inspection tasks, even without the participation of the Soviet Union or of "neutralist" nations who feel that their sovereign rights are impinged upon by simple forms of collaboration with an international agency, whose existence can and must become meaningful.

Perhaps a word or two is appropriate at this time on the original intent and spirit of the Atoms for Peace plan. The promises of the atom for "have-not" nations were perhaps overstated, but the original goal that stocks of nuclear materials for military purposes must be gradually and safely diminished through some international mechanism—and *why* not the IAEA?—remains valid. The mechanism of simple donation and expecting other nations to follow suit has been demonstrated to be wrong, but we must not cease our efforts in seeking other mechanisms to accomplish the same purpose.

It is in this spirit that the various control proposals for fissionable material have been tendered in preceding chapters. They do not import to be quick-acting panaceas for disarmament. They are suggested as the types of actions which might serve the dual purpose of building up experience in arms-control procedures and bringing together nations in solutions of partial, if not final, significance. A plan for the registration of nuclear materials in transit has been suggested, not because it provides a definitive solution, but because it could serve as a trial basis for inspection. Moreover, existing concepts of international law should be sufficient to enable establishment of at least this simple mechanism.

In addition to charging the International Atomic Energy Agency with some of its rudimental responsibilities, it was originally felt necessary to allow the Agency to assume some measure of integrity by giving it direct possession of stocks of nuclear materials. It is not possible to do this by ramming the principle of Agency possession of fissionable materials down the throats of bilateral recipients. Other means must be found to enable the Agency gradually to accumulate nuclear stocks and to become a preferred donor of such materials. It is suggested that a fissionable materials bank, built upon material rather than monetary contributions be created. In connection with this, there would be required a system of favorable exchange ratios between the various types of fissionable materials.

Actually, whether or not the International Atomic Energy Agency assumes the initiative as a broker for fissionable materials at a distant date in the future, the stocks, production, and utilization of nuclear fuels will become a more important index of economic strength than gold reserves and the flow of gold. The world many well convert some day to the "plutonium standard." Although the present price of nuclear fuel is some tenfold that of gold, at that future time when fantastic quantities of nuclear fuel are being consumed and generated, atomic fuel may become almost as cheap as gold. The possible physical quantities involved are also comparable for, if all of the U.S. electrical generating facilities were converted to atomic power and operated for the lifetime of the reactors, the weight of the fissionable fuel would approximate that of the gold now stored in U.S. vaults.

It is not the extreme monetary value, *per se,* of fissionable material which causes the most worry but the biological and political hazards. In the earlier control plans entirely too much emphasis was placed on accounting for the control of fissionable materials to a minute degree. There has been some recognition that the question of inspection has been overemphasized in previous discussions. This is undoubtedly true but changes will occur, not by eliminating the concept of inspection, but by changing the nature of the inspection process from something which at first would have been a strict policing arrangement to something which incorporates the other security factors relating to questions of nuclear safety, psychology, probability, etc. Thus the question of inspection, while it is necessary and cannot be eliminated, should be relegated to a position where it does not serve as a major barrier to further progress in arms control.

There is no doubt that negotiations for a nuclear test ban were hampered severely by an almost complete lack of technical understanding before and during the negotiations. Moreover, the effects of that lack lingered on long after better understanding became available. The wide range of uncertainties in the number of control points required, inspections, the yields which could be masked, and so on, served as focal points of argumentation and obstruction of the broader issues involved. It is imperative that there be adequate preparation for discussions of the broader aspects of arms control lest those discussions find themselves in similar difficulties.

In expressing the hope that somehow a way might still be found for the IAEA to assume its proper role in a general arms control arrangement, it must be emphasized that we have considered exclusively the nuclear problem. And any solution to this problem must be fitted into a more comprehensive arrangement involving delivery vehicles and guarantees of security from threats of conventional and unconventional means of warfare. It would seem obvious that the mere creation of an international institution, like the IAEA, does not in itself necessarily contribute to the solution of any sector of the problem.

3b. The establishment of uniform health and safety standards;
3d. The reconciliation of liability and indemnification practices;
3f. The promulgation of waste management standards.

These recommendations comprise a natural grouping. It is essential that they be implemented not only because of their implications for public safety but because of their possible relationships to a future arms control mechanism.

3c. The provision of technical assistance;

The more obvious, more immediately fruitful, sphere of consideration is the vast complex of nations in transition. Technically, economically, and politically, their aspirations and their consequent support of the Agency must be sustained in a realistic manner. But there is much evidence to indicate that " . . . there may [be] a tendency for technological change to accentuate regional disparities in levels of income and rates of growth."[4] The problem therefore is to find means for disseminating and adapting quite rapidly the great store of fundamental and applied knowledge in the economically advanced nations to the needs of those which are less provided, both in cognizance of that knowledge and in material resources. The difficulty to date, and probably the major reason why this dictum of increasing disparity with advancing technology is true, is that for the most part the attempt has been made to adapt the technologies of highly developed countries to those of the less developed countries without much consideration of the differing factors. Differences in physical and cultural characteristics, such as soils, minerals, food habits, religious outlook, and so on, must be incorporated as part of the whole complex task of adapting new technologies for the unprovided countries. There is also an often heard axiom, the validity of which is most questionable, that those countries need to go through the same

[4] Zvi Griliches, "Hybrid Corn and the Economics of Innovation," *Science*, July 29, 1960, v. 132, n. 3422, p. 280.

cycles of machinery and necessary adjunct skills through which the developed countries have passed. It is possible to bypass many intermediate, nonpertinent, technological steps—indeed, it is only through deliberate attempts of this kind that the gap will be narrowed.

At the same time one cannot catapult, drastically and blindly, to new technologies, for also inherent in these new technologies is a self-generating demand for funds and manpower which could sap the development budget of a state. For most technologies, including atomic energy, we are not at the point where we can say that certain very interesting breakthroughs already on the scene will indeed mean much for an underdeveloped country; but, on the other hand, we are also in a position of not being able to say with conviction that a certain number of technological developments will be useless for an underdeveloped area. Much more research needs to be done with the assistance and close cooperation of those whom we would aid if we are ever to know, for each technology, which of these positions is the definitive one. Stimulating this research and channeling it from proper donor to proper recipient should be the responsibility of the IAEA.

3e. The conduct of international research projects;

This also must be supported with emphasis on research conducted more closely, in a geographical and manpower sense, with the nations most concerned with these specific problems. At times there have been suggestions that new institutions connected with the IAEA be created—for example, a university for underdeveloped nations. While not rejecting them, one must approach such suggestions with caution. The standard political recipe—that of creating internationalized institutions—is often a dangerous one. International institutions are most likely to succeed if they can be effective first in bringing about national or regional reforms—the separate reforms which must exist before international cooperation can become truly operative. Most solutions which appear reasonable for the advanced and powerful nations make no sense at all for those countries in the early stages of economic development. The technologically advanced nations can and should support *basic* research, for example, and it is from those countries that im-

portant civilian by-products of atomic and space research will result. But for the smaller nations, one must question the feasibility
of the unlimited pursuit of knowledge—a pursuit which becomes
increasingly more expensive year by year and drains budgets which
could be put to better use in applying some of the basic ideas developed elsewhere to practical problems in their own countries. This
basic knowledge, which can be developed most efficiently in the
economically advanced countries, is a commodity which can be
given away freely without the donors being poorer for the gift.

CERN is sometimes offered as proof that international research
efforts are useful and productive. But CERN is a special case. It is
in pure physics that a tradition of cooperative endeavor was established through the simple circumstance that, back in the days
when the atom had not yet caught the attention of the politician,
essentially all the "elder-statesmen" physicists of today—Russian,
American and European—worked together in but two or three research centers in Europe. Today high energy physics, the subject
of research at CERN, is one of the few remaining fields of physics
which can be considered relatively pure. As a consequence of this
and of the cooperative traditions developed through two score
years, CERN is the outstanding cooperative international scientific center; this is not a simple tradition to maintain, for the conditions of the past no longer prevail.

    *4. A detailed study be made within the United States Govern-
ment of the steps to be taken to further foreign policy objectives in the field of atomic power. We believe that such a
study will show that an effective program need not be costly.*

This recommendation merely reflects the fact that there is still
no consistent over-all U.S. policy for atomic power abroad. One
cannot be too optimistic about a future government study. Again,
a "study" is the standard recipe for a problem. Previous studies
give little expectation that a new one would be more illuminating.

    *5. The United States Government continue to support actively
the programs of the Agency in the fields listed above by providing financial assistance, by supplying experts for special
assignments, and by encouraging competent technical men
to serve upon the Agency staff.*

What is lacking is a tenable policy and an IAEA inspired with a definite mission. With those, the resources called for would be more easily come by.

6. *The United States Government take under advisement various other suggestions contained in the body of this report.*

These other suggestions in the Advisory Committee's report relate to standard items such as fellowships, conduct of the Board of Governors, and so on. They are not particularly related to the stronger points of policy, but are the sort of things that emerge as a consequence of any policy.

It is in respect to the point of contact with the East in IAEA meetings that the only mention of the really basic problem is briefly hinted. The sidestepping of the issue of other relationships with the U.S.S.R., and how those relationships might contribute to a broader rapport, is one of the major weaknesses of the *Report of the Advisory Committee on U.S. Policy toward the International Atomic Energy Agency.*

Approaches to U.S.-Soviet Relations

The principal bilateral problem remains that of the interrelationships of the two great nuclear powers (with no offense intended to Britain and France!). The so-called science of Kremlinology is producing a most conflicting spectrum of advice and opinion on the military, technological, or political threat which the Soviet Union poses. Be that as may be, Soviet planning is not always perfect; it often contains elements of uncertainty—for they face dilemmas similar to ours.

Unfortunately, for more difficult problems, one must often resort to quite general suggestions of reform which tend to have a philosophical hue. Their effects, if any, will be seen only after an unpredictable passage of time. In the interim one must seek mechanisms, new "fixed points," for international participation which the Soviet Union will find difficult to resist. New modes of exchanging information and visits must be devised, for the present system of exchange visits is practically cultural in nature; and, although the visits, like "beautiful music and beautiful ballet, relieve some of the strain, they cannot deal with the basic issues."[5] Moreover, at the top level, there has never been a meeting of equivalent personalities in atomic energy matters. The peaceful and military atomic energy organizations are quite separate in the U.S.S.R., contrary to the organization of the U.S. Atomic Energy Commission. Should the Chairman of the U.S. AEC meet a representative of the U.S.S.R. State Committee for the Utilization of Atomic Energy, he would meet a man who does not personally bear the responsibility for the balancing of the military and nonmilitary aspects. Consequently, these discussions cannot really be serious. In situations where some people are more equal than others, we must have a better understanding of exactly with whom we are negotiating.

One can be much more firm on what is demanded in exchange. For example, since the invention of the cyclotron in the early 1930's by E. O. Lawrence, the United States has maintained a significant lead in the construction and application of accelerator machines and in the achievement of important experimental results. The Soviets appear to be anxious for a mutual project in this field.[6] Typically, until the United States put a man in orbital flight, space cooperation talks were simply talk. In December 1962, a rather interesting space agreement involving cooperation in meteorology and satellite communications was obtained.[7] Only by maintaining high-level technological achievement will it be possible to consummate further agreements of political significance with the U.S.S.R. There is much, technologically and politically, still to the advantage of the United States, and these are the assets which must not be wasted in the technique of reaching agreement with the Soviet Union. And now we shall dwell upon the "long-range" aspects of the problem.

The history of fifteen years of East-West contacts and of arms negotiations can be summarized in one sentence: The West insists on knowing what the situation is before and during the period of

[5] Brooks Atkinson, "U.S.-Soviet Differences Basic," *The New York Times* (Paris edition), November 22, 1960.

[6] V. Yemelyanov, "Nyeitron Ne Dolzhen Byt Nyeitralnym" ("The Neutron Cannot Be Neutral"), *Izvestia* (Moscow), June 18, 1961, p. 4.

[7] National Aeronautics and Space Administration, "US-USSR Join in Outer Space Program," Press Release 62-257, December 5, 1962 (mimeographed).

an arms control operation; the East insists that minimum information shall be known only after the operation is completed. We speak of the problems generated by new weapons suddenly ejected into an archaic political philosophy and blindly criticize what is easiest to criticize—the inadequate technical understanding of the politicians, and vice versa. But no reforms, no matter how effective in these areas, will even touch the problem if they do not include a reformulation of the basic stumbling block in our summarizing sentence, i.e., knowledge. The issue is as simple as that.

Asymmetric revision of basic concepts of the utilization and dissemination of information is not an adequate goal. The other philosophy—the philosophy which continues to emphasize secrecy—must also change. It is easy to explain, or indeed to rationalize, the Soviet "necessity" for secrecy, but rarely are the advantages of nonsecrecy for the Soviets brought to the fore. Not the least of these advantages is that the lack of knowledge and the uncertainty about the intentions of one nation has been throughout history one of the major reasons for the building up of military strength in other nations. What was not known about the very weak German atomic bomb program, rather than that which was known, hastened the development of the atomic bomb during World War II.

The application of the atom to peaceful ends introduces an excess of problems which, *in toto,* may convince one that atomic energy is more of a curse than a blessing. One should not be so foolish as to deny or to defend this conclusion; to progress, however, one must recognize the existence of that which exists and make the best of it. Though many of the peripheral problems (such as those relating to safety, insurance, patents, etc.) are difficult for the lawyer or technician, they will be solved. This can be said with certainty, but the host of other problems which bear upon the control and application of this monstrous force, and its relationships to the problems of man's existence, can only be approached by a monumental effort toward increasing man's understanding of that force.

The emphasis on the mystery of the atom, the coddled notion that even a slight comprehension of nuclear phenomena is beyond the ken of the average man, the bewilderment of the citizen when he views his scientific peers arguing vehemently and unscientifically about fallout—all this, compounded by the inability of the human body to see, smell, feel, or otherwise sense radiation, has created a very real barrier[8] to rational thought about nuclear problems.

Man's cogent acquaintance with radiation is but half a century old, and his first experience with it had been for the diagnosis of ailments and the treatment of some of his most fearful diseases like cancer. His first contacts with the power of the atom were the headlines that announced Hiroshima. It was this association that saturated his consciousness. Small wonder, then, that the first emotional impact of the Atoms for Peace plan, which promised vast enrichment of man's lot instead of destruction, was so immense. A large measure of the hope injected by the Atoms for Peace program resulted in apathy or disillusionment in many areas of the world. Can we, in realistic terms, revive this hope? If we cannot, there is little possibility that the world will ever move toward the peaceful resolution of the armament problem.

Toward this task, we are confronted by a basic rejection mechanism, a rejection which applies to the beneficent, no less than to the malevolent aspects, of the atom.[9] This mechanism is present even in a highly technological, highly informed society.

The public must rely upon the fourth estate for its nuclear facts of life. In turn, the press has adopted and pressed to its bosom, as with no other field of science, the conscience-stricken atomic scientist. The latter, after emphasizing in his own inimitable way the dilemma before us, usually decides that he and the public need more information. The lists of requirements usually resemble a curious mélange of titles of public documents that the scientist should have read, and of private documents which he cannot

---

[8] A suggested name: nucleomitophobia. (See *Today's Health,* publication of the American Medical Association, October 1961, p. 84.)

[9] An early insight into this phenomena is given in *Mental Health Aspects of the Peaceful Uses of Atomic Energy,* Technical Report Series, no. 151 (Geneva: WHO, 1958). The WHO discussions are of a necessarily preliminary nature. For a thoughtful presentation of this problem refer to "The Fear of Being Afraid," Chapter 1 in *Living with the Atom,* by Ritchie Calder (University of Chicago Press, 1962), pp. 22-42.

have read, i.e., the intelligence priorities of the Soviet state security organizations.

Press criticism of U.S. policies on the release of information is a popular pastime, yet where the publication of atomic information is concerned the United States certainly has been the most generous nation in the world. Even in the days before Atoms for Peace, the released information was sufficient to let any nation embark upon an atomic energy program commensurate with its physical and economic resources.

The intimate relationships of the peaceful uses of atomic energy with the armament program have been repeatedly emphasized. But in the United States there is relatively little of the peaceful atomic energy programs carried out by the U.S. Atomic Energy Commission which is now classified. Contrasted with this essentially open policy is (except for the sudden masses of information which were released at the Geneva Conference of 1955 and 1958) the slow leakage which certainly can reflect only a small fraction of the current Soviet effort in the peaceful atomic energy field. Generally, the ebb and flow of Soviet information relates inversely to their state of satisfaction with their exterior sources of information.

The coy peeking-game is complicated nowadays by the interests of other players (the Nth countries, which both the U.S. and the U.S.S.R. apparently want to keep just "interested," and Britain, France, and Mainland China) having more complicated relationships and demands. This fantastic magma calls for no simple solutions like unilateral wholesale declassification or sudden harsh security restrictions.

Unquestionably "in the long run, the safety of the world must be insured by enforceable international law, not by the perishable advantage of some specialized knowledge or development."[10] But the *short-run* tactics are important and often decisive in the long run. We are in the business of buying time for the solution of some of these problems; information is one of the media of exchange.

[10] Edward Teller, "Perilous Illusion: Secrecy Means Security," *The New York Times Magazine,* November 13, 1960, p. 29.

We strive for a completely open society, but will be defeated in our goal by a generosity which only enables the closed society to operate more closely. If the press feels denied, "... the fact is that it has not availed itself of the wealth of material which already exists. The reason for these inhibitions can best be discovered by members of the fourth estate."[11]

The image of the AEC as a bastion of security is firmly implanted and its walls will be stormed. And much beyond peaceful import, much of little significance and interest to the intelligent citizen, but of great interest to the trained observer, will be revealed. "For the facts of the matter are that this nation's foes have openly boasted of acquiring through our newspapers information they would otherwise hire agents to acquire through theft, bribery or espionage...."[12] To be fair, one should add to these sources some illuminating government publications and official pronouncements.

A compromise solution must be sought which will enable the press to fulfill its obligations of keeping a free society informed of the forces which could threaten its freedom and, at the same time, enable its government to maintain its bargaining position. Much of the responsibility does indeed rest with the press; but, in atomic matters at least, misunderstanding of classification policy is undoubtedly contributing to errors in the press and government alike.

How does one make maximum use of what has already been said? How does one balance the security value of the new development against what are sometimes very valid political reasons for open discussion? These questions used to be considered in the context of the United States vis-à-vis the U.S.S.R., but now this difficult problem is compounded by the Nth country.

Procedures and Personnel

The military and peaceful atoms (if they can be differentiated at

---

[11] I. I. Rabi, "The Cost of Secrecy," *The Atlantic Monthly*, August 1960, p. 42.
[12] President Kennedy's speech before the Bureau of Advertising of the American Newspaper Publishers' Association, New York, April 27, 1961, as reported by *The New York Times*, April 28, 1961, p. 4.

all) can claim more than their proper share in the development of a most potent form of modern thought anaesthesia—namely, the committee, which at a certain critical point in size becomes a conference. The latter phenomenon, which may crackle and fume a bit at its best but rarely produces an explosion of ideas, has not been described more succinctly than by Jacques Barzun:

In effect, the conference has become the world over, a substitute for work. That is its appeal. Take at any instant a census of the great talents of the world and you will find a large proportion preparing, attending or recovering from a conference. When you add to the burden of the physical event itself the mass of ancillary paperwork required, from the preparatory letterwriting to the transcripts of discussions that nobody reads (except to correct his own stammerings before publication), you may conclude that here make-believe reaches its apogee.[13]

Promulgating the make-believe beyond the conference chambers is a new breed of man, the professional committeeman, who in the years since World War II has learned to paraphrase quite effectively the evils of secrecy, the freedom of science, the hell of nuclear war, and other updated aphorisms of ancient concern. The committee is an ensconced institution of modern society and will not die, but there are growing signs of impatience with this mechanism and disappointment with what is has achieved.

Let us not malign *all* committees and conferences; there are those that deserve to be quoted and heeded. Nevertheless, a new type of individual is required to replace the committee experts, an individual not dependent on or constrained in thought by the sterility of the committee atmosphere. We are late in creating these individuals; a few are evolving in an environment of natural need. With a modest formal program and some changes in educational philosophy we could easily create the minimal number required.

Disproportionate attention has been paid to the creation of the institutions and machines, and to technical judgment. The major problems are not technical, nor can they be met through applying outmoded political solutions. A new type of mind must be devel-

---

[13] Jacques Barzun, *The House of Intellect* (New York: Harpers, 1959), p. 189.

oped—a mind which is essentially of managerial bent and adapted to a very special new environment.

Much of the sad state of affairs which exists in understanding the issues of the atomic age must be attributed to the simple fact that political issues are being handled by scientists who only dimly comprehend the mechanisms of statecraft, while many scientific decisions are being made by individuals who are perhaps politically astute but who either mistakenly believe that the basic facts of the atom are beyond their comprehension or assume they know enough.

For the most part, the American educational system does not allow the multilaterally talented individual of scientific bent to roam. The strict degree requirements at the graduate level demand a narrow specialization. Minor subjects are usually allowed only in a narrow sense of relationship to the major subject of specialization.

It is a commonplace to say that ours is a world growing increasingly more complex, requiring individuals knowledgeable in and capable of making decisions involving many facets of science, economics, and politics. It is high time that a few institutions, or perhaps a foundation, take steps to develop the individual who is well versed (though not narrowly specialized) in certain sciences, speaks several languages, and is actively committed to understanding the political-scientific issues of the day. The development of this multitalented individual should begin approximately at the senior level of the university and continue through the master's degree and the doctoral stages.

Government cooperation should be solicited in the form of offering the students assistantships at the various national atomic energy laboratories during the summer term. Some would be selected to work in fundamental research establishments like the U.S. national laboratories; a few may find their forte at the weapons and production installations. During an alternate summer, apprentice staff positions would be offered the students in the Atomic Energy Commission or the Department of State, either in the United States or at appropriate offices abroad. Participation at international conferences as junior aides should be encouraged as the opportunities arise. For the purposeful chap, the usual reaction pattern will be intoxication, bewilderment, disillusion, and finally an angry spur to independent effort.

Selection of candidates should be encouraged on a quiet basis throughout the academic community. The numbers of individuals required are not large—several tens trained each year would be sufficient to meet the needs and to inject into existing staffs of the Atomic Energy Commission, the Department of State, disarmament study groups, etc., the fresh element which hopefully would result in the generation of new ideas. At the minimum, we would place in the key positions individuals capable of at least understanding the many bewildering facets of our present nuclear-political dilemma.

The immediate personnel problem will have to be solved by redefining responsibilities and broadening the educational bases of the individuals already in the jobs. For specific tasks, government policy has often relied on studies and reports sponsored by private foundations, but the latter have thus far been relatively cautious of participating aggressively in the domain of atomic energy.

Much credit must be accorded to that unique by-product of U.S. free enterprise, the foundation. The foundations which provide for the international exchange of senior personnel, i.e., Guggenheim Awards, Ford Foundation Grants, Rockefeller Public Service Awards, Eisenhower Exchange Fellowships (as well as the exchanges under the Fulbright and Smith-Mundt Acts, using public funds), deserve much of the credit for the development of international understanding among scholars and artists of demonstrated accomplishment. By enabling a government official or scientific administrator to reside abroad for an extended period among counterpart associates, immeasurably more understanding can be achieved than through one- or two-week exchanges of international delegations, or by attendance at international scientific meetings. The vast majority of the scientific exchanges under foundation auspices have, however, been of an extremely specialized nature; and, of the many thousands of fellowships awarded, those who have gone abroad for the purpose of gaining insight into a combination of scientific, political and sociological problems are remarkably few and can probably be numbered on the fingers of one hand. Few such applications have been made to the foundations, nor have foundations specifically encouraged them. Since these aims are not being pursued elsewhere, it would be most heartening if some of the foundations would see fit to extend more aggressively their already impressive record of accomplishment into the scientific areas which must, in time, be integrated into almost every other aspect of life.

There are several key agencies with similar personnel problems, although the type of service differs in each, depending on what they are and what they will become. Atomic energy has lost much of its glamour to space; this is enabling, or forcing, the Atomic Energy Commission to assume the role of an ordinary government agency like the Federal Power Commission or the Federal Communications Commission. Technical knowledge of the atom is no longer confined to the Atomic Energy Commission; it is widely diffused in the universities, in industry and, to a growing extent, in the other federal agencies. Thus, the AEC is evolving into an agency primarily concerned with the control and provision of nuclear products for the physical security of our nation. It is not even clear that the responsibility for the production of fissionable material for peaceful uses will be forever retained by the AEC. Thus, the influence in foreign affairs of the technical agency for atomic energy will diminish.

That something has been lacking in nuclear policy formulation is evident, and the problem need be but briefly stated. Scant scientific competence had been available to an Office of the Special Assistant who advised the Secretary of State on atomic matters. Since mid-1962 nuclear responsibilities have been widely dispersed throughout the entire State Department. To counterbalance this situation, there is a Division of International Affairs in the AEC, with a measure of foreign policy experience. In the newly created United States Arms Control and Disarmament Agency a structure for effectively intermixing political and technical talent has been recognized, but it has yet to show its influence in peaceful atomic policy. Abroad, the Department of State has a number of Science Attachés with, however, no responsibility for atomic energy. The Atomic Energy Commission has several representatives abroad detached from any formal connection with the embassies; their main functions are to smooth difficulties in bilateral agreements already or about to be contracted. There is no doubt that individual competence is high in many of these posts, at home and abroad, but none of these representatives are asked or expected to be the astute, multitalented observer and policy formulator so urgently required. Surely this is one of the more simple of institutional reforms, but it must be instituted at a level higher than the Secretary or the Commission.[14]

By law, any release of classified information, transfer of special materials, or expenditure of funds in the international atomic energy program must be approved by the Joint Committee on Atomic Energy of the U.S. Congress. Actually, "agreements for cooperation" are not technically treaties and do not require Senate approval, so the Joint Committee has the decisive word on them. Thus, the Committee is in an extremely powerful position to alter or veto AEC and/or Department of State projects. The Committee's power is not confined to the realm of the peaceful atom, for,

> The Joint Committee on Atomic Energy is, in terms of its sustained influence within the Congress, its impact and influence on the Executive, and its accomplishments, probably the most powerful congressional committee in the history of the nation. There can be little doubt that, had Congress chosen to deal with atomic energy through conventional congressional committees, the history of our atomic energy program would have been quite different. Almost certainly, the national investment in atomic energy would have been substantially less, and our present level of technology considerably less advanced.[15]

For any major move within the realm of the benign atom, support or opposition of the Joint Committee is likely to be more important than the same forces within the AEC.

The members of the Joint Committee of course have their other

[14] For a fine highlighting of personnel problems in the broad area of arms control (problems similar to those found in the area of the peaceful atom) see the study, *Strengthening the Government for Arms Control,* PP-109, report of the Special Project Committee on Security through Arms Control of the National Planning Association (Washington: NPA, July 1960).

[15] Harold P. Green and Alan Rosenthal, *The Joint Committee on Atomic Energy: A Study in Fusion of Governmental Power,* report by the JCAE Study Project (Washington: The George Washington University, The National Law Center, 1961). Consult this reference for an interesting account of the metamorphosis of the Committee's power since 1947.

Congressional responsibilities; for some of them their atomic energy activities appear to command major interest. Few, if any, of the members can be said to be technically qualified, but the decade or more of service on the part of the senior members has imparted a surprisingly high level of understanding. Further, there has been more continuity of membership in the Joint Committee than in the Atomic Energy Commission. About a third of the members have served since 1946. Most of the members have overlapping memberships in related committees, like the armed services and appropriations committees, and thus are able to view the broader picture.

The Committee employs a competent small staff—a staff which is surely inadequate to handle the volume and scope of all the issues, peaceful and military, which come before it and which must be reviewed within several weeks, but into which has gone the long-term preparation of the mammoth Atomic Energy Commission staff. Technical consultants are available, but a technical appointment on the staff is an extreme rarity. The Joint Committee and its staff must rely on the reviews which are prepared for them by the various government agencies and upon a multitude of hearings and written communications. It is clear from the transcripts of the hearings that rapport on some subjects previous to hearings has been limited. Indeed, the hearings often have the appearance of two armies, with secret forces marshaled, suddenly meeting to do battle.

It is difficult to propose reforms without violating the principle of the separation of the legislative and administrative branches of the government, but some general advice should be heeded:

Vigorous Congressional leadership with the support of the President should prevent national policy from being frustrated by unsympathetic chairmen of committees and subcommittees. A national sense of the increased responsibilities of Congress for the making or breaking of foreign policies and programs should strengthen the hands of leadership, to make the intention of the whole Congress prevail.[16]

In this respect the observation of Green and Rosenthal is perti-

[16] "Text of American Assembly's Suggestions of Foreign Policy," *The New York Times,* October 10, 1960, p. 21.

nent: "Although the JCAE often exercises decisive influence in the formulation of national policy through its involvement in Executive processes, it is by no means clear that it bears commensurate responsibility or accountability."[17]

The foregoing discussion of personnel problems in government agencies concerned with atomic matters brings us again to the training of new talents able to cope with technological, political, economic, and social complexities of atomic energy. The person hypothesized will find his work, whether in the AEC, the State Department, or on a congressional staff, to be the most frustrating, though probably the most fascinating, he could ever encounter. Immensely difficult as the problems are, they are not unsolvable. Economic, social, and other changes not immediately connected with atomic energy provide the challenge to make atomic energy work for the nation in a nontechnical sense.

The first tasks of the "political-atomic servant," wherever he may find himself, will be to reconstruct for himself the history of the problems in negotiations and technology which interest him. These reconstructions will range from the analysis of the negotiations in the establishment of the International Atomic Energy Agency, the development of bilateral treaty arrangements, and so forth, to the highly complex considerations underlying nuclear fuel pricing, inspection, and utilization.

When the "political atomic servant" moves in political circles, he will understand how scientific "facts" are so often misused; and, when he moves in scientific circles, he will find disdain for the word "political." He will develop subtle, sometimes harsh techniques, for achieving agreement or compromise between the two camps. In getting a program rolling, he may on rare occasions find the support for a program greater than the physical resources can sustain; then his problem is renewed.

He may feel that he can best serve the interests of his own country and the interests of a broader community of nations, as well as following a greater cause, by becoming an international civil servant. In this he should be encouraged, but at the same time must be warned that to accomplish similar tasks in an international

[17] Cited, p. 292.

agency requires enormously more forebearance, patience, and tact. He will not only be frustrated in carrying out his mission, but conceivably must risk at times the displeasure of his own nation in the performance of his duties.

In visiting today the international organizations one finds an atmosphere of international service, most noticeably in the institutions of the European Community. As in no other organization, employees of Euratom regard themselves as citizens of Europe. This is a concept alien to De Gaulle's *l'Europe des Patries;* thus, the conflict between nationalism and internationalism proved disastrous for no less a personage than the President of Euratom, who was replaced late in 1961 by someone more attuned to the French line.[18] It will take time before conditions are such that the international civil servant will be able to consider himself a truly international citizen, however he may feel or try.[19]

Wherever he may serve, his primary task will be that of rediscovering, remolding the aims of Atoms for Peace, aims which in their greater measure are still valid. He must and will seek guidance from the small number of individuals who have contended with these problems during the last score of years; but, cognizant of their ratio of success to failure, he will seek the better way to cope with the newer circumstances.

The reader may regret that no grand concept has emerged from this study parallel to "Counterforce" for weapons employment, "Dumbbell" for the Atlantic alliance, or a host of other nostrums which have appeared in the past decade. As we have seen, the relation between the peaceful use of atomic energy, arms strategy, and arms control are entirely too complex to permit one grand plan of action. We must grasp the opportunities to solve the problems, piece by piece, as they arise—but always with an acute awareness of these relationships, the way they conflict with and complement each other. During the course of this book many suggestions have been boldly made—all of them seriously and perhaps some of them

[18] Jean Lecerf, "M. Chatenet remplace M. Hirsch à la Présidence de l'Euratom," *Le Figaro* (Paris), December 21, 1961; "Attack in E.E.C. over Euratom Appointment," *The Times* (London), December 22, 1961.

[19] " 'Le président français de l'Euratom n'est pas au service de la France,' déclare M. Hirsch," *Le Monde* (Paris), December 22, 1961, p. 4.

provocatively. In any event, they are all meant to be dissected and criticized; they are intended to goad and to stimulate alternative thoughts on these problems and, above all, to emphasize the necessity of devising "fixed points" to substitute for the frayed platitudes of nuclear politics. With other "solutions" that will undoubtedly occur to the reader and the analyst, an atmosphere of objective appraisal of them all must be developed.

Well into the "New Frontier," the United States finds itself carried higher and higher on the crest of a wave of technological achievement and hazard. But perhaps also being felt is a more subtle peril expressed by a retiring head of state, who seven years previously had envisioned in atomic science a hope yet uncrystalized:

Yet, in holding scientific research and discovery in respect, as we should, we must also be alert to the equal and opposite danger that public policy could itself become the captive of a scientific-technological elite.
It is the task of statesmanship to mold, to balance and to integrate these and other forces, new and old, within the principles of our democratic system—ever aiming toward the supreme goals of our free society.[20]

If public policy is indeed becoming captive of "a scientific-technological elite," it is because the public, which includes statesmen and scientists alike, has been presented with awesome technological prospects which appear to herald mostly destruction. With such a vista it is not surprising that policy becomes perhaps more aptly described as paralyzed rather than captive. A revitalized Atoms for Peace program—based not upon visionary promises of a cornucopia for all but rather upon more realistic technological analyses now possible and coupled step-by-step with imaginative, bold policy decisions—could alleviate greater dangers than that expressed above.

[20] "Text of President's Farewell Address to the Nation," *The New York Times,* January 18, 1961, p. 22.

Index

Acheson-Lilienthal report, 24-25
Action Committee for the United States of Europe, 153
ADAM reactor, 96
Agriculture: dual purpose fertilizer plant, 197; IAEA-Yugoslav irradiation research center, 214; uses of radiation in, 131, 140, 142-143, 148, 200; *see also* Water
Alaska, 93, 119
Albania, 178
Animas River (Colo.), 51
Apsara reactor, 191
Atlantic Alliance, 169-170
Atomic bomb: availability of data on, 18, 19, 22; "clean," 123; implosion type, 24; peaceful applications, *see* Nuclear explosions; predetonation, 24; production, 12, 17, 19-22, 111; testing, 23, 126-127; *see also* Test bans; Testing
Atomic energy: benefits and responsibilities to future, 103; early European contributions to study of, 150; fears of, 248; "have" nations, 147; influence of technical developments on international relations, 166; interest stimulated by Suez crisis, 84; prospects of economic applications, 38-39, 84, 85, 87, 89, 231-232; relationship of peaceful and military use, 4, 5, 9, 26, 235 258-259; role in strategy for peace, 3-9; and underdeveloped countries, 85-86
Atomic weapons, conversion to peaceful use, 28-29
Atoms for Peace, 3-4, 18, 79-80: accomplishments and failures, 230, 248; difficulties caused by plutonium, 18-19; and dissemination of information, 186, 187; early reactions, 3-4; effect on Atomic Energy Act, 6; food radiation research, 134, 136-137; and IAEA, 8; and the New Production Reactor, 38; objectives, 208-209, 258-259; role of plutonium, 28; successful ICA program, 204; and underdeveloped countries, 171, 188, 230, 232
Australia: as a nuclear power, 148; thorium deposits, 13; uranium deposits, 11; use of radiation, 139
Automation, 66-67

Baghdad Pact, 139
Barzun, Jacques, *quoted,* 251
Beaton, Leonard, *quoted,* 18
Belgium: bilateral agreement with U.S., 62; interest in nuclear ships, 106; IAEA research contract, 224; and maritime affairs, 58-59; and uranium prices, 223
Bhabha, Dr. Homi J., *quoted,* 65, 191-192
Bilateral agreements: with countries seeking nuclear independence, 64; restrictions on use of fissionable materials, 14; U.S.S.R.-Soviet bloc, 64; U.S. rights to plutonium purchase, 33; *see also* U.S. bilateral agreements
Brazil: acceptance of IAEA safeguards, 224; pact with Euratom, 205; thorium deposits, 13, 191;

Nuclear explosions (*Cont.*)
tion of reservoirs of geothermal heat, 120-121; international test agreements, 126-127; manufacture of fissionable materials, 121-122; manufacture of radioactive isotopes, 121; research on electromagnetic radiation, 122; *see also* Plowshare, Project

Nuclear materials, 72: European energy self-sufficiency, 87-88; legal distinction between "special" and "source," 13; price disparities, 38; registration of international trade in, 72-73; *see also* Fissionable materials

Nuclear propulsion, 104-116: aircraft, 112-113; locomotives and automobiles, 113; rockets and spaceships, 51-52, 113-114; U.S.S.R. research, 183-184

Nuclear propulsion, ships: and whaling, 108-109; countries interested in, 106; icebreaker *Lenin*, 107; international liability agreements, 58-59; merchant ships, 105-106, 111-112; *Nautilus*, 105-107; reluctance to permit harbor entry, 109-110; U.S. cooperation with allies on submarines, 68

Nuclear reactors: chemical production, 97; design changes to facilitate inspection, 67; dual-purpose, 141; fast, 20, 31-32; gas-cooled, 159, 166, 171; heat producing, 95-98; heavy water, 149, 171; liability insurance, 57; low temperature, 141; portable, 200-201; production of curies, 44-45; radioactive waste, 46-47; safety aspects, 59; side reactions, 13

Nuclear reactors, power producing: accident statistics, 56-57; advantages, 89; civilian use of military design, 93; controlled chain reac-

tion in, 12; costs, 65-66, 89, 94-95, 160, 196; direct generation of electricity, 94-95; economic competitiveness, 29, 89-94, 157-158, 231; kilowatt goals, 161-162; mass-produced, 94; obsolescence due to development of fusion process, 101; plutonium production, 21; plutonium-burning, 182-183; pressurized-water type, 105, 107; radioactive waste from, 46-47; refueling frequency, 30; small mobile systems, 92-93, 110; SNAP units, 114; thermal type, 30-31; in underdeveloped countries, 95; U.S.-Euratom joint program, 156-157, 161; use of "reject heat," 37, 202; use with conventional hydroelectric systems, 92

Oak Ridge, Tenn., 14
Oceanography, 48
Oil; *see* Fossil fuels
On the Beach, 17
Operation Candor, 3
Organization for Economic Cooperation and Development (OECD): Development Assistance Committee (DAC), 149; future of, 233, 235-237; nuclear aid to underdeveloped countries, 171; relationship to EEC, 164, 175; Saclay, France, center for food irradiation research, 137; U.S. membership, 8
Organization for European Economic Cooperation (OEEC), 8, 152-153: attempt to fix standards of safe radiation levels, 53; convention on liability in nuclear accidents, 58; reorganization into OECD, 164
Organization of American States (OAS), 205

Thermionic generation, 98
Thermoelectrical generation, 98
Thermonuclear energy, 101-102, 121
Thermonuclear research: advantages of U.S.-Europe cooperation, 102; ocean water as a fuel, 101; U.S.-U.S.S.R. cooperation, 103
Thorium: and breeding, 31; defined as "source material" in Atomic Energy Act, 13; deposits, 13, 191, 192-3; not usable for power in original state, 11
Transuranium Institute, Euratom research center, 172
Tritium, 102
Trombay, research reactor, 193
Turkey, 139

Underdeveloped countries: early promises of atomic energy, 188-189; economics of nuclear power in, 195; and EEC, 204; importance of water supply, 201-203; IAEA assistance, 9, 212-213; IAEA nuclear controls in, 191-192; nuclear applications suitable for, 136, 190, 196-200; opposition to controls, 196; other terms describing, 188-189; readiness for atomic age, 189; role in disarmament and control problems, 206-7; U.S. aid to, 204
Union of South Africa: offer of uranium to IAEA, 220; thorium deposits, 13; uranium deposits, 11; and uranium prices, 223
U.S.S.R.: All-Union Institution of Scientific and Technical Information (VINITI), 186-187; atomic testing, 4, 6, 73, 128, 185; attitude on Nth country problem, 76, 179; attitude toward inspection and control, 64-65, 70,

76, 185; bilateral agreements, 7, 9, 64, 179-182; Council of Mutual Economic Assistance (CEMA), 179; denunciation of Euratom, 153; interest in plutonium, 28, 182-183; and IAEA, 179, 209-210, 212, 218-219; non-bloc nuclear aid, 181, 194-195, 206; nuclear aid to China, 19, 180-181; nuclear icebreaker *Lenin*, 107; nuclear policy, 5, 184; nuclear power program, 37, 84, 91, 161, 182; nuclear research, 28, 174, 177-179 183; offer of uranium to IAEA, 220; offer of uranium to underdeveloped countries, 221; oil production and export, 84-85; participation in CERN, 152, 179; peaceful use of nuclear explosions, 117, 127-128; policy of secrecy, 15, 185; policy towards Plowshare, 117, 119, 127-128; production of uranium-235, 13-14; reaction to Atoms for Peace, 3-4, 18; State Committee for the Utilization of Atomic Energy compared to U.S. AEC, 246; uranium resources, 11; use of radioisotope applications, 133; work on centrifuge process, 16; *see also* U.S.-U.S.S.R. relations
United Kingdom: accident at Windscale, 41-42; Atomic Energy Authority, 159, 163; and Atoms for Peace program, 18; bilateral agreements, 7, 9, 63, 166, 192; changing concept of reactor program, 166, 194; contract for reactor construction in Italy, 159-160; cooperation with U.S. and Canada on atomic bomb, 150; Dragon, gas-cooled reactor, 166; economics of power reactors in, 30, 155, 161-162; effect of Suez crisis, 153-154; and Euratom, 115-

Publications of the

COUNCIL ON FOREIGN RELATIONS

FOREIGN AFFAIRS (quarterly), edited by Hamilton Fish Armstrong.

THE UNITED STATES IN WORLD AFFAIRS (annual). Volumes for 1931, 1932 and 1933, by Walter Lippmann and William O. Scroggs; for 1934-1935, 1936, 1937, 1938, 1939 and 1940, by Whitney H. Shepardson and William O. Scroggs; for 1945-1947, 1947-1948 and 1948-1949, by John C. Campbell; for 1949, 1950, 1951, 1952, 1953 and 1954, by Richard P. Stebbins; for 1955, by Hollis W. Barber; for 1956, 1958, 1959, 1960, 1961 and 1962, by Richard P. Stebbins.

DOCUMENTS ON AMERICAN FOREIGN RELATIONS (annual). Volume for 1952 edited by Clarence W. Baier and Richard P. Stebbins; for 1953 and 1954, edited by Peter V. Curl; for 1955, 1956, 1957, 1958 and 1959, edited by Paul E. Zinner; for 1960, 1961 and 1962, edited by Richard P. Stebbins.

POLITICAL HANDBOOK AND ATLAS OF THE WORLD (annual), edited by Walter H. Mallory.

THE ARABS AND THE WORLD: Nasser's Arab Nationalist Policy, by Charles D. Cremeans.

TOWARD AN ATLANTIC COMMUNITY, by Christian A. Herter.

THE SOVIET UNION, 1922-1962: A Foreign Affairs Reader, edited by Philip E. Mosely.

THE POLITICS OF FOREIGN AID: American Experience in Southeast Asia, by John D. Montgomery.

SPEARHEADS OF DEMOCRACY: Labor in the Developing Countries, by George C. Lodge.

LATIN AMERICA: Diplomacy and Reality, by Adolf A. Berle.

THE ORGANIZATION OF AMERICAN STATES AND THE HEMISPHERE CRISIS, by John C. Dreier.

THE UNITED NATIONS: Structure for Peace, by Ernest A. Gross.

THE LONG POLAR WATCH: Canada and the Defense of North America, by Melvin Conant.

ARMS AND POLITICS IN LATIN AMERICA (Revised Edition), by Edwin Lieuwen.

275

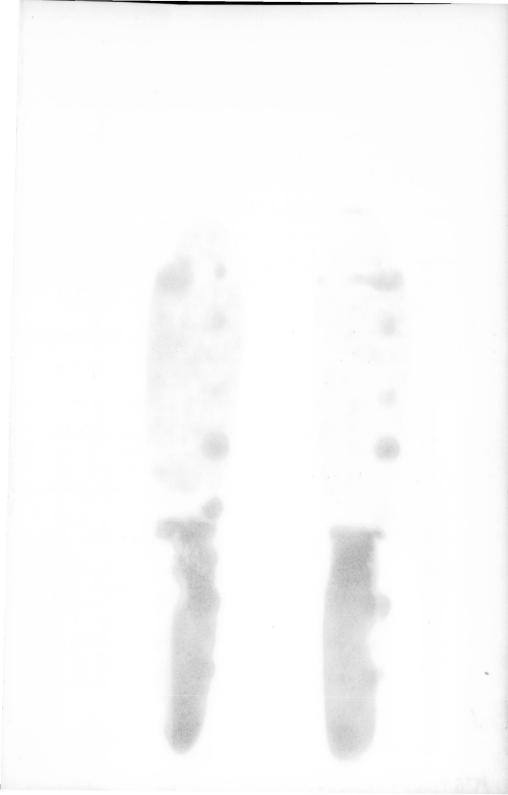

DATE DUE	